Physiology and Genetics of Tree-Phytophage Interactions

International Symposium

Gujan (France), August 31 - September 5, 1997

organized by
Institut National de la Recherche Agronomique (INRA)
International Union of Forestry Research Organizations (IUFRO)

INSTITUT NATIONAL DE LA RECHERCHE AGRONOMIQUE
147, rue de l'Université - 75338 Paris Cedex 07

Editeurs/ *Editors*

François LIEUTIER
INRA, CR d'Orléans
Unité de Zoologie Forestière
Avenue de la Pomme de Pin
BP 20619 - Ardon
F - 45166 Olivet Cedex, France

William J. MATTSON
Forestry Sciences Laboratory
North Central Forest Research Station
5985 Highway K
Rhinelander WI 54501, USA

Michael R. WAGNER
School of Forestry
Northern Arizona University
Box 15018
Flagstaff AZ 86011, USA

En vente / *For sale*

INRA Editions
Route de St Cyr, 78026 Versailles Cedex, France

ISBN : 2-7380-0883-6

Preface

Interactions between trees and phytophagous organisms represent an important fundamental process in the evolution of forest ecosystems. Through evolutionary time, the special traits of trees have lead the herbivore populations to differentiate and evolve in order to cope with the variability in natural resistance mechanisms of their hosts. Conversely, damage by herbivores has inevitably influenced the evolution of many aspects of tree structure (including biochemistry) and life history. The size of the trees, the diversity of structures in an individual, as well as the variation in physiological status during the year and through ontogeny have created a large number of ecological niches for herbivores. Reciprocally, the high diversity of herbivores and their behaviours have favoured a wide variety of tree structures to evolve in many directions to thwart attacks. Consequently, a high diversity of tree-herbivore relationships has evolved suggesting reciprocal adaptations.

Environmental factors have also played an important role in the evolution and diversification of these interactions, acting both directly on the organisms and indirectly through modifications of tree susceptibility and herbivore aggressiveness. Because tree-herbivore interactions are at the root of forest food chains and also because they strongly influence the other plant-animal relationships, the tree-herbivore interactions are among the key processes operating in forest ecosystems.

The main objective of the biologist is to understand how Nature operates and what are the place and role of humans in the biosphere. The forest biologist, for that purpose, aims at discovering general patterns of organisation in the forest ecosystem and explaining their dynamic structure. Understanding the interactions between trees and herbivores is thus a basic requirement. To reach the above objective, the dynamics of plant-herbivore interactions must be studied at both the proximate (mainly physiological) and the ultimate (genetic) levels, while taking into account the environmental and human impacts on the forest ecosystems. The knowledge of this dynamics should thus contribute to defining how to protect forests against severe herbivore damage, but also to defining the rules that must be followed in order to make the human requirements of forests compatible with forest preservation and sustainability.

As part of the above approach, the scope of the book is mainly devoted to tree resistance to biotic aggressions and to other tree-phytophage interactions conditioning tree resistance. Understanding the mechanisms involved will help in better managing pests and forest ecosystems.

Because the genetic variability of the living organisms is the basic material on which the natural selection operates, the first part of the book is focused on tree resistance and its variability and tree selection for resistance. The second part of the book deals with variability and biology of herbivore populations. The third part presents the effects of tree resistance on aggressors, and the forth one gives examples of the reciprocal effect of aggressors on the tree. Because the expression of all biological phenomena, as well as their persistence through evolutionary time are modulated and controlled by environmental factors, the fifth part examines how external factors affect tree-aggressors interactions and resistance expression. A variety of aggressors is considered in each part, ranging from fungi to various insect groups and to mammals, thus giving a wide view on tree-phytophage interactions. The final section proposes synthetic theories and mechanisms for tree resistance to biotic aggressions.

This book results from a symposium held in Gujan (Landes, France) from August 31 to September 5, 1997, organized by 4 working parties of the International Union of Forestry Research Organizations (IUFRO) corresponding to the whole subject group S7.01 "Physiology and genetics of tree-phytophage interactions". These working parties are S7.01-01 "Tree resistance to pathogens", S7.01-02 "Tree resistance to insects", S7.01-03 "Tree resistance to mammals" and S7.01-05 "Effect of environmental factors on resistance expression". The Organizing Committee was composed of François Lieutier (France), William J. Mattson (USA) and Hervé Jactel (France).

Before their acceptance for publication, all papers presented in this book were submitted to at least two reviewers belonging to the Scientific Committee, and one of the senior editors of the Symposium.

*****

We would like to thank these institutions for economical and other kinds of support :

The Institut National de la Recherche Agronomique (INRA), France

the International Union of Forestry Research Organizations (IUFRO)
the Conseil Régional d'Aquitaine
the Association pour la Protection de la Forêt Aquitaine (APFA), France
the staffs of the Forest Entomology Program (INRA of Orléans and Pierroton, France).

Editors are also grateful to Paul Romary (INRA, France) for taking in charge several practical tasks during the preparation of the Symposium and for harmonising the presentation of the various articles.

François LIEUTIER
William J. MATTSON
Michael R. WAGNER

Scientific Committee

ALFARO René I.	Forestry Canada, Victoria, BC, Canada
ARBEZ Michel	INRA, Pierroton, France
BASTIEN Catherine	INRA, Orléans, France
BERRYMAN Alan A.	Washington State University, Pulman, WA, USA
CHRISTIANSEN Erik	Norwegien Forest Research Insitute, Ås-NLH, Norway
DAY Keith R.	University of Ulster, Coleraine, UK
DELATOUR Claude	INRA, Nancy, France
DREYER Erwin	INRA, Nancy, France
DU MERLE Paul	INRA, Avignon, France
EVANS Hugh	Forestry Commission, Wrecclesham, UK
FÜHRER Erwin	Universität für Bodenkultur, Vienna, Austria
GERI Claude	INRA, Orléans, France
GREGOIRE Jean-Claude	Université Libre de Bruxelles, Belgique
HERMS Daniel A.	Ohio State University, OH, USA
JACTEL Hervé	INRA, Pierroton, France
LÅNGSTRÖM Bo	Swedish University of Agricultural Sciences, Uppsala, Sweden
LEATHER Simon	Imperial College, Ascot, UK
LIEUTIER François	INRA, Orléans, France
LORIO Peter	USDA, Pineville, LA, USA
LUNDERSTÄDT Jorg	Georg-August Universität Göttingen, Deutschland
MATTSON William J.	North Central Forest Research Station Rhinelander WI, USA
MAUPHETTES Yves	Université du Quebec, Montréal, Canada
NIEMELA Pekka	University of Joensuu, Finland
RAFFA Kenneth F.	University of Wisconsin, Madison, WI, USA
ROQUES Alain	INRA, Orléans, France
ROUSI Matti	Finnish Forest Research Institute, Punkaharju, Finland
SOUSA SANTOS Maria N.	Estaçao Florestal Nacional, Oeiras, Portugal
TEISSIER DU CROS Eric	INRA, Avignon, France
VETROVA Valentina	Sukachev Institute of Forest, Krasnoyarsk, Russia
WAGNER Michael R.	Northern Arizona University, Flagstaff, AZ, USA
WINGFIELD Michael	University of Pretoria, Pretoria, South Africa
YE Hui	Yunnan University, Kunming, Yunnan, P.R. China

Contents

Physiology and Genetics of Tree-Phytophage Interactions
Gujan (France), August 31 - September 5, 1997
Ed. INRA, Paris, 1999 (Les Colloques, n°90)

Introductory lecture:

Improvement of tree resistance to biotic aggressions: the geneticist point of view

C. BASTIEN

INRA, Station d'Amélioration des arbres forestiers
45160 Ardon, France

RESUME

As in crop and animal breeding, the original goal of forest tree breeding was to increase yield or more specifically the economic value of large scale intensive timber production. Faced to diseases and insect attacks, the tree breeder has to identify or create varieties not necessary totally immune but with reasonable tolerance to biotic factors.

In contrast with agricultural crops, most tree populations used for breeding are essentially managed but unselected populations which have often developed different disease resistance mechanisms through coevolution. One essential step of the geneticist's approach is therefore to describe as precisely as possible the available genetic variation. Difficulties in evaluating tree resistance at individual or population levels are discussed. The needs for research on both genetic variability of the pest and environmental effects on the host-pest interaction are outlined. Today, optimal estimation of genetic values can take advantage of complementary approaches such as classical quantitative genetics and DNA information. From a more basic point of vue, knowledge on the inheritance of resistance mechanisms and on resistance overcoming will be improved.

All advanced tree breeding programs recognize the need for durable disease and insect resistance. The short term development of resistant varieties is then limited to predictable risks and captures the high genetic gains promised by a narrowing of the genetic basis. Biological risk of pest attack resulting from genetic uniformity is reduced by packaging a maximum of major and minor genes involved in resistance components. Because within-host genetic diversity through time and space is only one of the numerous factors controlling durability, appropriate complementary deployment strategies must be developed. For a given species, long term durability must be considered at the population level in which individuals share the different genes involved in resistance mechanisms. Management of breeding populations rely on recurrent but moderate selection to increase frequencies of interesting alleles for predictable and unpredictable risks. Maintenance of genetic diversity involving introduction of variability from new genetic pools is also a major concern of this scheme. To achieve these goals, late assessment of several resistance traits, complexity of resistance mechanisms, and multiple selection criteria of tree breeding programs justify the use of marked-assisted selection.

INTRODUCTION

If local adaptation and volume production are still the main selection objectives of most tree breeding programs in the world, more attention is paid to resistance to biotic aggressors as indirect criterion to improve stem form or even as major selection objective in response to increasing declined plantation forestry. In some advanced breeding programs such as those of radiata pine in New-Zealand or slash pine in Southeastern USA, disease or insect attacks become a major obstacle to fully realize the gain expected from intensive silviculture and tree improvement (Carson and Carson, 1989, Doudrick et al., 1996, Dieters et al., 1996).

Expression of genetic gain for tree resistance against biotic aggressors

Depending on the economical impact of the species, genetic gains have first been achieved through selection of the best natural populations or provenances or by a larger narrowing of the genetic basis through family or clonal selection.

Genetic gain for resistance to biotic aggressions is evaluated in the selected tree population and not in the pest population. Genetic gain is positive when substantial damage reduction is observed. It is considered optimal when these damages decrease to an economically tolerable level. Total immunity or absence of damages is not looked for anymore. The term "resistance" will express hereafter the relative amount of pest attacks regardless of any underlying mechanisms. Genetic improvement is one potential means to reduce damages in forests but its potential success is limited both by the economical compromise between production traits, and resistance and by biological limits offered by genetic variability. Now it has become widely recognized that forests are not only specific plant production areas for human needs but also important and sometimes endangered ecosystems in the biosphere. During the last decade, biodiversity has become the subject of much public dialogue and more attention is paid to a reasoned management of genetic variability not only at the species level but mainly at the ecosystem or landscape scale. Reduction of genetic diversity due to tree improvement is often translated in terms of risks with forest health. In fact, clear evidence of widespread devastation by pests of plantations with genetically improved material is lacking. Moreover, communications outside the genetic community are required to explain that gene conservation efforts are in effect where tree improvement programs exist. Development of rigorous testing and selection strategies for resistance to biotic aggressions addresses at the moment one major question to discuss not only among geneticists : how much genetic diversity is necessary for forest health ?

What does genetic resistance mean ?

When improvement of tree resistance to biotic aggressions is trusted to geneticists and tree breeders, that means that within the tree species or genus considered, genetic resistance mechanisms are suspected. In fact the response of the host can be considered as genetic resistance only if genetic variability exists for this response and if this response is genetically inherited. Describing the genetic variability and the inheritance of resistance mechanisms are then two basic activities of breeding programs for resistance.

Since most tree breeders are still at the early stage of domesticating relatively wild species, they are interested in describing insect and disease-host interaction at different scales :

1- For many tree species, resistance variation among populations has been revealed in different provenance tests including populations sampled over the entire range of the species (Ruby and Wright, 1976, Wu *et al.,* 1996). If in some cases as for lodgepole pine, geographical patterns have been identified, their causes are not so obvious to define (Wu *et al.,* 1996). They can correspond to true differences in allelic frequencies for resistance loci but also simply to phenological mechanisms of escape (Desprez-Loustau and Dupuis, 1994).

2- Frequently higher intrapopulational variation has been demonstrated and exploited in breeding programs for many pest-tree interaction systems (Pichot and Teissier du Cros, 1993, Bastien *et al.,* 1995, Meagher and Hunt, 1996). Population resistance probably reflects the joint involvement of different resistance mechanisms distributed over different individuals. This individual level must be considered as the basic level of host variation for a better understanding of resistance mechanisms at physiological, histological, chemical or genetic levels. For long-lived organisms such as forest trees, development of improved varieties for durable resistance requires to go back to a population or sub-population level in which frequencies of resistance alleles are increased through selection and genetic recombination.

3- Potential interest of interspecific hybridization has been demonstrated for resistance traits as for other traits and is intensively exploited in poplar breeding (Florence and Hicks, 1980). Natural hybridization zones provide interesting information on how the genetics of tree resistance is affected and how this modification affects in turn the evolution and ecology of the biotic aggressors (Floate and Whitham, 1993).

Multidisciplinary research needs to improve selection for durable resistance

In order to achieve durable resistance through a recurrent scheme consisting in describing and manipulating genetic variability, tree breeders are faced to some limiting scientific obstacles :

1- one major step in breeding for tree resistance is the development of repeatable and reliable screening techniques, which can be applied at low cost on large amount of individuals (600 to 1000 genotypes). Improvement of evaluation methodology is also important to increase knowledge on host-parasite interactions.

2- for a better management of genetic diversity, research emphasis should be placed on a better understanding of physiological, biochemical, and molecular factors of qualitative and quantitative resistance.

3- recent improvement in using molecular markers coupled with gene cloning should permit a better understanding of resistance overcoming. Thanks to them, new methods for construction of durable resistance must be developed.

These three points will be now discussed.

EVALUATION OF TREE RESISTANCE TO BIOTIC AGGRESSORS

Limits of genetic field tests

Most knowledge on the structure of host genetic variability for their response to biotic aggressors comes from classical genetic tests such as provenance, progeny or clonal forest or nursery tests (Wu et al., 1996, Sluder, 1993, Pichot and Teissier du Cros, 1993). In these experiments, the genotypes each replicated 10 to 100 times, are spatially distributed according to an experimental design chosen for an optimal control of local fertility effects. Tree resistance is generally evaluated after natural attacks by a damage severity score.

From the breeder's point of view, such evaluation offers many advantages :

- the assessment of the host-aggressor interaction is close to the economical impact and the expected genetic gain calculated on this scale will be close to the actual economical gain.
- selection process hopefully involves most of the underlying resistance mechanisms and thus durability over time might be better guaranteed.

From the geneticist's point of view, such an evaluation method is often inadequate for the understanding of tree-pest interaction patterns. There is no control of the variability of the aggressor, neither of the level and homogeneity of attacks (Doudrick et al., 1996a). In Europe, first generation of poplar clonal selection for rust resistance was based on evaluation in natural conditions without any control of the aggressor variability. Unfortunatly, the development of specific and unstable resistance to a given race of the pathogene could not be suspected and great disappointment invaded the scientific community ten years later when the selection was revealed ineffective.

Limits of artificial or laboratory tests

Thanks to the experience of pathologists, entomologists and ecologists, artificial resistance tests improve the control of the aggressor variability, the level and homogeneity of attack or infection, and the environmental conditions such as temperature or humidity level.

In routine selection, artificial screening techniques may show limits:

- the experimental size and correlatively the number of genotypes tested may be limited by technical facilities (Desprez-Loustau, 1990);

- artificial conditions may not always mimic the complexity of natural conditions favoring the tree-pest interaction. Poor correlations between results of artificial screening and field evaluation might exist. For instance, ...

Screening techniques based on leaves or cut-shoots or more generally on tree parts are appreciated because they are non destructive and repeatable (Desprez-Loustau, 1990, Lefèvre *et al.,* 1994). Early evaluation on seedlings also considerably increase selection efficiency per unit time (Martinsson, 1987).

In controlled conditions, host-pest interaction can be described simultaneously with traits referring to the host tree and with traits referring to the aggressor biology (Lefèvre *et al.*, 1997, Auger *et al.*, 1991). This breakdown of tree-aggressor interaction is a first step to the identification of the underlying resistance mechanisms.

Limits of biochemical markers

Indirect selection based on biochemical indicators of various families of compounds has looked promising but has seldom been translated into successful screening techniques.

General theories of plant defenses share the basic assumption that secondary compounds are responsible for plant resistance (Schopf, 1986). Variations of specific groups of chemicals such as terpenes or phenolics have been linked to host response to different biotic aggressors without any proof of their causal relationships (table 1). First approaches to come closer to the genetic basis of resistance mechanisms have used 2D protein electrophoresis to trap variations of the primary metabolites and corresponding enzyme activities (Ekramoddoullah *et al.*, 1993).

Table 1. Various types of biochemical indicators linked to tree response to different biotic aggressors.

Group of compounds	Tree-aggressor interaction	Reference
Phenolics		
stilbenes	*Picea sitchensis - fungi*	Woodward and Pearce, 1988
	Picea abies - C.polonica	Brignolas *et al.*, 1995
	Pinus taeda - C. minor	Hemingway *et al.*, 1977
	Pinus sylvestris - O.brunneo	Lieutier *et al.*, 1996
Flavonoids	*Pinus sylvestris - L. wingfieldii*	Bois, 1996
	Pinus sylvestris - Diprion pini	Auger *et al.*, 1991
	Picea abies - C.polonica	Brignolas *et al.*, 1995
	Larix decidua - Ips cembrae	Jung *et al.*, 1994
	Populus tremuloides - C. conflictana	Clausen *et al.*, 1989
Terpenes	*Pinus sylvestris - Tomicus piniperda*	Langström *et al.*, 1992
	Pinus taeda - Cronartium fusiforme	Rocwood, 1973
	Pinus pinaster - Dioryctria sylvestrella	Jactel *et al.*, 1997
Proteins	*Pinus lambertiana - Cronartium rubicola*	Ekramoddoullah and Hunt, 1993

Table 2. Minimum absolute values of genetic correlation between an indirect indicator and a resistance target trait for a relative selection efficiency (RE) superior or equal to 1 and for different combinations of heritabilities.

r_G minimum	$h^2_{resistance\ trait}$		
$h^2_{indicator}$	***0.2***	***0.4***	***0.6***
0.2	1.00	RE <1	RE <1
0.3	0.82	RE <1	RE <1
0.4	0.71	1.00	RE <1
0.5	0.63	0.89	RE <1
0.6	0.58	0.82	1.00
0.7	0.53	0.76	0.93
0.8	0.50	0.71	0.87

To interest indirect selection for tree resistance, biochemical markers do not need to be causally related to resistance. Selection efficiency is only determined by relative values of heritability for the indicator and target trait (h^2_{marker}, $h^2_{resist.}$) and by the absolute value of their genetic correlation (r_G) (Falconer, 1981).

$$ER = |r_G| \frac{h_{marker}}{h_{resist.}}$$

Because resistance to biotic aggressors is often related to fitness, heritability estimates of tree resistance traits are often comprised between 0.4 and 0.8 in optimal experimental design (Dieters *et al.*, 1996, Doudrick *et al.*, 1996b, Pichot and Teissier du Cros, 1993). Simulations of indirect selection relative efficiency for varying values of heritabilities and genetic correlation show that for such values, potential biochemical markers must have a high heritability and must be highly correlated to the target trait (table 2). Unfortunately, large environmental and physiological within-tree variation often reduces heritability of biochemical variables even in precise experimental conditions.

One danger of biochemical indirect selection is to restrict selection on only one underlying mechanism except if biochemical selection is defined as multitrait selection with one or several biochemical indicators per target resistance component.

Nevertheless, biochemical markers keep their interest in selection for resistance which can be evaluated only at late stage of tree development or which need heavy, costly and destructive methods (Auger *et al.*, 1991, Lieutier *et al.*, 1994, Jactel *et al.*, 1997). In that case maximum selection efficiency will not be achieved but a minimum genetic gain will be expected.

Advantages of tree-aggressor interaction decomposition

Although monogenic resistance mechanisms have been identified in forest trees (Kinloch and Byler, 1981), most of tree-aggressor interactions are complex responses involving several mechanisms controlled by many loci with probably epistatic effects. A first step used by tree geneticists to identify the different genes involved, is to breakdown tree response into components with supposed simple inheritance pattern. This approach is illustrated by the decomposition of poplar resistance to Melampsora larici-populina rust in the INRA breeding program (Lefèvre *et al.,* 1997) which is described hereafter.

Operational clonal selection is based on assessment of symptom intensity after natural inoculation. The observations are made at the end of summer after several natural cycles of infection. A 0-9 score is assigned to each ramet of the experiment. The natural inoculum in Orléans nursery is a mixture of different races which varies in its qualitative and quantitative composition every year (Pichot and Teissier du Cros, 1993, Pinon *et al.*, 1995).

For a better understanding of genetic basis of the qualitative and quantitative resistance observed at intra and interspecific levels, breakdown of resistance into epidemiological components is done independently for 4 known pathogen races in laboratory tests. Leaf-disks are sprayed with controlled inoculum suspension and maintained in growth chamber under controlled temperature (19°C) and photoperiod (16h light). Development of symptoms is observed during a 15 days-period. The latent period, the number of uredia, the average size of uredia are assessed on each leaf-disk and are used to calculate a susceptibility index (Lefèvre *et al.*, 1997) :

susceptibility index = (number of uredia)x(average size of uredia)/(latent period)

Since susceptibility index evaluated for the different pathogen races are closely linked to field resistance, genotype ranking based on laboratory tests can be considered confident for selection (Lefèvre *et al.*, 1997). Moreover, the susceptibility index for the most common two races are also highly correlated. The two epidemiological components linked respectively to infection intensity and sporulation are nearly independent within *Populus trichocarpa* species. Tree breeders would have the choice to select either *Populus trichocarpa* genotypes with few uredia of medium size, either genotypes with many uredia of small size.

Needs for a complete analysis of tree-aggressor-environment interaction

The phenotypic response of a tree to biotic aggressors is determined by an interactive function involving three major terms :

- the genetic information carried by the tree
- the genetic information carried by the aggressor which may induce specific response from the host
- the environmental conditions such as temperature, humidity,...

In selection experiments, tree breeders often concentrate on the host genetic variability for a given aggressor in given environmental conditions. Only few experiments analyze jointly host and insect or pest genetic variability (Quencez, 1995, Lefèvre *et al.*, 1997). Joint analysis of host and pest genetic variability should have high research priority in order to better understand site effect, specific resistance, overcoming events and coevolution process.

If varying environment changes the genotype resistance performances, GxE interaction could seriously limit durability of tree resistance over time and space. Estimations of GxE interaction are often limited to comparison of genotype rankings over field or laboratory tests. However, the range of environments prospected rarely reports limiting factors such as severe drought. Rigorous factorial experiments must be established in order to measure GxE interaction in very contrasted environments which may simulate the varying climate conditions over a 30-40 years period.

IDENTIFICATION OF PHYSIOLOGICAL AND MOLECULAR BASIS OF TREE RESISTANCE

Genetic variability for durable resistance will be fully exploited if all the underlying mechanisms are identified through complementary histological and biochemical studies. If quantitative genetics has proved to be an efficient method to estimate genetic value and to predict genetic gain, it is unsuited for dissecting complex resistance characters into discrete loci or for defining the roles of individual genes.

Molecular markers offer tree geneticists a possibility to answer basic genetic questions such as :

- the number of genes involved in tree resistance
- the distribution of genes over linkage groups
- the mode of gene action (additivity or dominance)
- the existence of interaction between genes ? (epistasis)

There are two molecular genetic approaches to understand and manipulate resistance traits with continuous phenotypical distribution (RTL = Resistance Trait Loci).

One is to complete a saturated linkage map with a suitable pedigree and to tag characters of interest with multiple genetic markers. Use of DNA codominant markers such as restricted fragment length polymorphism (RFLP) enables detection of heterozygotes and can be used to tag even recessive traits. The detection of RTL-marker associations is based on cosegregation analysis. A significant phenotypic difference between classes at a particular locus indicates that a RTL is probably nearby (Young, 1996, Nance *et al.*, 1992). Firstly developed for annual crops, specific theory is now available for forest trees for which inbred lines are not available.

Several host-disease interactions are under analysis on sugar pine, slash pine or poplar (Devey *et al.*, 1995, Newcombe and Bradshaw, 1996, Villar *et al.*, 1996). Interesting results will soon be obtained on the genetic architecture of complete or partial resistance at both intra and interspecific levels. But practical limits of RTL mapping can easily explain why no complex tree-insect interaction is under break down with the same tools.

1- Creating advanced pedigree selected for divergence for the resistance response needs time (Strauss *et al.*, 1992).

2- High number of individual trees must be evaluated jointly for their genotypical value for the markers and for their phenotypical resistance performance (Strauss *et al.*, 1992, Young, 1996). Efficiency of RTL detection is also tightly linked to the phenotypical scoring method of resistance. We go back here to the problem of improvement of tree resistance evaluation in genetic experiments.

3- The lack of linkage desequilibrium in forest tree populations requires evaluation of RTL-marker associations for different genetic backgrounds before using gene mapping for marker-assisted selection (Strauss *et al.*, 1992).

Theoretical considerations limit the use of RTL mapping for gene cloning and gene transformation in trees. QTL mapping is mainly based on random genomic DNA probes which give no information on gene function (Nance *et al.*, 1992, Strauss *et al.*, 1992). Resulting maps are linkage maps and not physical maps; precise location of loci is not known (Strauss *et al.*, 1992).

The alternative approach to begin RTL identification is to use genes with known metabolic function, cloned from other model species (Davis and Lawrence, 1994, Nance *et al.*, 1992). If co-segregation of such candidate genes and RTL is confirmed, the effective involvement of the candidate gene must be checked through genetic transformation.

DEVELOPMENT OF BREEDING STRATEGIES FOR DURABLE TREE RESISTANCE

All advanced tree breeding programs over the world recognize the need of durability of disease and insect resistance. Low durability or biological risks are often associated to increasing genetic uniformity resulting from selection.

Balance between development of improved genetic stocks and need for genetic variability conservation is provided by separate short-term and long-term breeding activities (Namkoong, 1991).

1- Short-term activities (corresponding to the present generation) are then limited to predictable biological risks and capture high genetic gains due to the narrowing of the genetic basis.

2- Long-term activities rely on recurrent but moderate selection to increase frequencies of resistant alleles in breeding populations of large size. Gene resource conservation provides genetic stocks for both predictable and unpredictable risks.

Short-term breeding activities

As underlined by Carson and Carson (1989), "durability is a property of host populations which has no real meaning at the level of individual genotypes ".

In theory, breeding for durable resistance could only be achieved partially for clonal forestry. The most effective strategy is to pyramide major genes for both qualitative and quantitative resistance in one genotype. If classical breeding is today the most common tool, marker-assisted selection will enable breeders to select directly on the basis of genotype rather than phenotype which can be especially helpful for time-consuming evaluation of resistance performance (Bernatzky and Mulcahy , 1992, Young, 1996). In order to accelerate recombination which is particularly long for forest tree, gene transformation could be used when available.

Most forest tree improved varieties are produced in seed orchards which include 20 to 50 selected parents. Provided that the subset of selected genotypes combines different resistance mechanisms or alleles, such artificial populations decrease the risk of resistance overcoming. Decomposition of resistance mechanisms is here the prerequisite step of both classical index selection or marker-assisted selection.

Because within-host genetic diversity is only one of the numerous factors controlling durability, appropriate complementary deployment strategies must be developed (Carson and Carson ,1989). Simulations of optimal patterns of planting in time and space are required.

Long-term breeding activities

In long-term breeding programs, durability is also considered at the population level in which individuals share the different genes involved in resistance mechanisms. To ensure that optimal genetic variability is included in the breeding populations, the effective population size should range between 600 to 1000 genotypes (Namkoong, 1991).

Management of genetic variability for various resistance components is facilitated by the creation of separate sub-populations for each resistance component. After resistance evaluation with adapted screening techniques , recombination of elite trees is done separately within each subpopulation in order to increase allele frequencies of the corresponding resistance component. Only recurrent selection based on moderate selection intensity can ensure a simultaneous pyrimiding of major and minor resistance genes in one or few genotypes (Cox, 1995). Once more, marker-assisted selection can play an efficient role in the selection process. At any given time, tree breeders can select elite genotypes from the different breeding sub-populations and create a varietal mixture which will combine different sets of resistance mechanisms. If new biotic aggressions appear or if the impact of a known aggressor increases, introduction of genetic variability for resistance patterns in improved material can be envisaged from the genetic resources conservation network.

CONCLUSION

To develop durable multiple resistance mechanisms, tree breeding requires deeper understanding of inheritance of resistance mechanisms in different environmental conditions and at different scales from the single gene to the entire tree. The achievement of these objectives will be accomplished by joint work of entomologists, pathologists, tree physiologists, molecular geneticists, ecologists. If tree breeders are able to answer about the control of biotic aggressions when sufficient genetic variability exists, their response is generally limited to the species level. In some cases, durability of pest resistance must be foreseen at the ecosystem level and management of genetic variability must not be only supported by tree breeders but also concerns policy approaches.

REFERENCES

AUGER M.A., JAY-ALLEMAND C., BASTIEN C., GERI C., 1991. Comestibilité de différents clones de pin sylvestre pour *Diprion pini* (Hym., Diprionidae) II- Relations entre le contenu des aiguilles de pins sylvestres et la mortalité des larves de *Diprion pini L.*. Journal of Applied Entomology, 111, 78-85.

BASTIEN C., GÉRI C., AUGER M.A., CHARPENTIER J.P., JAY-ALLEMAND C., 1995. *Spécificité des réactions de défense du pin sylvestre vis à vis du défoliateur Diprion pini.* AIP-INRA "Etude de la co-évolution des populations végétales domestiquées face à leurs agents pathogènes ou ravageurs", 21 Juin 1995, 63-74.

BERNATZKY R., MULCAHY D.L., 1992. Marker-aided selection in a backcross breeding program for resistance to chestnust blight in the American chestnut. *Canadian Journal of Forest Research,* 22 (7), 1031-1035.

BOIS E., 1996. *Rôle des composés phénoliques dans la résistance du pin sylvestre aux attaques de Scolytidae et de leurs champignons associés.* Thèse IIe cycle, Université d'Orléans, 152 p.

BRIGNOLAS F., LACROIX B., LIEUTIER F., SAUVARD D., DROUET A., CLAUDOT A.C., YART A., BERRYMAN A.A., CHRISTIANSEN E., 1995. Induced responses in phenolic metabolism in two Norway spruce clones after wounding and inoculations with Ophiostoma polonicum, a bark beetle associated fungus. *Plant Physiology,* 109, 821-827.

CARSON S.D., CARSON M.J., 1989. Breeding for resistance in forest trees - a quantitative genetic approach. *Annual Review of Phytopathology,* 27, 373-395.

CLAUSEN T.P., REICHARDT P.B., BRYANT J.P., WERNER R.A., POST K., FRISBY K., 1989. Chemical model for short-term induction in quaking aspen (*Populus tremuloides*) foliage against herbivores. *Journal of Chemical Ecology,* 15, 2335-2346.

COX T.S., 1995. Simultaneous selection for major and minor resistance genes. *Crop Science,* 35, 1337-1346.

DAVIS J.M., LAWRENCE S.D., 1994. Strategies to identify genes involved in forest tree defense. *Forest Genetics,* 1 (4), 219-226.

DESPREZ-LOUSTAU M.L., 1990. A cut-shoot bioassay for assessment of *Pinus pinaster* susceptibility to *Melampsora pinitorqua. European Journal of Forest Pathology,* 20, 386-391.

DESPREZ-LOUSTAU M.L., DUPUIS F., 1994. Variation in the phenology of shoot elongation between geographic provenances of maritime pine (*Pinus pinaster*)- implications for the synchrony with the phenology of the twisting rust fungus *Melampsora pinitorqua. Annales des Sciences forestières,* 51, 553-568.

DEVEY M.E., DELFINOMIX A., KINLOCH B.B., NEALE D.B., 1995. Random amplified polymorphic DNA markers tightly linked to a gene for resistance to white pine blister rust in sugar pine. *Proc. Natl. Acad. Sci. U.S.A.,* 92, 2066-2070.

DIETERS M.J., HODGE G.R., WHITE T.L., 1996. Genetic parameter estimates for resistance to rust (*Cronartium quercuum*) infection from full-SIB tests of Slash Pine (*Pinus eliottii*), modelled as functions of rust incidence. *Silvae Genetica,* 45 (4), 235-241.

DOUDRICK R.L., SCHMIDTLING R.C., NELSON C.D., 1996a. Host relationships of fusiform rust disease. I. Infection and pycnial production on slash pine and nearby tropical relatives. *Silvae Genetica,* 45 (2/3), 142-149.

DOUDRICK R.L., SCHMIDTLING R.C., NELSON C.D., 1996b. Host relationships of fusiform rust disease. II Genetic variation and heritability in typical and South Florida varieties of Slash pine. *Silvae Genetica,* 45 (2/3), 149-153.

EKRAMODDOULLAH A.K.M., HUNT R.S., 1993. Changes in protein profile of susceptible and resistant sugar pine foliage infected with white pine blister rust fungus, *Cronartium rubicola*. *Canadian Journal of Plant Pathology*, 15, 259-264.

FALCONER D.S., 1981. Introduction to quantitative genetics, Longman, New-York.

FLOATE D.K., WHITHAM T.G., 1993. The « hybrid bridge » hypothesis : host shifting via plant hybrid swamps. *American Naturalist*, 141, 651-662.

FLORENCE L.Z., HICKS R.R., 1980. Further evidence for introgression of *Pinus taeda* with *Pinus echinata*: electrophoretic variability and variation in resistance to *Cronartium fusiforme*. *Silvae Genetica*, 29, 41-43.

HEMINGWAY W.,MC GRAW G., BARRAS S.J., 1977. Polyphenols in *Ceratosystis minor* infected *Pinus taeda* : Fungal metabolites, phloem and xylem phenols. *J. Agric. Food. Chem.*, 25, 717-722.

JACTEL H., KLEINHENTZ M., RAFFIN A., MENASSIEU P., 1997. Comparison of different selection methods for the resistance to *Dioryctria sylvestrella* Ratz. (Lepidoptera : *Pyralidae*) in *Pinus pinaster* Ait. IUFRO S7.01 Symposium "Physiology and genetics of tree-phytophage interactions", Arcachon 31/08-05/09 1997.

JUNG V.P. ROHDE M., LUNDERSTÄT J., 1994. Induzierte resstenz im leigewebe der europäischen *lärche Larix decidua* (Mill) nach befall durch den groben lärchenborkenkäfer *Ips cembrae* (Heer) (Col., Scolytidae*). Journal of Applied Entomology,* 117, 427-433.

KINLOCH B.B., COMSTOCK M., 1981. Race of *Cronartium rubicola* virulent to major gene resistance in sugar pine. *Plant Disease*, 65, 604-605.

LANGSTRÖM B., HELLQVIST C., ERICSSON A., GREF R., 1992. Induced defence reaction in Scots pine following stem attacks by *Tomicus piniperda. Ecography*, 15, 318-327.

LEFÈVRE F., PICHOT C., PINON J., 1994. Intra- and interspecific inheritance of some components of the resistance to leaf rust (*Melampsora larici-populina* Kleb.) in poplars. *Theoretical and Applied Genetics*, 88, 501-507.

LEFÈVRE F., GOUÉ-MOURIER M.C., FAIVRE-RAMPANT P., VILLAR M., 1997. A single gene cluster controls incompatibility and partial resistance to various *Melampsora larici-populina* races in hybrid poplars. *Phytopathology* (accepted for publication)

LIEUTIER F., BRIGNOLAS F., PICRON V., YART A., BASTIEN C., 1994. Can phloem phenols be used as markers of Scots pine resistance to bark beetles ? In : USDA For. Serv. Gen. Techn. Rep. NC-183 (Ed.): Dynamics of forest herbivory : quest for pattern and principle, p.178-186.

LIEUTIER F., SAUVARD D., BRIGNOLAS F., PICRON V., YART A., BASTIEN C., JAY-ALLEMAND C., 1996. Changes in phenolic metabolites of Scots pine phloem induced by *Ophiostoma brunneo-ciliatum*, a bark beetle associated fungus. *European Journal of Forest Pathology*, 26, 145-158.

MARTINSSON O., 1987. Scots pine resistance to pine twist rust. Conformity between the resistance found in an artificial environment and field trials. *Silvae genetica*, 5 (1), 1520.

MEAGHER M.D., HUNT R.S., 1996. Heritability and gain of reduced spotting vs. Blister rust on Whestern White pine in Briush Columbia, Canada. *Silvae genetica*, 45 (2-3), 75-81.

NAMKOONG G., 1991. Maintaining genetic diversity in breeding for resistance in forest trees. *Annual Review of Phytopathology*, 29, 325-342.

NANCE W.L., TUSKAN G.A., NELSON C.D., DOUDRICK R.L., 1992. Potential applications of molecular markers for genetic analysis of host-pathogen systems in forest trees. *Canadian Journal of Forest Research*, 22 (7), 1036-1043.

NEWCOMBE G., BRADSHAW H.D.Jr., 1996. Quantitative trait loci conferring resistance in hybrid poplar to *Septoria populicola*, the cause of leaf spot. *Canadian Journal of Forest Research*, 2, 1943-1950.

PICHOT C., TEISSIER DU CROS E., 1993. Susceptibility of P.deltoides Bartr. to *Melampsora larici-populina* and *M. allii-populina*. II. Quantitative analysis of a 6x6 factorial mating design. *Silvae Genetica,* 42 (4/5), 188-199.

PINON J., LEFEVRE F., VILLAR M., POPE-DE-VALLAVIEILLE C., 1995. Structure et dynamique des populations de races de rouille dans des populations cultivées et sauvages de peupliers. AIP-INRA "Etude de la co-évolution des populations végétales domestiquées face à leurs agents pathogènes ou ravageurs", 21 Juin 1995, 123-133.

QUENCEZ C., 1995. *Incidence de la biodiversité du ravageur Diprion pini L. (Hym. Dipronidae) sur la résistance de différents clones de pin sylvestre (Pinus sylvestris L.).* Mémoire de DEA de biologie forestière, Université Henri Poincaré Nancy I, p 25.

ROCKWOOD D.L., 1973. Monoterpene-fusiform rust relationships in loblolly pine. *Phytopathology*, 63, 551-553.

RUBY J.L., WRIGHT J.W., 1976. A revised classification of geographic varieties of Scots pine. *Silvae Genetica*, 25, 169-175.

SCHOPF R., 1986. The effect of secondary needle compounds on the development of phytophagous insects. *Forest Ecology and Management*, 15, 54-64.

SLUDER E.R., 1993. Results at age 15 years from a half-diallel cross among 10 Loblolly pines selected for resistance to fusiform rust (*Cronartium quercuum* f. sp. *fusiforme*). *Silvae Genetica,* 42 (4/5), 223-230.

STRAUSS S.H., LANDE R., NAMKOONG G., 1992. Limitations of molecular-marker-aided selection in forest tree breeding. *Canadian Journal of Forest Research*, 22 (7), 1050-1061.

VILLAR M., LEFÈVRE F., BRADSHAW H.D., TEISSIER DU CROS E., 1996. Molecular genetics of rust resistance in poplars (*Melampsora larici-populina* Kleb./*Populus* sp.) by bulked segregant analysis in a 2x2 factorial mating design. *Genetics*, 143, 531-536.

WOODWARD S. PEARCE R.B., 1988. The role of stilbenes in resistance of Sitka spruce (*Picea sitchensis* (Bong.) Carr.) to entry of fungal pathogens. *Physiological and Molecular Plant Pathology*, 33, 127-149.

WU H.X., YING C.C., MUIR J.A., 1996. Effect of geographic variation and jack pine introgression on disease and insect resistance in lodgepole pine. *Canadian Journal of Forest Research*, 26, 711-726.

YOUNG N.D., 1996. QTL mapping and quantitative disease resistance in plants. *Annual Review of Phytopathology*, 34, 479-501.

Chapter 1

Tree Resistance Variability and Tree Selection for Resistance

Physiology and Genetics of Tree-Phytophage Interactions
Gujan (France), August 31 - September 5, 1997
Ed. INRA, Paris, 1999 (Les Colloques, n°90)

Interaction of the white pine weevil (*Pissodes strobi* Peck) and its hosts : arguments for coevolution

R.I. ALFARO[1], E.T. TOMLIN[2], J.H. BORDEN[2], K. LEWIS[1].

[1]*Pacific Forestry Centre, Canadian Forest Service, Victoria, BC. Canada. V8Z 1M5*

[2]*Centre for Pest Management, Dept. of Biological Sciences, Simon Fraser University, Burnaby, BC, Canada. V5A 1S6*

RESUME

The white pine weevil, *Pissodes strobi* Peck, is a serious pest of spruce (*Picea* spp.) and pine (*Pinus* spp.) regeneration in North America. Damage from this insect has forced forest managers to eliminate the planting of Sitka spruce (*Picea sitchensis* (Bong.) Carr), in much of coastal British Columbia. Genetic resistance to weevil damage has been demonstrated for both spruce and pine in Canada. To deploy host resistance in an Integrated Pest Management System it is critical to understand the processes which underlie this phenomenon. This paper reviews what we know of genetic resistance in the weevil/spruce system and considers if there are arguments that could be made to favor a hypothesis of coevolution of the weevil and its hosts.

INTRODUCTION

The white pine weevil, *Pissodes strobi* Peck (Coleoptera: Curculionidae) is the most serious native pest of regenerating Sitka (*Picea sitchensis* (Bong.) Carr), white (*P. glauca* (Moench) Voss), and Engelmann spruce (*P. engelmanni* Parry) and their hybrids, in western North America. In eastern North America its hosts include eastern white pine, *Pinus strobus* L., Jack pine, *Pinus banksiana* Lamb., Norway spruce, *Picea abies* (L.) Karst, Scots pine, *Pinus sylvestris* L., white spruce, and red spruce, *Picea rubens* Sarg (Humble *et al.*, 1994).

Genetic trials in British Columbia have revealed resistance to this weevil as determined by reduced number of attacks per tree (Alfaro and Ying 1990; Alfaro *et al.*, 1996a; Kiss and Yanchuk 1991; Ying 1991), and much research has focused on determining the mechanisms of resistance. Resistant genotypes are now available for commercial use. However, we must carefully consider how these genotypes are to be deployed to minimize the coevolutionary interactions between the weevil and its host that could render these trees susceptible.

Ehrlich and Raven (1964), proposed that the evolution of plant secondary substances, and the stepwise evolutionary responses to these by phytophagous organisms, have been the dominant factors in the evolution of butterflies and other phytophagous insects. While it has been generally accepted that coevolution influences plant-insect interactions, the importance of plant chemistry, the mechanisms by which coevolution proceeds, and the importance of coevolution relative to other influences has been vigorously debated (Slatkin and Smith 1979; Thompson 1982; Futuyma 1983; Gould 1988; Berenbaum and Zangerl 1988; Thompson 1994). Coevolution may be reciprocal or diffuse (Janzen 1980; Fox 1981; Strong *et al.*, 1984; Fox 1988), and may only occur in the case of intimate associations between a herbivore and its host (Fox 1988).

For coevolution to occur, herbivores must impose selection on their host plant. To demonstrate this, the defensive trait must be genetically variable and subject to some form of selection (Rausher 1996). Determining the selection pressure affecting host range requires: examination of the ecological factors affecting host selection, genetic analyses of host preference and larval performance, and physiological and biochemical studies on how insects cope with plant defenses, such as noxious compounds (Thompson 1988).

This paper reviews what we know of genetic resistance and ecological determinants of host selection in the weevil-spruce system; it considers if there are arguments that could be made to favor a hypothesis of coevolution of the white pine weevil and its hosts.

Intimate association between weevil and host

The eggs are laid from late April to June in punctures made by females in the bark just below the buds of the terminal (year-old) shoot. The larvae mine downward beneath the bark of the terminal shoot (leader), feeding in the phloem, girdling and killing the terminal. By midsummer, they construct oval pupal cells in the wood and pith, and pupate within a "cocoon" of wood fibers. Most adults emerge from the leaders in late August and September, feed on the stem and branches, and then overwinter primarily in the duff (Alfaro 1994). Occasionally, and especially in the interior of British Columbia, adults will re-attack below the previously attacked leader. Because *P. strobi* kills the apical shoot, the ability of the host tree to compete for apical dominance is reduced. Repeatedly attacked trees may become suppressed and may eventually die.

Geographic sources of resistance

Genetic studies in British Columbia have demonstrated significant family variation in the attack index, with high heritability of resistance (h^2i=0.39, h^2f=0.7, King *et al.*, 1997). Capitalizing on this variation, a coevolution model would predict that populations subjected to high herbivory would tend to develop high resistance levels. Ying (1991) postulated that extreme selection pressure in high weevil hazard zones in British Columbia increased the proportion of resistant trees in these areas. This statement seems to be holding true in British Columbia. Variation in the resistance of white spruce to *P. strobi* was related to ecoclimatic conditions of the place of origin of the trees (Alfaro *et al.*, 1996a). Parents from locations with high weevil hazard or high weevil populations yielded the highest proportions of resistant trees. These sites are primarily of low elevation and latitude, especially in Moist-Warm habitats of the Sub-Boreal-Spruce (SBS) biogeoclimatic zone. For Sitka spruce, known geographic sources of resistant genotypes are mainly at the edge of its range where warm, dry summers favour the weevil. These sources are the Haney area of the Fraser Valley, the eastern border of Vancouver Island and the inland Skeena River area, where Sitka and white spruce hybridize. However, resistance has not developed in all such areas, e.g., the north east corner of the Olympic Peninsula and adjacent areas in Washington State.

Defenses of spruce against weevils

(i) Defenses at the site of weevil oviposition

Resin canals play an important role in tree defenses and have evolved numerous times in the plant kingdom (Farrell *et al.*, 1991). Weevil resistant trees in Sitka and white spruce families had significantly denser resin canal systems in the cortex of the apical shoot (the weevil's oviposition site and larval habitat) than those in susceptible families(Alfaro *et al.*, 1997; Tomlin and Borden 1994, 1997a). Similar differences occur in the resin canal density of *Pinus strobus* (Stroh and Gerhold 1965). These studies demonstrated significant family variation and potential for selection. However, Tomlin and Borden (1997b) indicated that some resistant genotypes may rely on resistance mechanisms other than resin canal density.

Alfaro (1996) and Jou (1971) found that resin canal density in the bark of Sitka spruce is higher in the apical shoot than in the lower internodes (Fig. 1). Resin canal density decreases as the leader ages through the season, due to increasing leader diameter, addition of phloem layers to the cortex, and occlusion of existing canals.

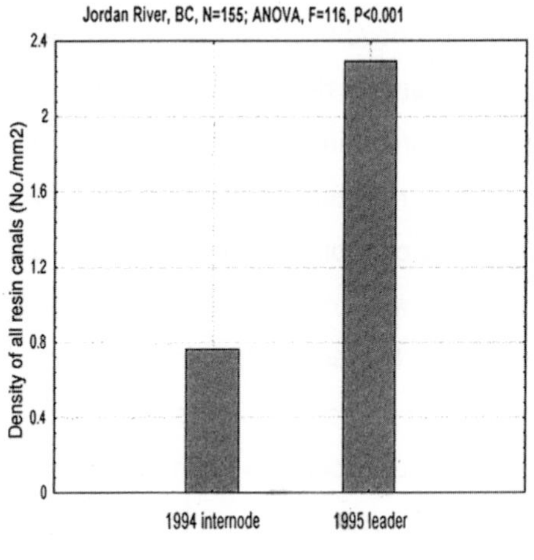

Fig. 1. Resin canals have a higher density in the leader (site of oviposition and larval development) than in the one-year old internode. This decrease in resin canal density with age happens in resistant and susceptible trees. Based on 155 trees from Jordan River, British Columbia.

(II) Reduced apparency

Tomlin and Borden (1997a) found that most resistant clones of Sitka spruce have lower amounts of volatile foliar terpenes than susceptible clones. It was hypothesized that these trees were avoiding attack by weevils through reduced apparency (Feeney 1975).

(III) Resin composition

Tomlin and Borden (1996) observed higher amounts of resin acids in the cortex of resistant Sitka spruce genotypes when compared to susceptible genotypes. Resin acids could be involved in determining adult host selection by acting as repellents or they may reduce growth and survival of larvae.

(IV) Induced resinosis.

Dissection of white and Sitka spruce leaders in which weevil attack had failed (eggs had been laid but no adult emergence occurred), demonstrated the existence of an induced defense reaction (Alfaro 1995; Alfaro *et al.*,1996b). The response was initiated shortly after feeding and oviposition in the attacked shoot and consisted of the cambium switching from producing normal tracheids and parenchyma ray cells to the production of traumatic resin canals, arranged in a ring fashion in the developing xylem. Artificial wounding experiments demonstrated that resistant trees are capable of a faster and repeated response whereas susceptible trees respond more slowly and generally produce a single ring of traumatic resin canals (Tomlin and Borden 1997b). Moreover, increased production of monoterpenes near the site of wounding raises the terpene to resin acid ratio, apparently resulting in highly fluid resin which could readily "drown" eggs and first instar larvae (unpublished results).

Weevil adaptations to avoid defenses

(i) Adaptations to sabotage or circumvent bark resin canal defenses

Microscopic observations of weevil feeding and oviposition cavities in the leader indicate that *P. strobi* avoids puncturing resin canals while feeding (Stroh and Gerhold 1965; Overhulser and Gara 1975; Alfaro 1995). Consuming the tissue around the resin canals effectively cuts the epithelial cell (which produce the resin) from their food supply in the vascular bundles, leading to deactivation and death of the resin canal structure (Fig. 2). In addition, Overhulser and Gara (1981) observed that resin canals adjacent to oviposition punctures became occluded, and presumably deactivated.

When confined to high-resin-canal resistant trees, gravid females oviposited low in the stem, below the leader, where resin canal density was reduced by the increase in stem diameter (a dilution effect) (Alfaro 1996).

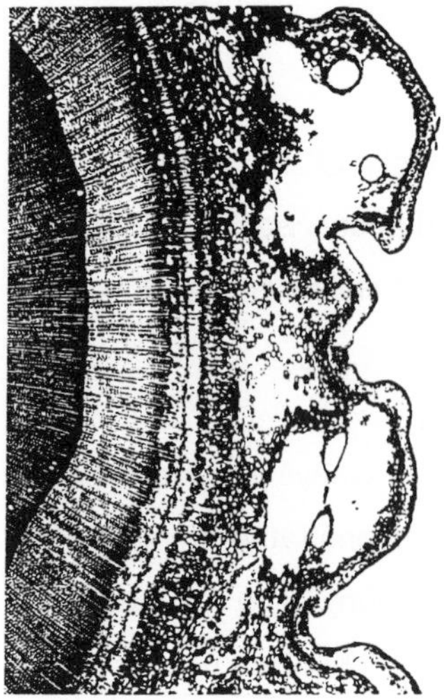

Fig. 2. Cross section of a spruce leader after feeding by *Pinus strobi.* The weevil has consumed the tissues around resin canals while avoiding puncturing them. This isolates the resin canals from their nutrient supply in the vascular bundles.

(ii) Mass egg laying and larval aggregation: adaptations to quickly overcome induced defenses.

Mass oviposition (numerous eggs deposited in a short time) and larval aggregation seem to be adaptations enabling *P. strobi* to deal with induced defenses. These behaviours ensure quick colonization of the cortex and secure that at least some individuals will survive the tree defenses. Mass attack that severs resin ducts is common in bark beetles (Scolytidae) (Rudinsky 1962, Raffa 1991). Resin flows for a short time until the resources of the host are depleted, and the tissue becomes suitable for colonization.

(iii) Host selection behaviour.

Tomlin and Borden (1996) showed that weevils are able to avoid at least some resistant genotypes of Sitka spruce by detecting the presence of feeding and oviposition deterrents. In addition, Hamel *et al.*, (1994) observed that eastern *P. strobi* prefer Norway spruce, an introduced host, over two native hosts, eastern white pine and white spruce.

(iv) Adaptations to reduce genome waste.

Gara and Wood (1989), Sahota *et al.*, (1994) and Leal *et al.*, (1997) indicate that female weevils confined to the leaders of resistant trees do not mature or regress their ovaries. Thus, a female weevil may detect an unsuitable host and, via endocrine feed-back, shut off oviposition. We interpret this as an adaptation of female *P. strobi* to conserve its genome in the likelihood that a more suitable host would be found.

Synchrony of weevil and tree phenology

The work of Hulme (1995) and the authors (unpublished) indicates that resistant and susceptible spruce families have different phenologies, a trait that is under strong genetic control (Cannell *et al.*, 1985). Resistant families start development earlier in the season than susceptible families, apparently leaving susceptible trees vulnerable during a critical oviposition window. Weevils lay eggs only if the leader is in a susceptible stage, i.e., its phenology has progressed to the point at which resin canal density is low, and offspring survival is likely. Resistant trees seem to go through this susceptible window early in the season when few weevils may be available for attack. Later, when more weevils are active, trees are capable of resisting attacks via induced resinosis. It appears that the weevil has countered these seasonally variable resistance levels (Hulme 1995) by development of a life cycle with significant variation, particularly with respect to the amount of heat required to complete the various life stages (emergence from overwintering, timing of colonization of the leader). A variable life cycle ensures that some weevils within a population will be in synchrony with the host.

Using DNA markers, mean expected heterozygosity and percent polymorphic loci were shown to average 0.24 and 71.8 respectively within populations of *P. strobi* in British Columbia (Lewis 1995). Thus, populations of the weevil appear to be quite rich in genetic variation and this could be reflected in highly variable behavioral attributes within and between populations.

Should coevolution be considered?

Pissodes strobi has an intimate association with its host. Resistant populations of spruce are correlated with high weevil densities, and defensive traits are correlated with resistance to attack by weevils in the field. Weevils show evidence of several types of adaptation to host defenses, and there is phenotypic, and almost certainly genotypic variation in the life cycles of both the weevil and its hosts. Assuming that *P. strobi* and its hosts have coevolved, and that the capacity for coevolution persists, resistant genotypes must be used in a manner which avoids selection for weevil biotypes that will overcome resistance.

REFERENCES

ALFARO R.I., 1994. The white pine weevil in British Columbia: biology and damage. Pp. 7-22 in: *The White Pine Weevil: Biology, Damage and Management.* FRDA Report No. 226, R.I. Alfaro, G. Kiss, and R.G. Fraser (eds.). Proceedings of a symposium held January 19-21, 1994 in Richmond, British Columbia.

ALFARO R.I., 1995. An induced defense reaction in white spruce to attack by white pine weevil. *Can. J. For. Res.* 25:1725-1730.

ALFARO R.I., 1996. Feeding and oviposition preferences of the white pine weevil on resistant and susceptible Sitka spruce clones in laboratory bioassays. *Environ. Entomol.* 25: 1012-1019.

AlFaro R.I, HE F., Tomlin E., KISS G. 1997. Resistance of white spruce to the white pine weevil related to resin canal density. *Can. J. Bot.* In Press.

ALFARO R.I., HE F., KISS G.K., KING J., YANCHUK a. 1996a. Resistance of white spruce to white pine weevil: Development of a resistance index. *For. Ecol. Manag.* 81:51-62.

ALFARO R.I., KISS G.K., KING J.,YANCHUK A., 1996b. Variation in the induced resin response of white spruce to attack by the white pine weevil. *Can. J. For. Res.* 6: 967-972.

ALFARO R.I., YING C.C., 1990. Levels of Sitka spruce weevil, *Pissodes strobi* (Peck), damage among Sitka spruce provenances and families near Sayward, British Columbia. *Can. Ent.* 122: 607-615.

BERENBAUM M., ZANGERL., 1988. Stalemates in the coevolutionary arms race: syntheses, synergisms and sundry other sins. Pp. 113-132 in: K.S. Spencer, (ed). Chemical mediation of coevolution. *Academic Press*, N.Y.

CANNEL M.G.R., MURRAY M.B., SHEPPARD L.J., 1985. Frost avoidance by selection for late budburst in *Picea sitchensis. J. Appl. Ecol.* 22:931-941.

EHRLICH P.R., RAVEN P.H., 1964. Butterflies and plants: a study in coevolution. Evolution 18: 586-608.

FARRELL B.D., DUSSOURD D.E., MITTER C., 1991. Escalation of plant defense: Do latex and resin canals spur plant diversification. *Am. Nat.* 138: 881-900.

FEENEY P., 1975. Plant apparency and chemical defense. *Rec. Adv. Phytochem.* 10: 1-39.

FOX L.R., 1981. Defense and dynamics in plant-herbivore systems. *Amer. Zool.* 21: 853-864.

FOX L.R., 1988. Diffuse coevolution within complex communities. *Ecology* 69: 906-907.

FUTUYMA D.J., 1983. Evolutionary interactions among herbivorous insects and plants. Pp. 207-231 in D.J. Futuyma and M. Slatkin, (eds). *Coevolution.* Sinaur Assoc., Sunderland, Mass.

GARA R.I., WOOD J.O., 1989. Termination of reproductive diapause in the Sitka spruce weevil, Pissodes strobi (Peck) (Col., Curculionidae) in western Washington. *J. Appl. Ent.* 108: 156-163.

GOULD F. 1988. Genetics of pairwise and multispecies plant-herbivore coevolution. Pp. 13-55. in K.S. Spencer, (ed). *Chemical mediation of coevolution. Academic Press,* N.Y.

HAMEL M., M, Bauce E., LAVALLEE R., 1994. Feeding and oviposition preferences of adult white pine weevil (Coleoptera: Curculionidae) in Quebec. *Environ. Entomol.* 23:923-929.

HUMBLE L.M., HUMPHREYS N., VAN SICKLE G.A., 1994. Distribution and hosts of the white pine weevil, Pissodes strobi (Peck), in Canada. Pp. 68-75 in: *The White Pine Weevil: Biology, Damage and Management.* FRDA Report No. 226, R.I. Alfaro, G. Kiss, and R.G. Fraser (eds.). Proceedings of a symposium held January 19-21, 1994 in Richmond, British Columbia.

HULME M., 1995. Resistance of translocated Sitka spruce to damage by Pissodes strobi related to tree phenology. *J. Econ. Entomol.* 88:1525-1530.

JANZEN D.H., 1980. When is it coevolution? *Evolution* 34: 611-612.

JOU S.-M., 1971. *The resin canal system in Sitka spruce,* Picea sitchensis *(Bong.).* M.Sc. Thesis, University of Washington, Seattle. 88 p.

KING J.N., YANCHUK A.D., KISS G.K., ALFARO R.I., 1997. Genetic and phenotypic relationships between weevil *(Pissodes strobi)* resistance and height growth in spruce populations of British Columbia. *Can. J. For. Res.* 27: 732-739.

KISS G.K., YANCHUK A.D., 1991. Preliminary evaluation of genetic variation in interior spruce in British Columbia. *Can. J. For. Res* 21: 230-234.

LEAL I., WHITE E.E., SAHOTA T.S., MANVILLE J.F., 1997. Differential expression of the vilellogenin gene in the spruce terminal weevil feeding on resistant versus susceptible host trees. Insect Biochem. Molec. *Biol.* 27 (6): 569-575.

LEWIS K.G., 1995. *Genetic variation among populations of* Pissodes strobi *(white pine weevil) reared from* Picea *and* Pinus *hosts as inferred from RAPD markers.* M.Sc. Thesis, Faculty of Forestry, University of British Columbia, Vancouver. 232 p.

OVERHULSER D.L., GARA R.i., 1975. *Studies on Sitka spruce weevil- Host interactions with emphasis on spruce defense mechanisms.* University of Washington, Centre for Ecosystem Studies, College of Forest Resources, Seattle, Washington. 45 p.

OVERHULSER D.L., GARA R.I., 1981. Occluded resin canals associated with egg cavities made by shoot-infesting *Pissodes. For. Sci.* 27: 297-298.

RAFFA K.F., 1991. Induced defensive reactions in conifer-bark beetle systems. In: *Phytochemical induction by herbivores,* D.W. Tallamy and M.J.Raupp (eds.). John Wiley and Sons Inc. N.Y.

RAUSHER M.D., 1996. Genetic analysis of coevolution between plants and their natural enemies. *Trends in Genetics* 12: 212-217.

RUDINSKY, J.A., 1962. Ecology of the Scolytidae. *Ann. Rev. Entomol.* 7:327-348

SAHOTA T.S., MANVILLE J.H., WHITE E., 1994. Interaction between Sitka spruce weevil and its host *Picea sitchensis* (Bong) Carr.: A new resistance mechanism. *Can. Entomol.* 126: 1067-1074.

SLATKIN M., SMITH J.M., 1979. Models of coevolution. *Quarterly Review of Biology* 54: 233-263.

STRONG D.R., LAWTON J.H., SOUTHWOOD SIR. R., 1984. Pp. 200-219 in: *Insects on plants. Community patterns and mechanisms.* Blackwell Scientific Publications, Oxford.

STROH R.C., GERHOLD H.D., 1965. Eastern white pine characteristic related to weevil feeding. *Silvae Genetica* 14: 160-169.

THOMPSON J.N., 1982. Pp. 37-58 in: *Interaction and coevolution.* John Wiley and Sons, N.Y.

THOMPSON J.N., 1988. Coevolution and alternate hypotheses on insect/plant interactions. *Ecology* 69: 893-895.

THOMPSON J.N., 1994. Pp. 203-276 in: *The Coevolutionary Process.* Univ. of Chicago Press, Chicago, Ill.

TOMLIN E., BORDEN J.H., 1994. Development of a multicomponent resistance index for Sitka spruce resistant to the white pine weevil. Pp. 117-133 in*: The White Pine Weevil: Biology, Damage and Management.* FRDA Report No. 226, R.I. Alfaro, G. Kiss, and R.G. Fraser (eds.). Proceedings of a symposium held January 19-21, 1994 in Richmond, British Columbia.

TOMLIN E., BORDEN J.H., 1996. Feeding responses of the white pine weevil, *Pissodes strobi* (Peck) (Coleoptera: Curculionidae), in relation to host resistance in British Columbia. *Can. Entomol.* 128: 539-549.

TOMLIN E., BORDEN J.H., 1997a. Thin bark and high density of outer resin ducts: interrelated resistant traits in Sitka spruce against the white pine weevil (Coleoptera: Curculionidae). *J. Econ. Entomol.* 90:235-240.

TOMLIN E., BORDEN J.H., 1997b. Multicomponent index for evaluating resistance by Sitka spruce to the white pine weevil (Coleoptera: Curculionidae). *J. Econ. Entomol.* 90:704-714.

YING C.C., 1991. Genetic resistance to the white pine weevil in Sitka spruce. B.C. Ministry of Forests Res. *Note No. 106.* Victoria, B.C. Canada.

Physiology and Genetics of Tree-Phytophage Interactions
Gujan (France), August 31 - September 5, 1997
Ed. INRA, Paris, 1999 (Les Colloques, n°90)

Screening Norway spruce (*Picea abies* (L.) Karst.) for resistance to white pine weevil (*Pissodes strobi* (Peck))

R. LAVALLÉE, G. DAOUST, D. RIOUX

Natural Resources Canada, Canadian Forest Service, Laurentian Forestry Centre, P.O. Box 3800, Sainte-Foy, QC G1V 4C7, CANADA

RESUME

This study reflects the initial steps in the development of Norway spruce trees resistant to white pine weevil and suitable for Quebec conditions. Weevils were caged on the terminal leaders of 67 clones over two years. Adults of the new generation were counted and weighed alive and the number of oviposition and feeding punctures, the length of the leaders and the length of damage under the bark were measured. Also, another group of 8 clones was used to test the influence of insect feeding on the formation of traumatic resin canals. Results demonstrated that the number of feeding and oviposition punctures was not affected by clones. The adult mean weight, the number of nymphal chambers, and the damage length were significantly affected by clone and per year. The use of a relative performance index to reduce the clone*year interaction is discussed. Also, observations under the microscope demonstrated that insect punctures induced the formation of traumatic resin canals into the xylem as well as into the live bark.

INTRODUCTION

Norway spruce (*Picea abies* (L.) Karst.) was introduced as a reforestation species in Quebec in the 1920s. The majority of the current plantations come from older plantations managed as seed stands. Since 1964, more than 200 million seedlings have been planted in Quebec. This species was very popular between 1984 and 1994, with a peak of 18 million seedlings planted in 1988. At present, fewer than 2 million seedlings are planted annually. This decline is largely caused by the white pine weevil (*Pissodes strobi* (Peck)), which produces damage similar to that observed on white pine (*Pinus strobus* L.) (Lavallée *et al.*, 1990). In 1996, the weevil was present in 77% of the Norway spruce plantations in Quebec (G. Gagnon, Pers. Comm.) and more generally in 26% of the Quebec spruce plantations (Ministère des Ressources naturelles du Québec, 1997).

Few methods are available to control weevil populations. Among them, tests are conducted to demonstrate if it is possible to enhance natural biological control by modifying the procedure for removing infested leaders (Lavallée *et al.*, 1997). In addition, as previous studies demonstrated that site characteristics can play a key role in population dynamics (Archambault *et al.*, 1993; Lavallée *et al.*, 1996), better site selection and a survey into specific stands could reduce the impact of the weevil. Likewise, other strategies such as using resistant trees in reforestation programs could help in the development of an integrated pest management system for Norway spruce. In western Canada, tree resistance to white pine weevil has been documented on Sitka and white spruce (Alfaro *et al.*, 1997, Tomlin and Borden, 1997). In eastern North America, tree resistance to white pine weevil has been reported for Norway spruce (Holst, 1955; 1963; Coleman *et al.*, 1987) but resistant Norway spruces are still not available for reforestation.

Caged insects can be used to test insect-plant resistance screening (Smith *et al.*, 1994). The objectives are to study the variability in the biological performance of the white pine weevil placed on Norway spruce clones and to identify resistant genotypes for a breeding program. The aptitude of Norway spruce to resist white pine weevil attack by producing defense mechanisms is also evaluated.

MATERIALS AND METHODS

Insect collection and rearing in spring

Weevils were collected in an 8-year-old Norway spruce plantation located near Saint-Gédéon (46°02'50"; 70°40'20") at the beginning of the oviposition period in 1994 (17-22 May) and 1996 (27-31 May). Insects were kept on fresh branch sections at 2°C, which allows feeding but not oviposition, and they were sexed before use according to Lavallée *et al.* (1993).

Resistance screening

Field work was conducted in 1994 and 1996 in a 10-year-old (1994) clonal bank located near Valcartier, 50 km north of Quebec City. This clonal bank contained 260 Norway spruce clones from which 67 were selected for their rusticity and good growth capacity. Each clone was represented by 10 ramets (5 ramets / block). There was no randomization of the clones inside each block. In 1994, fewer than 1% of the ramets were attacked by a natural weevil population.

On the terminal leader of two ramets per block, three males and three females were caged in a fine-mesh cloth sleeve before tree growth resumed. Adults were introduced at the beginning of June (9 June 1994; 7 June 1996) and left in cages until August. In 1996, the same experimental design was used except that two other ramets were selected to avoid any possible induction effect of a previous host.

The leaders were collected in August (16 August 1994; 14 August 1996) to document the insect biological performance. At that time of the year, larval development is completed but adults of the new generation are still inside the leaders (Lavallée *et al.*, 1990). Insects previously introduced were removed from the cages and leader length was measured. Leaders were kept individually in cardboard cylinders under greenhouse conditions to allow the emergence of the new adult generation from mid-July to mid-September. Leaders were observed daily and each collected adult was individually weighed alive. At the end of emergence, some external characteristics related to insect behavior (number of oviposition and feeding punctures; damage length under bark) were noted and thereafter leaders were dissected to determine the number of nymphal chambers. A new variable expressing the insect performance was calculated with the ratio of number of oviposition punctures over the number of nymphal chambers.

After the appropriate transformation to achieve variance homogeneity and normality of the residuals, partial correlation coefficients were calculated with the MANOVA instruction (GLM procedure, SAS Institute Inc., 1990).

Induction effect

In 1996, in the same clonal bank, eight clones were selected to study the influence of weevil feeding and oviposition on bark growth. Two ramets per clone per block were selected for insect treatment and control. Two adults of each sex were introduced into a similar sleeve cage on 10 June and were allowed to feed and oviposit over 15 days. Then, intact and attacked leaders were cut and sample sections of the shoot taken as soon as possible while the other leaders were stored at 2°C until being used.

For routine light microscopy, the samples were fixed with 2.5% glutaraldehyde in 0.1 M sodium cacodylate buffer (SCB) (pH 7.2) for 2-3 h, rinsed three times with SCB before postfixation with 1% OsO_4 in SCB for 1 h. They were gradually dehydrated with ethanol and embedded in Epon 812. Sections (1 μm) were stained with toluidine blue O and safranin O and observed with a Reichert Polyvar microscope.

For fluorescence microscopy, some samples were embedded in Tissue-Tek O.C.T. compound at -15°C. Sections (20 μm) were obtained with a Reichert Histostat cryomicrotome. The sections were stained with phloroglucinol-HCl to quench the autofluorescence of lignin and the autofluorescence of the resin and suberin was revealed using the BP 330-380 exciter filter with a DS 420 separator mirror and a LP 418 barrier filter (violet illumination).

RESULTS AND DISCUSSION

Resistance screening

The number of oviposition and feeding punctures made by caged adults was not significantly affected by clones (Table 1). This could indicate that under no-choice conditions, in which the insect has to feed to survive, these criteria might not be informative. According to Raffa and Berryman (1982b), feeding stimulant and incitant are present in the bark of resistant and susceptible lodgepole pine.

Other variables like the adult mean weight, the number of nymphal chambers, the length of damage under the bark and leader length were statistically affected by the clone (Tab. 1). From all the criteria studied, the number of nymphal chambers seems to be the most useful in relation to population dynamics. The significant variation between clones in the number of nymphal chambers indicated that survival is affected by the clones. In cages, under these no-choice conditions where the insects cannot leave the plant, we measured antibiosis (*sensu* Painter, 1951) where egg hatching, insect growth and survival were affected (Smith *et al.*, 1994).

Table 1. Analysis of variance on insect performance and leader length for both years of treatments.

	Oviposition punctures		Feeding punctures	
	F	Pr	F	Pr
Clone (C)	1.2	0.1927	1.2	0.2495
Year (Y)	5.6	0.0208	130.0	0.0001
Y*C	1.3	0.1396	1.0	0.5271
	Adult mean weight		Nymphal chambers	
	F	Pr	F	Pr
Clone (C)	3.0	0.0001	3.5	0.0001
Year (Y)	8.9	0.0040	4.2	0.0433
Y*C	1.5	0.0457	2.0	0.0032
	Length of damage under bark		Leader length	
	F	Pr	F	Pr
Clone (C)	3.4	0.0001	3.1	0.0001
Year (Y)	38.4	0.0001	537.4	0.0001
Y*C	2.1	0.0014	1.8	0.0084

Table 2. Partial correlation between variables in 1994 and 1996.

	r	Pr
Adult mean weight	-0.05	0.7339
Leader length	0.36	0.0023
Feeding punctures	0.03	0.7908
Oviposition punctures	0.039	0.7523
Nymphal chambers	-0.126	0.3097
Damage under bark	0.118	0.3402
Performance index	-0.209	0.0899

However, using the ratio of number of oviposition punctures over the number of nymphal chambers, an index that is more related to tree resistance could be developed. This performance index integrates the insect pressure exerted on the tree by oviposition intensity and also the insect development success by the number of nymphal chambers. This index was calculated and shown to be significantly affected by clone ($P<0.01$) but not by year ($P=0.62$) and the year*clone interaction ($P=0.21$) was not significant. Therefore, this value could reflect more precisely the host-insect interaction.

With some of the variables under study, the year*clone effect is particularly important to consider since it indicates that the response expressed one year may be different the year after. It also means that a clone considered as resistant one year may not be resistant the year after. This aspect is also expressed by the partial correlation coefficients between the data of a single variable obtained during two years when only the leader length and the performance index were significant at 10% (Tab. 2). The clonal variation between years is difficult to explain but important to consider. As mentioned by Smith *et al.* (1994), resistance is dependent on several interacting factors involving the insect, the plant and the environment. Working with the pine reproduction weevil (*Cylindrocopturus eatoni*), Miller (1950) observed a year to year variability in the resistance of his hybrid pines. In the present study, weather conditions may have played an important role in modulating plant and insect response. If we consider only rain precipitation, June 1994 was a rainy month (month=213 mm; mean=110 mm) compared with July (month=168 mm; mean=119 mm). In 1996, it was the opposite trend between June (month=143; mean=110) and July (month=231 mm; mean=118). Miller (1950) observed that irrigation improved tree vigor and helped vigorously growing trees to better survive reproduction weevil attack. Tree physiology and insect development may have been differently affected by the availability of water at different growth periods. Hulme (1995) reported that resistance status may be affected by tree phenology and tree phenology can be affected by water availability (Kozlowski *et al.*, 1991).

Induction

Examinations under the microscope showed the regular formation of a band of traumatic resin canals in the xylem (Fig. 1), as reported by Alfaro (1995). It was also possible to confirm the observations of Overhulser and Gara (1981) that some of the extant resin canals located

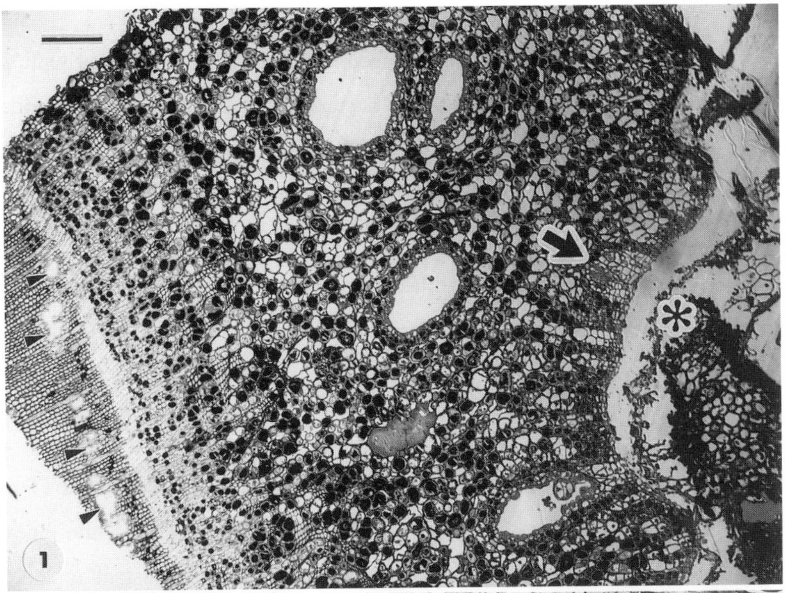

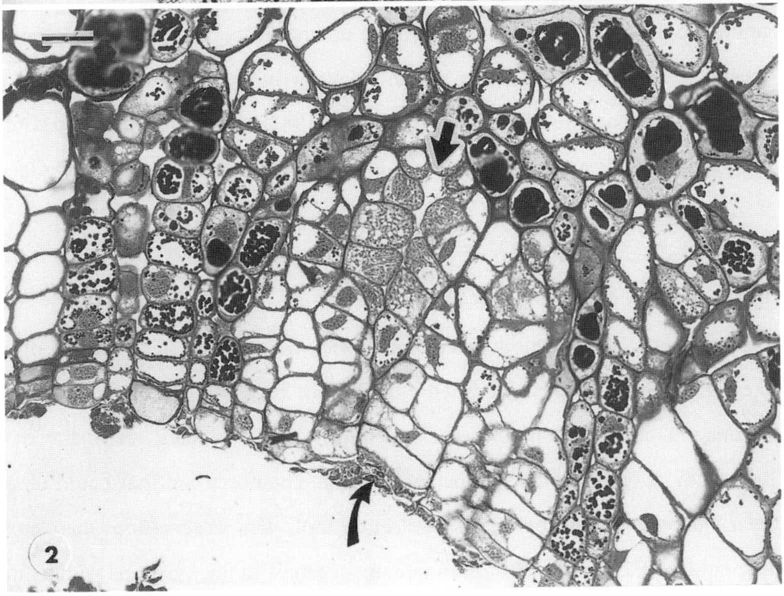

Figure 1. Overview of bark tissues adjacent to a cavity (*) caused by the insect that is partially filled with remains of necrotic cells. Constitutive resin canals are shown in the cortex as are some traumatic resin canals formed in the xylem (arrowheads). The arrow points to an area containing a traumatic resin canal that is presented at higher magnification in Figure 2. Bar = 200 μm.

Figure 2. High magnification of the area pointed to by the arrow in Figure 1. A traumatic resin canal (arrow) bordered by cells with dense cytoplasm is in formation next to a cavity made by the insect. It was common to observe separations within the band of suberized cells (curved arrow) forming the necrophylactic periderm that likely indicated that these cells were not well penetrated by the embedding medium. Bar = 30 μm.

either in the vicinity of the egg chambers or the feeding holes became occluded with time as a result of the proliferation of epithelial cells. The occurrence of a necrophylactic periderm was also noted around the punctures made by the insect, as regularly described following wounding (Biggs, 1992) or infection. The formation of new resin canals adjacent to the weevil punctures (Figs. 1 and 2) was also observed. As revealed under violet illumination, these cavities were often filled with resin but it was frequently difficult to link the presence of this resin with extant resin canals, so it is postulated that these new resin canals, mainly located in the cortex, and even some of the cells lining the insect wounds might react and produce a part of the resin found in these insect cavities.

As demonstrated for white spruce (Alfaro *et al.*, 1997) and for Sitka spruce (Tomlin and Borden, 1997), constitutive resin canals were associated with resistance to white pine weevil. This anatomical feature could help identify Norway spruce clones resistant to the weevil. Likewise, traumatic resin canal formation might be another important factor to consider. Like with bark beetles, the induced response to the invasion might be more important than the constitutive defense mechanisms (Raffa and Berryman, 1982a). As with other types of defense reactions, to be efficient this response should occur rapidly to drown eggs and young larvae.

CONCLUSION

These screening tests demonstrated that insect weight and the number of nymphal chambers are significantly different between clones. The development of an index that could consider the amount of food available (leader length, volume of bark, etc.), the oviposition intensity, the length of damage, the number of nymphal chambers and that could also remove the clone*year interaction could be a useful selection tool. Our observations also showed that insect feeding induced the formation of traumatic resin canals in the xylem as well as in the live bark. Finally, it is important to document the time and site variability in a resistance expression that may be relevant to different factors such as the physiological status of the insect and of the tree that can both be affected by weather conditions and site quality.

REFERENCES

ALFARO R.I., 1995. An induced defense reaction in white spruce to attack by the white pine weevil, *Pissodes strobi*. *Can. J. For. Res.*, 25, 1725-1730.

ALFARO R.I., HE F., TOMLIN E., KISS G., 1997. White spruce resistance to white pine weevil related to bark resin canal density. *Can. J. Bot.*, 75, 568-573.

ARCHAMBAULT L., MORISSETTE J., LAVALLEE R., COMTOIS B., 1993. Susceptibility of Norway spruce plantations to white pine weevil attacks in southern Quebec. *Can. J. For. Res.*, 23, 2362-2369.

BIGGS A.R., 1992. Anatomical and physiological responses of bark tissues to mechanical injury. *In:*Blanchette R.A. and Biggs A.R. (Eds.): *Defense mechanisms of woody plants against fungi.* Berlin, Springer-Verlag, p. 13-40.

COLEMAN N.N., NIEMAN T.C., BOYLE T.J.B., 1987. *Growth, survival, and stem form of a 22-year-old Norway spruce progeny test.* Canadian Forestry Service, Petawawa National Forestry Institute, Inf. Rep. PI-X-73.

HOLST M.J., 1955. Breeding for weevil resistance in Norway spruce. *Z. Forstgenetik,* 4, 33-37.

HOLST M.J., 1963. *Growth of Norway spruce (*Picea abies *(L) Karst.) provenances in eastern North America.* Ottawa, Ont., Can. Dep. For. Publ. No. 1022.

HULME M.A., 1995. Resistance of translocated Sitka spruce to damage by *Pissodes strobi* (Coleoptera: Curculionidae) related to tree phenology. *J. Econ. Entomol.*, 88, 1525-1530.

KOZLOWSKI T.T., KRAMER P.J., PALLARDY S.G., 1991. The *physiological ecology of woody plants.* Academic Press, San Diego, 657 p.

LAVALLEE R., BONNEAU G., COULOMBE C., 1997. Mechanical and biological control of the white pine weevil. Canadian Forest Service, Laurentian Forestry Centre, Inf. Leafl. 28 (in preparation).

LAVALLEE R., GUERTIN C., MORISSETTE J., COMTOIS B., 1990. Observations sur le développement du charançon du pin blanc chez l'épinette de Norvège au Québec. *Rev. entomol. Qué.*, 35, 31-44.

LAVALLEE R., ALBERT P.J., KAPOOR N.N., 1993. Techniques for sexing live adults of the white pine weevil *Pissodes strobi* Peck (Coleoptera: Curculionidae). *Can. Entomol.*, 125, 745-747.

LAVALLEE R., ARCHAMBAULT L., MORISSETTE J., 1996. Influence of drainage and edge vegetation on levels of attack and biological performance of the white pine weevil. *For. Ecol. Manage.*, 82, 133-144.

MILLER J.M., 1950. *Resistance of pine hybrids to* the *pine reproduction weevil.* Forest research notes, USDA For. Serv. California For. Range Exp. Stn., Report No. 68.

MINISTERE DES RESSOURCES NATURELLES DU QUÉBEC, 1997. *Insectes et maladies des arbres.* Québec 1996. Direction de la conservation des forêts, Publication no RN97-3056.

OVERHULSER D., GARA R.I., 1981. Occluded resin canals associated with egg cavities made by shoot infesting *Pissodes. For. Sci.*, 27, 297-298.

PAINTER R.H., 1951. *Insect resistance in crop plants.* Macmillan, New York, 520 p.

RAFFA K.F., BERRYMAN A.A.,1982a. Physiological differences between lodgepole pines resistant and susceptible to the mountain pine beetle and associated microorganisms. *Environ. Entomol.,* 11, 486-492.

RAFFA K.F., BERRYMAN A.A., 1982b. Gustatory cues in the orientation of *Dendroctonus ponderosae* (Coleoptera: Scolytidae) to host trees. *Can. Entomol.*, 114, 97-104.

SAS INSTITUTE INC. 1990. *SAS/STAT user's guide.* Version 6, Vols. 1 and 2, SAS Institute Inc., Cary, NC.

SMITH C.M., KHAN Z.R., PATHAK M.D., 1994. *Techniques for evaluating insect resistance in crop plants.* CRC Press, Florida, 320 p.

TOMLIN E.S., BORDEN J.H., 1997. Multicomponent index for evaluating resistance by Sitka spruce to the white pine weevil (Coleoptera: Curculionidae). *J. Econ. Entomol.*, 90, 704-714.

ACKNOWLEDGEMENTS

The authors thank Pamela Cheers for editing the text and Diane Paquet for her word processing work.

Physiology and Genetics of Tree-Phytophage Interactions
Gujan (France), August 31 - September 5, 1997
Ed. INRA, Paris, 1999 (Les Colloques, n°90)

Resistance to galling adelgids varies among families of Engelmann spruce (*Picea engelmani* P.)

WILLIAM J. MATTSON[1], ALVIN YANCHUK[2], GYULA KISS[3], BRUCE BIRR[1]

[1] *Forestry Sciences Laboratory, North Central Forest Research Station ,
5985 Highway K, Rhinelander, WI 54501*
[2] *Research Branch, British Columbia Ministry of Forests ,
1450 Government Street, Victoria, B.C., Canada V8W 3E7*
[3]*Kalamalka Research Station, British Columbia Ministry of Forests
3401 Reservoir Road, Vernon, B.C., V1B 2C7*

RESUME

Cooley gall adelgids, *Adelges cooleyi*, and round gall adelgids, *Adelges abietis*, differentially infested 110 half-sib families of Engelmann spruce, *Picea engelmannii* at 9 study sites in British Columbia. There was a negative genetic correlation (-0.53) between the infestations of the two gall-forming species. Cooley gall abundance exhibited a negative genetic correlation (-0.66) with tree growth, whereas round gall abundance exhibited a positive genetic correlation (0.79) with growth. Heritability (h^2) of resistance against the adelgids averaged about 0.60 for Cooley galls and 0.20 for round galls

INTRODUCTION

World-wide, there are 30 species of spruce (*Picea* spp: Pinaceae) which serve as the primary host for the majority of the 49 or so species of primitive aphids in the family Adelgidae (Carter 1971, Ghosh 1983). Each adelgid species typically causes a uniquely shaped gall to form on the developing shoots of susceptible spruces. Such galls can persist on the affected trees for many years depending on the species of gall-maker and the species and environment of the host spruce, thereby leaving a useful index to a tree's general resistance. For example, in undisturbed plantations in northern Minnesota, we have found galls that were formed as long as 30 years earlier (Mattson et al. 1994).

Usually, the impact of adelgids on tree growth and survival appears inconsequential. But, to be sure, no one has ever measured their long-term impacts on bud demography. Cooley galls, caused by *Adelges cooleyi*, for example, typically kill their subjugated shoots. Round galls caused by A. *abietis* and A. *lariciatus*, on the other hand, do not kill the shoot but allow it to grow in an apparently substandard manner. Ragged spruce galls caused by *Pineus similis* can cause hormonal imbalances in young seedling stems, triggering a cork-screw growth-habit that predisposes them to snow damage. In rare cases, some highly susceptible individual trees have nearly all of their shoots attacked by adelgids and consequently are rendered uncompetitive and eventually die (Mattson, pers. obs). In western North America where there are 15 species of adelgids, it is not uncommon to find galls from as many as 4 species on the same host plant, as is the case for Engelmann spruce, P. *engelmannii*, Sitka spruce, P. *sitchensis*, white spruce, P. *glauca*, and the vast hybrid swarm called interior spruce (mostly P. *engelmannii* x *glauca*) in interior British Columbia.

Numerous field studies in Europe and North America have reported substantive, consistent differences among individual trees in their resistance to the galling adelgids (e.g. see Mattson et al. 1994, Mattson et al. 1998), thereby implying that resistance has an important genetic component to it. For example, Mattson et al. (1998) estimated that broad sense heritability (H^2) of resistance against *Adelges abietis* was about 0.86 (the theoretical maximum being 1.0), using one clonal orchard of *Picea abies* in the southern Paris basin. Of course, such limited studies (i.e. one «population» of trees, one environment, one population of aphids) give but only a glimpse of the possible genetic bases of spruce resistance to adelgids.

This study was undertaken to further basic understanding about the genetics of spruce resistance to insects. Specifically, we investigated the hypothesis that there is substantive family level variation in Engelmann spruce resistance to two common, shoot-galling adelgids: the native, Cooley spruce gall aphid, A. *cooleyi*, and the introduced (from Eurasia), round spruce gall aphid, A. *abietis*, both of which produce very distinctive galls (Rose and Lindquist 1977). We also investigated the heritability (h^2) of such resistance and tested for genetic correlations between plant resistance to the two species of adelgids and between tree growth and resistance. We predicted that (a) tree resistance to one adelgid species would be positively correlated with resistance to the second adelgid owing to trees employing the same or very similar resistance mechanisms against both species, and (b) tree resistance and growth would be positively correlated because the most likely mechanisms of resistance would be rapid inducible defenses, such as strong and swift hypersensitive reactions, that are dependent on vigorous growth (Herms and Mattson 1992, 1997).

METHODS

This study was overlaid on a genetic trial utilizing 110 half-sib Engelmann spruce families originating from the east Kootenay region in S.E. British Columbia. Families were planted in linear, 10 tree plots, replicated in 2-3 blocks at each of 9 different, widely separated geographic sites. Trees were about 15 years of age, and ranged in height from 2-5 m in September 1994 when measurements were made. The first 5 living trees of all families in each replicate were scored for numbers of Cooley and round galls by a pair of forestry technicians. Each tree was examined (one person on each side) for two, 30-second intervals (using a timer) during which Cooley galls were counted, and then round galls counted. Such a brief inspection period was sufficient to provide a reliable difference among differently infested trees. For example, there was a strong linear regression relationship ($p < 0.01$, $r^2 = 50\text{-}75\%$) between such 30 second counts by forestry technicians and one minute counts (virtually 100% censuses) done on the same trees by two highly experienced gall workers (wjm & bab). Usually, the 30 second counts allowed the measurement of nearly all of the galls on lightly infested trees, and at least one-third to one half of them on the heavily infested trees. Tree heights (cm) and tree diameters (mm) were likewise measured at the same time. The round galls were initiated primarily by A. *abietis*, but there may also have been a small fraction of superficially similar round galls caused by A. *lariciatus*, though its distribution in S.E.. British Columbia is not well substantiated. Because over 11,000 trees were to be examined, it was not economically feasible to attempt to definitively segregate these two species of round gall makers, if indeed they occurred together. Therefore, the round gall counts may represent cumulative infestations of two species of adelgids. Due to misunderstandings, the whole tree gall counts were converted to a numerical index, and recorded as infestation classes: 0=0, 1=1-10, 2=11-20, 3=21-30, 4=31-40, 5=41-99 galls.

For statistical analyses and tests, we used the numerical indices directly, but furthermore we converted them back into a semblance of the original data by using a random number generator to pick a gall number within the appropriate numerical range covered by the index assigned to a tree. All such generated numbers (x) were then converted to their $\log_e (x+1)$ equivalent for meeting the assumptions of ANOVA. We used two ANOVA models. One was for analyzing separately each geographic locale or site: $X_{ijn} = \mu + F_i + R_j + F_iR_j + e_{ijn}$, where F is family, R is replicate, and FR are family by replicate interaction effects, e is residual error among individuals. The second was for analyzing the pooled data set across all sites: $X_{ijkn} = \mu + S_k + R_j (S_k) + F_i + F_iS_k + F_i R_j (S_k) + e_{ijkn}$, where S is site. Because of computational overload problems with an unbalanced design arising from missing observations, the pooled data set was manipulated to create a perfectly balanced data set consisting of 82 families and three individual trees per replicate (2) at all study sites. Hence, those statistics for the pooled study refer to this reduced data set, and consist of the class counts for galls. Statistics shown for the individual sites are based on the full set of 110 families, all replicates, and all individual trees, but using the random counts. In every ANOVA, all effects were considered random effects. To estimate the magnitudes of genetic correlations (r_g), and narrow-sense, individual heritabilities (h^2), we computed the variance components for the main effects, and their interactions, and then followed standard estimation protocols (Becker 1984, Falconer 1989, Kiss and Yanchuck 1991, Stonecypher 1992).

RESULTS and DISCUSSION

Variation among sites and families

Cooley galls were common at all 9 sites, but as expected, their abundance differed substantially and significantly among sites (Tables 1,2). For example, they averaged about 7 galls/tree at the least infested site, and 31 galls/tree at the most infested site. Analyses of variance confirmed that there were also substantive, significant ($p<.001$) differences among half-sib families (F) in their resistance to A. cooleyi at all 9 sites. According to a variance components analysis on the overall model testing all of the sites together, family effects accounted for 8.6 % of the total variation (Table 2). At the most heavily infested sites, the majority (>75 percent) of families were in middle to high range infestation classes, i.e. medium to light-heavy infestation classes. Only very few families were in the extremes, i.e. in very light and very heavy infestation categories. This implies that nearly all families are moderately to highly susceptible to A. cooleyi.

Round galls were much less common than Cooley galls at 6 of the 9 sites, but at 3 sites they were equally abundant (Tables 1,2). At the least infested location, round galls averaged about 2/tree, whereas at the most infested location they averaged about 34/tree. Analyses of variance revealed that there were highly significant family effects ($p < .001$) on round gall numbers/tree at all 9 sites. According to a variance components analysis on the overall model, family effects accounted for 2.4% of the total variation (Table 2). At the most heavily infested sites, the majority of spruce half-sib families fell into the medium and heavy infestation classes. As was the case for Cooley gall susceptibility, only few families fell into the very light and very heavy infestation classes. Thus, almost all families are moderately to highly susceptible to the round gall adelgids.

Tree size effects on galling

Because larger trees have larger canopies and offer more potential growing points for adelgid infestations, and families varied significantly in growth rates, we plotted mean galls/tree/family against family diameter (d.b.h.) and height to search for

Table 1. Mean number of galls ($\log_e(x + 1)$) per tree at nine different research sites, and the probability of a larger F value in randomized, complete block design testing the null hypotheses that there are no family, replicate, and family x replicate effects on gall counts per tree. Study sites are ranked in ascending order according to the mean abundance of Cooley galls per tree.

	Cooley galls:				Round galls:			
Study Sites:	mean	Fam	Rep	FxR	mean	Fam	Rep	FxR
E.WhiteRiver	1.768	<.001	0.24	0.07	0.959	<.001	0.06	<.010
Lodge Creek	1.918	<.001	<.001	0.07	1.554	<.001	<.001	<.001
Roche Creek	2.162	<.001	0.07	<.01	2.547	<.001	0.1	<.001
Jumbo Creek	2.513	<.001	<.001	<.001	0.539	<.001	<.010	<.010
Perry Creek	2.733	<.001	<.001	<.001	2.689	<.001	0.02	<.001
Bloom Creek	2.825	<.001	0.09	<.010	3.309	<.001	0.225	<.001
Lussier River	3.137	<.001	0.05	<.010	2.429	<.001	<.001	<.010
Horse Creek	3.173	<.001	0.41	0.12	1.338	<.001	0.47	0.04
WdvrmereCk	3.233	<.001	<.01	<.001	1.755	<.001	0.247	<.001

Table 2. Analysis of variance of data pooled from all sites, using gall class counts, showing degrees of freedom (df), Mean Squares (MS) and components of variance for the main effects for both Cooley and round gall analyses.

		Cooley Galls		Round Galls	
Source of Variation	df	MS	Variance Comp.	MS	Variance Comp.
Sites	8	315.5*[a]	0.62	502.4*	0.99
Reps(sites)	9	91.5*	0.04	13.2*	0.05
Families	81	12.5*	0.20 (8.6%)[b]	4.5*	0.05 (2.4%)[b]
FxS	648	1.8*	0.08	1.7*	0.06
FxR(sites)	729	1.3*	0.15	1.3*	0.19
Error	2952	0.9	0.87	0.7	0.74

[a] * significant ($p<0.001$) effects, [b] percentage of total variance

any such potential relationships. Universally, there was a very poor to negligible relationship between mean Cooley gall counts/tree/family and mean family d.b.h. and height (Table 2.). On the other hand, quite the opposite was true for round galls. Round gall numbers per family clearly increased linearly with mean family height (and diameter) at all study areas, ranging from about 1-3 galls/m of height at the most lightly infested areas, to about 7-12 galls/m of height at the most severely infested areas (table 4.).

To remove the effects of family growth rate which is potentially confounded with the inherent resistance/susceptibility of families, we divided galls/tree by tree height (m) and then transformed the ratio (r) using a $\log_e$ r +.01) transformation before running analyses of variance. We did not employ height as a true covariate in ANOVA because the regression relationship of galls on height was not perfectly collinear among all 110 families.

Converting raw gall counts to galls per unit height did not remove family effects; they were still very highly significant ($p < 0.001$) at all study sites (Table 3.). Although, standardizing galling by height did not eliminate family effects from the model, it did rearrange the individual infestation rankings of families, but largely within their original quartiles. For example, most of those families ranking in the highest and lowest infestation quartiles on the basis of galls/tree still occurred within the highest and lowest infestation quartiles, respectively, after standardization by tree height. However, the internal rankings of almost all these families changed relative to one another. For example, at Bloom Creek, the mean change in round gall family infestation rank (old rank-new rank) was +2.8 for the highest infestation quartile. In other words, the average family increased in mean gall loading by about 3 ranks. For the lowest infestation quartile, the mean change in family rank was -3.5, meaning that rank dropped by more than 3 (i.e. lower average gall loading). Only 5 new families moved into the highest infestation quartile, the other 22 just changed their rank orders. The same was true for the lowest infestation quartile. Therefore, we conclude that there are real and substantive family effects on galling that are confounded to only a small degree with the effects of family growth rates.

Table 3. Statistics for linear regressions of mean Cooley and round gall counts/tree/family versus mean family tree height (cm) at each of 9 study areas. If zero occurs in the slope columns, slopes are not significantly from different from zero. Otherwise, slopes are significantly ($p < .05$) larger than zero. Each regression is based on $\geq$ 216 observations.

	Cooley galls:		Round galls:	
Study Sites	Slope	r^2	Slope	r^2
BloomCrk	-0.0443	0.05	0.0954	0.17
E.WhiteRvr	0.0000	0.00	0.0217	0.29
HorseCrk	0.0378	0.05	0.0204	0.33
JumboCrk	0.0194	0.02	0.0129	0.31
LodgeCrk	0.0138	0.03	0.0483	0.46
LussierRvr	0.0000	0.00	0.1196	0.48
PerryCrk	0.0000	0.00	0.0319	0.12
RocheCrk	0.0220	0.09	0.0722	0.33
WindvCrk	0.0000	0.00	0.0276	0.21

Table 4. Mean number of $\log_e$ (galls/meter of tree height + 0.01) at nine different research sites, and the probability of a larger F value in randomized, complete block design testing the null hypotheses that there are no family, replicate, and family x replicate effects on gall per unit of height per tree. Study sites are ranked in ascending order according to the mean abundance of Cooley galls per tree.

Study	Cooley galls:				Round galls:			
Sites:	mean	Fam	Rep	FxR	mean	Fam	Rep	FxR
E.WhiteRiver	-0.016	<.001	0.09	0.03	-2.002	<.001	0.04	<.001
Lodge Creek	0.199	<.001	<.001	0.016	-0.592	<.001	<.001	<.001
Roche Creek	0.445	<.001	0.10	<.001	1.105	<.001	0.73	<.001
Jumbo Creek	1.003	<.001	<.001	<.010	-3.217	<.001	<.001	<.010
Perry Creek	1.006	<.001	<.001	<.001	0.954	<.001	0.03	<.001
Bloom Creek	1.198	<.001	0.33	<.001	1.789	<.001	0.24	<.001
Lussier River	1.887	<.001	0.06	<.010	0.857	<.001	<.002	<.030
Horse Creek	1.839	<.001	0.31	0.49	-1.132	<.001	0.55	0.010
WdvrmereCk	2.098	<.001	<.01	<.001	-0.057	<.001	0.325	<.001

Genetic correlations between galling and tree growth

To investigate possible genetic relationships between gall infestations and tree growth rates, we calculated the genetic correlations (r_g) between Cooley and round gall infestations and $height_m$ at each of the nine study sites, and on the entire, pooled data set (Table 5). In the case of Cooley galls, all correlations were negative, ranging in value from -0.02 to -.0.79. The pooled data set gave r_g = -0.21. The consistent association implies that the tree's traits for fast growth and resistance to Cooley gall aphids are positively linked, as might be the case if resistance depended on rapid inducible

Table 5. Genetic correlations (r_g) between adelgid gall infestations and tree growth ($height_m$), and between Cooley (C) and round (R) galls levels per tree, and estimates of the heritability (h^2) of resistance against adelgids using two measures of infestation, gall no./tree and gall no./m at each of 9 study sites in British Columbia. Each estimate in the table is based upon measurements on approximately 1000-2000 trees, except for the pooled sites.

Study Sites	Genetic correlations:				Heritability (h^2) estimates:			
	C.galls vs height	R.galls vs height	R.galls vs C.galls no./tree	R.galls vs C.galls no./m	C.galls no. Per tree	R.galls no. per tree	C.galls no./m	R.galls no./m
Bloom Creek	-0.79	0.36	-0.51	-0.31	1.0+	0.41	1.0+	0.17
E. White River	-0.49	1.0+	-0.54	-0.71	0.34	0.13	0.44	0.09
Horse Creek	-0.26	1.0+	0.03	-0.59	0.35	0.26	0.44	0.11
Jumbo Creek	-0.42	0.84	-0.49	-0.61	0.32	0.26	0.39	0.21
Lodge Creek	-1.0+	0.62	-1.0+	-1.0+	0.28	0.05	0.32	0.00
Lussier River	-0.37	0.84	-0.48	-0.69	0.95	0.51	1.0+	0.26
Perry Creek	-0.61	1.0+	-0.33	-0.69	0.83	0.12	0.85	0.00
Roche Creek	-0.02	0.84	0.19	0.38	0.78	0.17	0.84	0.09
Wdvrmere Creek	-0.55	0.74	-0.93	-0.85	0.69	0.18	1.0+	0.11
Pooled Sites	-0.66	0.79	-0.53	n.a.[1]	0.61	0.20	n.a.	n.a.

1 n.a. not available, because analysis was not done for the particular variable of concern.

defenses (such as hypersensitive reactions) which are swiftest and strongest in vigorously growing tissues. On the other hand, for round galls quite the opposite was found. All correlations were positive, ranging from 0.36 to 0.84. The pooled r_g estimate was 0.92. Because round and Cooley gall resistance have different relationships to tree growth, it implies that the resistance mechanisms against them are different.

Correlations Between Cooley and round gall adelgids

To obtain a synoptic view of family resistance to both Cooley and round gall adelgids, we ranked each spruce family according to its percent departure from the grand mean resistance level of all 110 families at each of the 9 study sites. For example, at each locale, every family was rescaled for the two gall types using the following formula: ($_{family}$ $gall_i$ mean-local $gall_i$ grand mean)/local $gall_i$ grand mean x 100, where means are from log_e (x+1) data. These new variables, percent deviations, were then used in a randomized block ANOVA, with study areas treated as blocks, to test again for family differences.

As before, there were highly significant ($p < 0.001$) family effects on the rescaled measures of resistance to galling. To demonstrate the families' resistance relationships to both Cooley and round gall adelgids, we plotted mean round gall rank against mean Cooley gall rank for all 110 families (Figure 1). The result was an obvious left to right sloping scattergram. Such a pattern implies a negative genetic correlation between the resistance traits for these two adelgids. Sixty-eight percent of the families fell into the upper left (27 percent) and lower right (41 percent) quadrants of the graph. Only a meager 11 percent of the families occurred in the lower left quadrant where susceptibility to both species of adelgids is below the grand mean. Therefore, typically, when one resistance trait is high, then the other is low, and vice versa. Contrary to this trend, only one family, f-126, had substantially low levels of both adelgids: its infestations were on average 23 percent below the grand mean for Cooley galls, and 32 percent below the grand mean for round galls. At the other contrary extreme, family f-80, had the highest combined level of both adelgids: its infestations were on average about 20, and 23 percent higher than the respective grand means for Cooley and round galls.

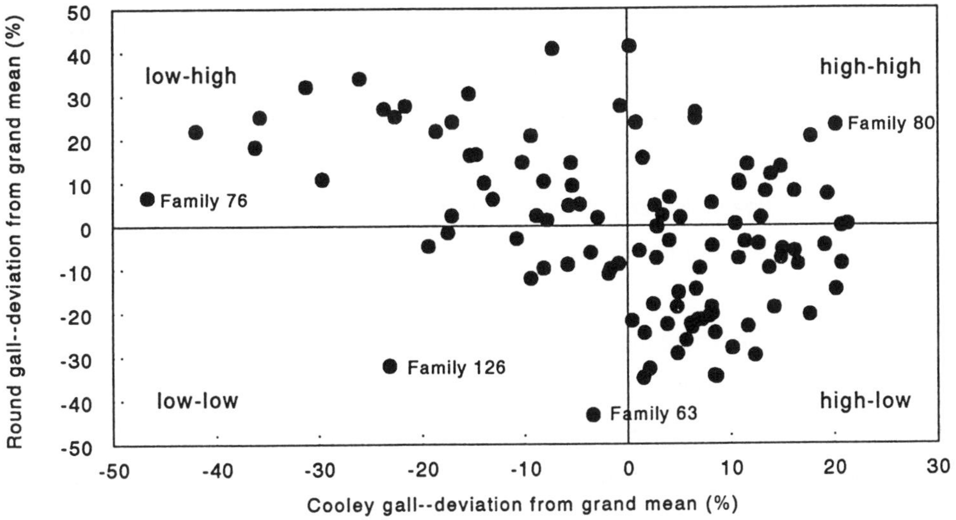

Figure 1. Plot showing the mean round and Cooley gall infestation ranks of each of 110 spruce families, using a family's average percent deviation from the grand mean round and Cooley gall infestation level of all trees, at each of 9 study sites. In other words, each point is the mean of 9 individual deviations measurements for a single family, showing its tendency to be higher, or lower than others with respect to infestations by round and Cooley gall adelgids. For example, Family 126 is identified in the lower left (low-low) quadrant, exhibiting below average levels of both galling adelgids.

Genetic correlations between Cooley and round gall infestations

Using the $\log_e (x+1)$ gall counts, we found that there were negative genetic correlations (-0.33 to -0.93) between Cooley and round gall infestations per tree at 7 of 9 sites (Table 5). At 2 sites the correlations were near zero or positive (0.03 and 0.19). Using the entire data (all sites) set in the pooled model gave a substantial, negative genetic correlation of -0.53.

Estimating heritabilities of resistance to adelgids

Heritability estimates depend on the environment in which they are measured, the particular genetic structure of the populations, and a bevy of other factors. Therefore, we computed heritability estimates for each of the 9 study locales, realizing that insect population size and its genetic structure may vary substantially among them.

For Cooley adelgids, h^2 values ranged from 0.28-0.95 with one estimate exceeding 1.0, owing to estimation errors (Table 5). The pooled estimate and its standard error over all sites was 0.61 $\pm$ 0.11.

For round gall adelgids, h^2 values ranged from 0.05-0.51 (Table 5). The pooled estimate and its standard error over all sites was 0.20 $\pm$ 0.05.

Because each heritability estimate was usually based on about 1000 individual tree measurements, derived from 110 families, the precision of the estimates are reasonably good. For example, the sampling variances of h^2 estimates are approximately 32 x h^2/1000 (Falconer 1989), and thus its standard errors are approximately (sqrt (32 x h^2)) / 1000. Although we only calculated standard errors for the overall h^2 estimates (after Becker 1984), it is evident that heritabilities were significantly larger than zero.

CONCLUSIONS

Heritability estimates varied widely across individual sites, but the overall estimates confirmed that h^2 was substantially larger (~0.6) for Cooley galls, than for round galls (~0.2). This may suggest that there is more genetic variation present for Cooley gall resistance, but the lower level of attack by round gall adelgids may have caused the heritability estimates to be less than those for Cooley gall resistance. Not surprisingly, for both gall adelgids there was a tendency for the highest heritability estimates to be linked to the sites with highest insect densities, as has been observed elsewhere by Strong et al. (1993) for a cecidomyiid leaf-galling fly on willow, Salix spp in Sweden.

Nevertheless, these values indicate there are good levels of genetic variation in resistance to both gall-forming insects on interior spruce, and breeding for resistance would be possible. However, relationships between height growth and resistance to both gall forming insects were quite different. Cooley gall abundance was negatively correlated with height growth which suggests faster growing families are more resistant. Whereas, for round gall adelgids, faster growing families are more susceptible. This would make breeding for resistance against both insects more difficult as very few genotypes would be segregating for positive attributes for all three traits (i.e., growth and Cooley and round gall adelgid resistance).

Adjustments to the data to account for differential attack among large and small trees, suggested that tree size per se does not largely change the probability that a tree will be attacked and that family pedigree is more important. Ideally one should know the impact of galling aphids on tree growth which would then permit an assessment of the benefit of developing lines of trees resistant to gall forming adelgids. Unfortunately, nothing is really known about the impact of such gall formers on tree survival and growth.

Understanding of the genetics of tree resistance to phytophagous insects is in its infancy. More research is clearly needed in order to be able to effectively employ natural mechanisms of plant resistance against potential tree pests.

REFERENCES

BECKER W.A., 1984. *Manual of quantitative genetics.* Wash. State Univ. Press, Pullman.

CARTER C.I., 1971. Conifer woolly aphids (Adelgidae) in Britain. *Forestry Comm. Bull.* 42: 1-41

FALCONER D.S., 1989. *Introduction to quantitative genetics.* John Wiley, N.Y., 438 pp.

GHOSH A.K., 1983. A review of the family Adelgidae from the Indian subregion (Homoptera: Aphidoidea). *Oriental Insects* 17: 2-29.

HERMS D.A. and MATTSON W.J., 1992. The dilemma of plants: to grow or defend. *Quart. Rev. Biol:* 67: 283-335.

HERMS D.A., and MATTSON W.J., 1997. Trees, stress, and pests, pp. 13-25, In*: Plant health care for woody ornamentals,*. Univ. Ill. Coop. Ext. Service, Urbana-Champaign, 223 p.

KISS G.K. and YANCHUK A.D., 1991. Preliminary evaluation of genetic control of weevil resistance of interior spruce in British Colombia. *Can J. For. Res.* 21: 230-234.

MATTSON W.J., BIRR B.A., and LAWRENCE R.K., 1994. Variation in the susceptibility of North American white spruce populations to the gall-forming adelgid, Adelges abietis (Homoptera: Adelgidae) pp. 135-147, In Price, P., Mattson, W.J., and Baranchikov, Y. (eds.) The ecology and evolution of gall-forming insects. USDA Forest Serv. GTR NC-174, St. Paul, Mn., 222 p.

MATTSON W.J, LEVIEUX J., and PIOU D., 1998. Genetic and environmental contributions to variation in the resistance of Picea abies to the gall-forming adelgid, *Adelges abietis* (Homoptera: Adelgidae). pp. 304-315, in Csoka, G., Mattson, W.J., Stone, G.N., and Price, P.W. (eds.) *The biology of gall-forming arthropods,* USDA For. Serv. GTR NC-199, St. Paul, Mn 303 p.

ROSE A.H. and. LINDQUIST. O.H., 1977. Insects of eastern spruces, fir, and hemlock. *For. Tech. Rept.* 23, Ministry of Supply and Services, Ottawa. 157 pp.

STRONG D.R., LARSSON S. and GULLBERG U., 1993. Heritability of host plant resistance to herbivory changes with gallmidge density during an outbreak on willow.. *Evolution* 47: 291-300.

STONECYPHER R.W., 1992. Computational methods, pp. 195-228, in Fins, L., Friedman, S.T., and Brotschol, J.V..(eds.) *Handbook of quantitative forest genetics.* Kluwer Academic Publishers, London. 403 p.

Physiology and Genetics of Tree-Phytophage Interactions
Gujan (France), August 31 - September 5, 1997
Ed. INRA, Paris, 1999 (Les Colloques, n°90)

Cupressus sempervirens L. vs. Cypress seed chalcid, *Megastigmus wachtli* Steiner: genetic and evolutionary relationships

A. ROQUES[1], E. CARCREFF[2], J.Y. RASPLUS[3]

[1] *INRA, Zoologie Forestière*
Ardon 45160- Olivet, France
[2] *INRA, Unité de Recherches Forestières*
Domaine de l'Hermitage, Pierroton, 33610- Cestas, France
[3] *INRA, Génétique et Biologie Evolutive*
Rue Croix de Lavit, 34090- Montpellier Cedex, France

RESUME

The host range of *Megastigmus wachtli* Seitner (Hymenoptera: Torymidae), a chalcid species naturally attacking the seeds of Mediterranean Cypress, *Cupressus sempervirens* L., was surveyed during 1994-97. The chalcid attacked seven cypress species over 15 native and exotic species introduced in Europe. Differences in attack was attributed to the variation in the phenology of seed development among species. Adult emergence in natural sites was shown to vary from late June (Greece) to October (Tunisia), whereas it did not vary in arboreta. This behavior is assumed to be adaptative, adjusting to the variation in phenology of seed development with a geographic location. The sequencing of the cytochrome b gene of mtDNA only revealed a low variability in populations of *M. wachtli* but permitted the differentiation of a new species related to *C. atlantica* in Morocco. Analyses of DNA microsatellites showed that populations from Crete and the Dodecannese islands (natural range) were characterized by high polymorphism, though clearly differing from each other. Populations from France, Italy, and Tunisia (introduction range) were characterized by a very low polymorphism. It suggested that these populations originated from Cretan seeds introduced by Ancient Greeks or Romans. The origin of the Tunisian population in the stand of Makthar is controversial, but the seed chalcid may be a good marker, suggesting the stand's introduced origin. Finally, the phylogenetic tree obtained for the populations of *M. wachtli* was compared to that known for the populations of *C. sempervirens* from isozyme studies.

INTRODUCTION

The Mediterranean evergreen cypress, *Cupressus sempervirens* L. (Cupressaceae), originates from the eastern part of the Mediterranean basin where its natural range extends from North Iran to Crete and Dodecannese islands (Vidakovi 1991). However, this species has been introduced on a large scale throughout southern Europe and northern Africa for at least two millennia, first by the Ancient Greeks, and then by the Romans (Baumann 1982). Once established, the species then propagated freely along the Mediterranean coast. In addition, two other native cypress species, *C. atlantica* Gaussen and *C. dupreziana* Camus, occur as relicts on very small areas in Morocco and Algeria, respectively. A fourth, but exotic species, *C. lusitanica* Mill., has been naturalized in Portugal where it forms large stands (Vidakovi 1991).

Although the insect pests damaging cones and seeds of cypresses have received little attention, a cypress seed chalcid, *Megastigmus wachtli* Seitner (Hymenoptera: Torymidae), appears to be present throughout the native range of *C. sempervirens* (Çanakcioglü 1959; Roques *et al.*, 1997), and in the introduced range as well (Roques and Raimbault, 1986; Guido *et al.*, 1995; Ben Jamaa and Roques, 1997). Because the larvae can only develop in cypress seeds, chalcid survival is entirely dependant on cone abundance, and the chalcid life cycle is closely synchronized with the development of cypress seeds (Roques and Raimbault, 1986). The close relationships between cypress seeds and chalcids suggest that variations in insect biology and genetic diversity of chalcid populations may reflect the history of cypress introductions into the different Mediterranean countries.

Thus, our objective was to survey the populations of *M. wachtli* in the natural and introduced range of the Mediterranean cypresses in order to: (i) confirm the host specificity of seed chalcids; (ii) look for variation in insect biology and impact according to the geographic location; (iii) assess the genetic diversity of chalcid populations by analyzing sequence variations in mtDNA and DNA microsatellites; and, (iv) compare insect and tree diversity.

MATERIAL AND METHODS

Seed collection, survey of chalcid host range and adult emergence period

A total of 73 sites distributed throughout the Mediterranean basin were surveyed during 1994- 1997 (Fig. 1). Twenty stands were sampled in the natural range of *C. sempervirens* in Greece and Turkey whilst 40 plantations were sampled in the area where this species was introduced. Collections also were made in two natural stands of *C. atlantica* in Morocco, one plantation of *C. dupreziana* in Algeria, and five naturalized stands of *C. lusitanica* in Portugal. In addition, 5 arboreta and comparative plantations (Le Rouet, Les Caunes, Le Caneiret, Ceyreste, and Antibes) were sampled in southern France. These arboreta included a total of 15 exotic species of *Cupressus* originating from Asia, North America, and Central America. The "Le Rouet" arboretum specifically included trees issued from seeds originating from 10 natural provenances of *C. sempervirens*, of which five could be compared to samples collected in the original stands.

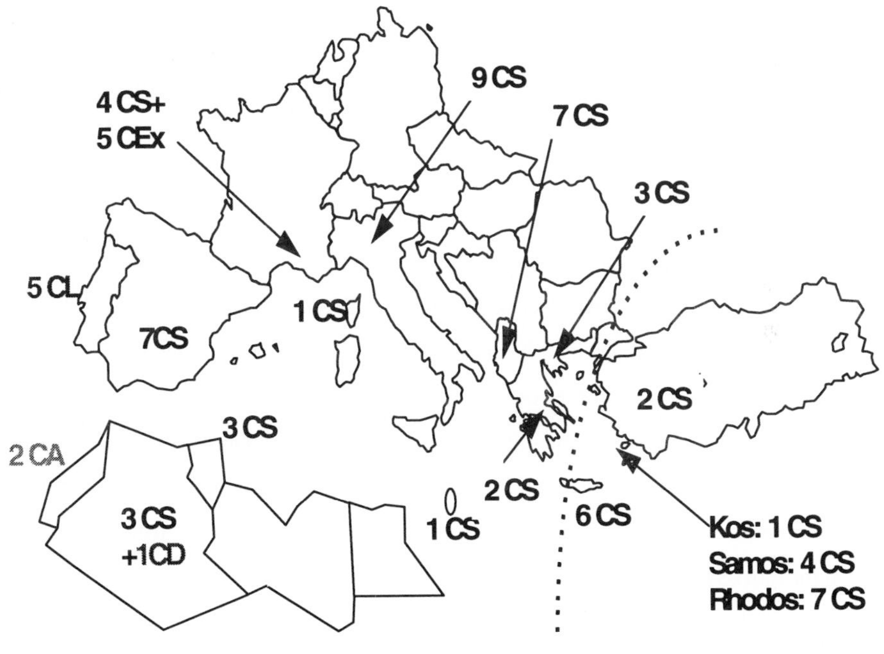

Figure 1. Geographic distribution of the surveyed sites. CS: *Cupressus sempervirens*; CA: *C.atlantica*; CD: *C.dupreziana*; CL: *C. lusitanica*; CEx: exotic species of *Cupressus*.

In each site, 100 mature 2-year-old cones were collected on 10 cone-bearing selected at random (when the cone crop allowed it) every year in late spring (i.e., before the emergence of adult chalcids). In the arboreta, we randomly collected 100 cones per cypress species and per provenance each year. Half of the cones were dissected and the seeds extracted. Each seed lot was individually irradiated with X-rays, using a Faxitron-43855® apparatus (20 Kv, 3 mA, 4 min) and X- rays sensitive films (Kodak ® "Industrex M"). The proportion of insect-infested seeds were assessed from the radiographic images. The remainder of the cones were placed into rearing boxes stored in an outdoor insectary at Orléans, France. The emergence pattern of both sexes of seed chalcids was monitored daily in order to investigate possible differences in the emergence period among geographic origins of the infested seeds. At emergence, adults are frozen (-80°) until DNA analyses were carried out.

Genetic analysis of seed chalcid populations

Sequencing of the cytochrome b gene

We analyzed 10 individuals from each of nine different populations of *M.wachtli*, and individuals from seeds of Chinese cypresses (*M. duclouxianae* Roques et Pan), junipers (*M. amicorum* Bou ek, *M. bipunctatus* Swederus, *M. pingii* Roques et Sun), and Douglas-fir (*M. spermotrophus* Wachtl). Total DNA was extracted from single individuals following standard phenol-chloroform extractions (Sambrook *et al.*, 1989). Polymerase chain reactions (PCR) were realized on the central part of the "cytochrome b" gene of mitochondrial DNA (mtDNA), using the primers CP1 (5'-GATGATGAAATTTTGGATC-3') and CP2 (5'-CTAATGCAATAACTCCTCC-3') which were defined from the sequencing of mtDNA in *Drosophila yakuba* (Douglas and Wolstenholme, 1985). Sequencing was done using the primers CP1 and CB1 (5'- TATGTACTACCATGAGGACAAATATC- 3') (Crozier *et al.*, 1995), CB1 being considered as an internal primer because it is located between CP1 and CP2 on the gene. An 800 pb- part was thus amplified on the cytochrome b gene, and we obtained a 631 pb-sequence using an automatic sequencing apparatus (Applied Biosystems® 373A). Data were analyzed using CLUSTAL V software (Higgins *et al.*, 1992). Genetic distances were measured using the Kimura method (Kimura, 1980). The phylogenetic trees were built from the Neighbor-joining algorithm (Saitou and Nei, 1987) using the MEGA software (Kumar *et al.*, 1993). The phylogenetic analyses were realized using the PAUP 3.1.1 software (Swofford, 1993), the domestic bee, *Apis mellifica* L., being used as an outgroup. A bootstrap procedure with 1000 iterations was used to test for parsimony and distance in the phylogenetic trees.

Analysis of DNA microsatellites

Because of the haplodiploid sex determination in Hymenoptera, only females were used in the study. A total of 195 females from four natural stands of *C. sempervirens* (Crete, Samos, Kos, Rhodos) and five plantations located in the introduced range (mainland Greece, France, Italy, Tunisia) were analyzed. Additional analyses were made on chalcids from Morocco (host *C.atlantica*). The isolation and characterization of microsatellite loci followed a technique detailed by Carcreff *et al.* (1997). Polymorphism was measured as both the number of alleles per locus and the expected level of heterozygosity in Hardy-Weinberg equilibrium. The allelic frequencies and the level of heterozygosity were estimated using Nei's formulae, $D= n\,(1-\Sigma\, p_i^2)/(n-1)$, $Hc= 2n\,(1-\Sigma\, p_i^2)/(2n-1)$, where n is the number of individuals and p_i the haplotypic (D) or allelic (Hc) frequency (Nei, 1978; Nei and Tajima, 1985). The calculations were made using the GENEPOP software (Raymond and Rousset, 1995).

The phylogenetic tree was built using the same algorithm as for cytochrome b. The distance between shared alleles (DSA) was calculated between individuals and populations (Chakraborty and Jin, 1992). For each locus, the distance equals to one when two individuals have no allele in common, to zero when they show the same alleles, and to 0.5 in other cases. DSA among individuals corresponds to the mean distance observed for all of the studied loci. DSA among populations corresponds to the mean distance observed for the individuals of each population. DSA was finally used to built dendrograms of populations and individuals (J.M. Cornuet, unpublished software). A bootstrap procedure with 2000 iterations was used for testing the population dendrogram.

RESULTS AND DISCUSSION

Host range of *Megastigmus wachtli*

The host range of *M. wachtli* seems limited (Fig. 2). In arboreta, seed chalcids were found on the native Mediterranean cypresses but also on four *Cupressus* species introduced from California (*C. abramsiana* C.B. Wolf, *C. arizonica* Greene, *C. bakeri* Jepson, and *C. goveniana* Gord.). The percentage of attacked cones significantly differed with the cypress species (ANOVA: $F_{15,64}$=8.018, P<0.001), but no arboretum effect was observed (ANOVA with arboretum as covariate: $F_{1,63}$=2.550, P=0.115). *C. sempervirens* was significantly more infested than exotic species (Tukey test; P>0.01) but chalcid damage was not significantly different among *C. atlantica, C. dupreziana* and the four infested American species (Tukey test; P>0.05).

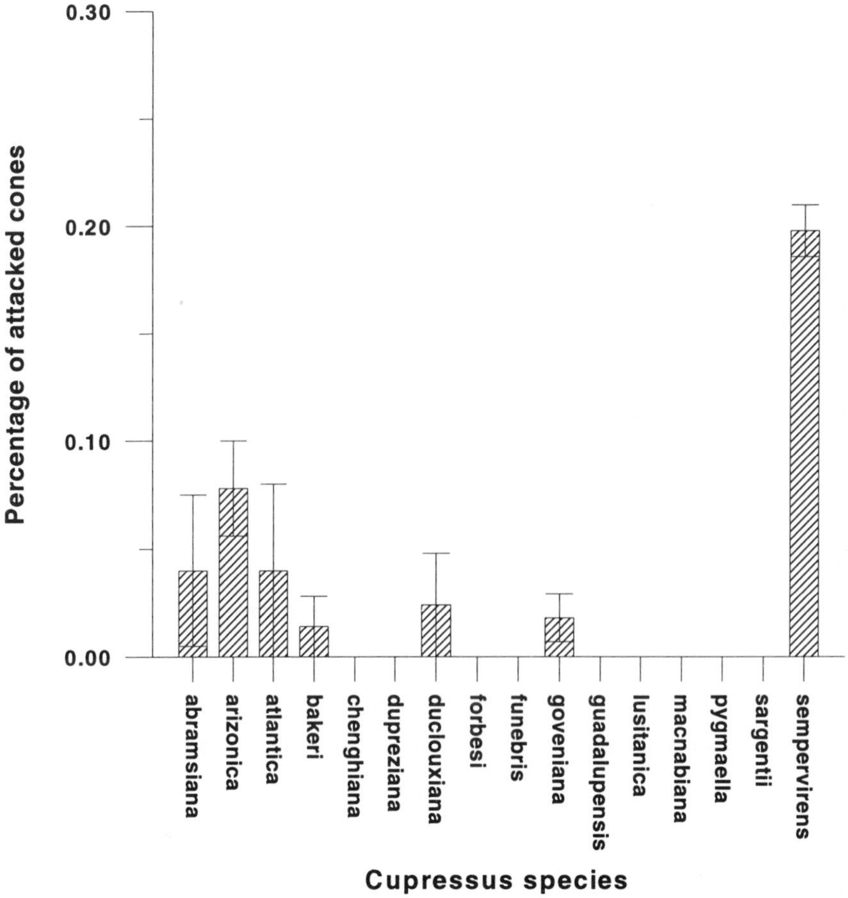

Figure 2. Mean cone damage caused by *Megastigmus wachtli* on cypress species planted in five arboreta of southern France, 1995.Vertical bars represent standard errors.

None of the Asian cypress species was attacked wherever the arboreta. By contrast, three species of *Megastigmus* seed chalcids are recorded from the natural range of Asian cypresses (Roques *et al.* 1995; Xu and He,1995) whereas no chalcid species is known thus far in the native range of the 12 *Cupressus* species growing in North and Central America (Hedlin et al., 1981). In fact, the attack of a cypress species by *M. wachtli* seems related to the timing of the seed cone development cycle of *C. sempervirens.* Species with seed maturation initiated in summer are susceptible to be attack, adult emergence of *M. wachtli* occurring at that time (cf. below). Species with an earlier seed maturation (e.g., Asian cypresses) are not colonized in the introduced range in absence of introduced chalcids whose cycle fits that of the host. For instance, in south China *M. duclouxianae* oviposits in April- May into the seeds of *C. duclouxiana* (Roques *et al.*, 1995).

Variation in seed chalcid damage with geographic location

Cone attack was highly variable with site and year in the natural stands (Fig. 3b; ANOVA $F_{5,24}$=55.945, P<0.001), but comparatively higher than in the areas where *C. sempervirens* was introduced (ANOVA: $F_{1,58}$=17.072, P<0.001). However, natural provenances planted in the "Le Rouet" arboretum did not show any difference in cone damage (Fig. 3a; ANOVA:$F_{8,36}$=1.714, P=0.129).

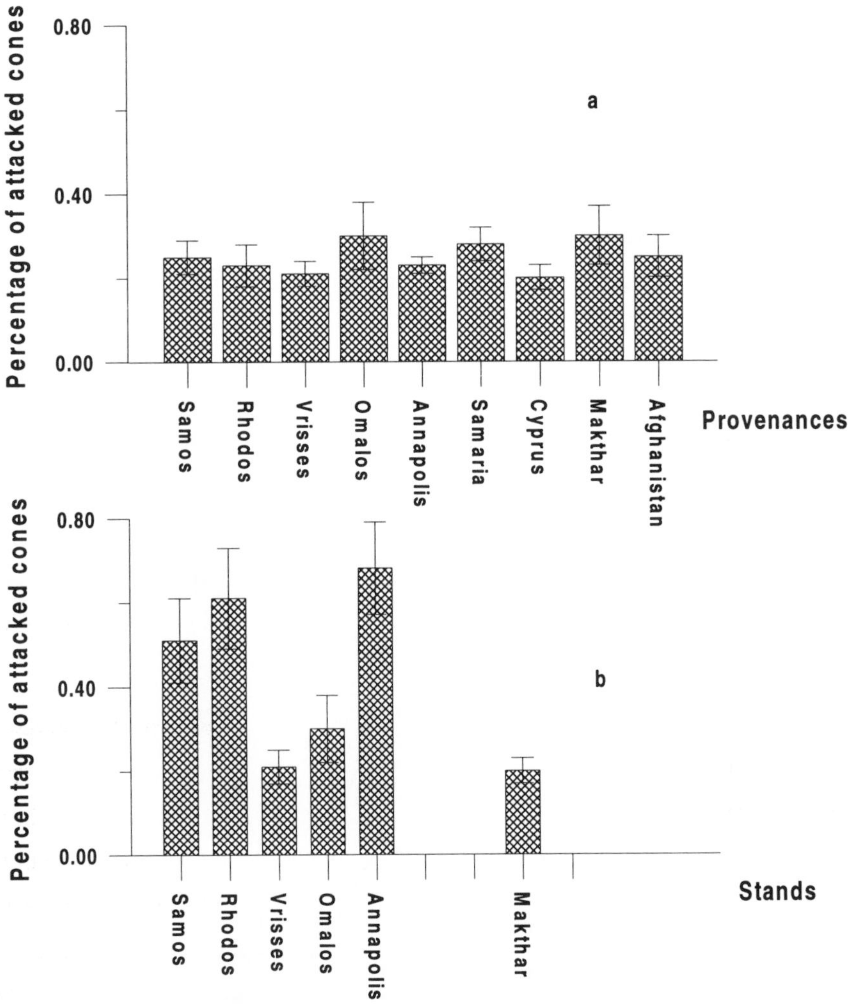

Figure 3. Variation in cone attack by *Megastigmus wachtli* with stands and provenances of *Cupressus sempervirens* in 1995. a) trees from natural provenances planted at the Le Rouet arboretum; b) stands of Greece (natural range) and Tunisia (Makthar). Vertical bars represent standard errors.

We therefore suggested that damage difference between natural and introduction areas probably resulted from difference in masting patterns rather than from difference in tree susceptibility. In natural areas, cypress trees behave like most conifer trees, showing large annual variations in cone crop. Thus, an inverse relationship exists between the proportion of insect-caused damage and the annual change in cone crop size, as it occurs in most other cone insects (Turgeon *et al.*, 1994). By contrast, most cypress trees usually flower every year in the areas of introduction.

Variation in emergence of adult chalcids with geographic location

The period of adult emergence varied with location (Fig. 4). Chalcids emerged earlier in natural sites of Greece than in France and Tunisia. Adult emergence was especially late in Morocco (October). However, adults issued from the Greek natural provenances planted at the Le Rouet arboretum emerged synchroneously to the chalcids developing in other plantations of southern France.

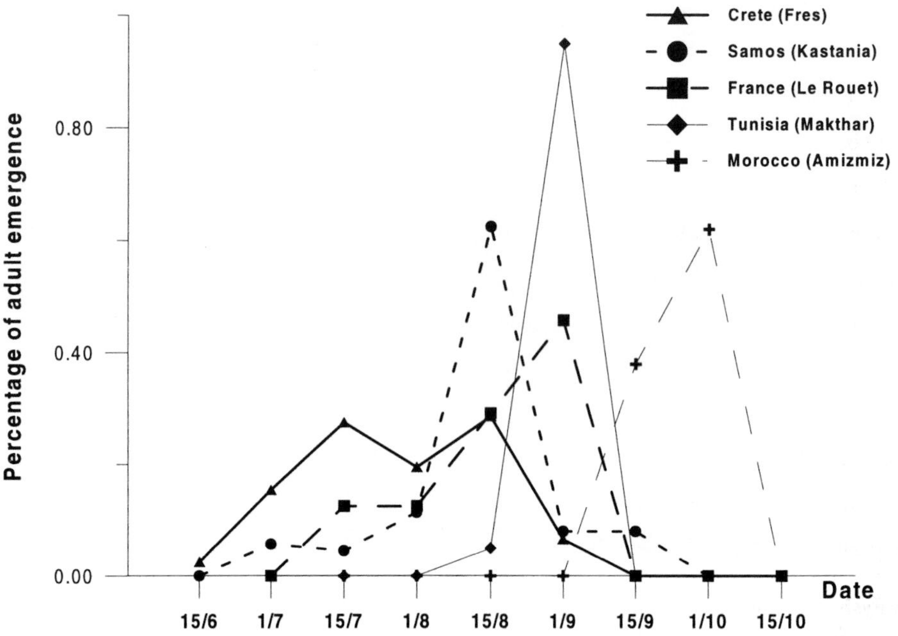

Figure 4. Variation in the emergence period of adult seed chalcids in different locations of the natural (Crete, Samos) and introduced range (France, Tunisia) of *Cupressus sempervirens*, and in the natural range of *C. atlantica* (Morocco).

The emergence period seems thus adaptative to the local conditions of seed cone development, chalcid egg-laying being necessarily synchronized with the onset of seed maturation to allow further larval development (Guido *et al.*, 1995). However, no comparative data about the variation in phenology of seed development with location were available to test this hypothesis.

Results of sequencing of cytochrome b gene

A very low variability in gene sequence was observed among populations of *M.wachtli,* only 15 over 631 nucleotides being substituted (i.e., 2.4%), except in the population developing on *C. atlantica* in Morocco. The mean nucleotidic frequency varied from 34.8 to 36.2 for A, 41.3 to 42.8 for T, 11.3 to 13.2 for C, 10.2 to 10.8 for G, and the mean rate A-T was 0.774. In the Moroccan population the nucleotidic frequency was the following: A= 34.9, T= 41.2, C= 13.2, G= 10.8. Because of the genetic distance, chalcids attacking *C. atlantica* probably correspond to a species different from *M. wachtli.* The rate of mtDNA substitution having been estimated to $1.2*10^{-8}$ substitution/ silent site/ year (Brower, 1994), the divergence of the Moroccan species can be dated to ca. 2 million years ago. This period corresponds to the glaciation of the late Pliocene and early Quaternary Eras.

Fig. 5 compares the phylogenetic trees obtained from parsimony and neighbor joining methods, respectively. The Asian species, *M. duclouxianae*, did not seem closely related to the Mediterranean populations attacking cypress seeds, and may originate from an evolutive lineage different from that of *M. wachtli.* Although minor differences were observed, both methods separated *Megastigmus* spp. attacking Eurasian species of *Juniperus* from these developing in seeds of *Cupressus sempervirens* and *C. atlantica.* These data confirmed the isozyme results previously obtained by Roux and Roques (1996). However, the phylogenetic trees also revealed a monophyletic origin for the species related to *Cupressus* and *Juniperus* because of maximal bootstrap values. This result suggests a common ancestor for the *Megastigmus* spp. attacking the two Cupressaceae genera, and thus confirms the phylogenetic proximity of *Cupressus* and *Juniperus* (Gadek and Quinn, 1993).

Analysis of DNA microsatellites

A total of five loci was studied. The number of alleles per locus varied from six to 35. Populations from Crete showed the larger locus variability and the larger number of alleles (67) whilst the Italian populations were the less polymorphic (10 alleles).

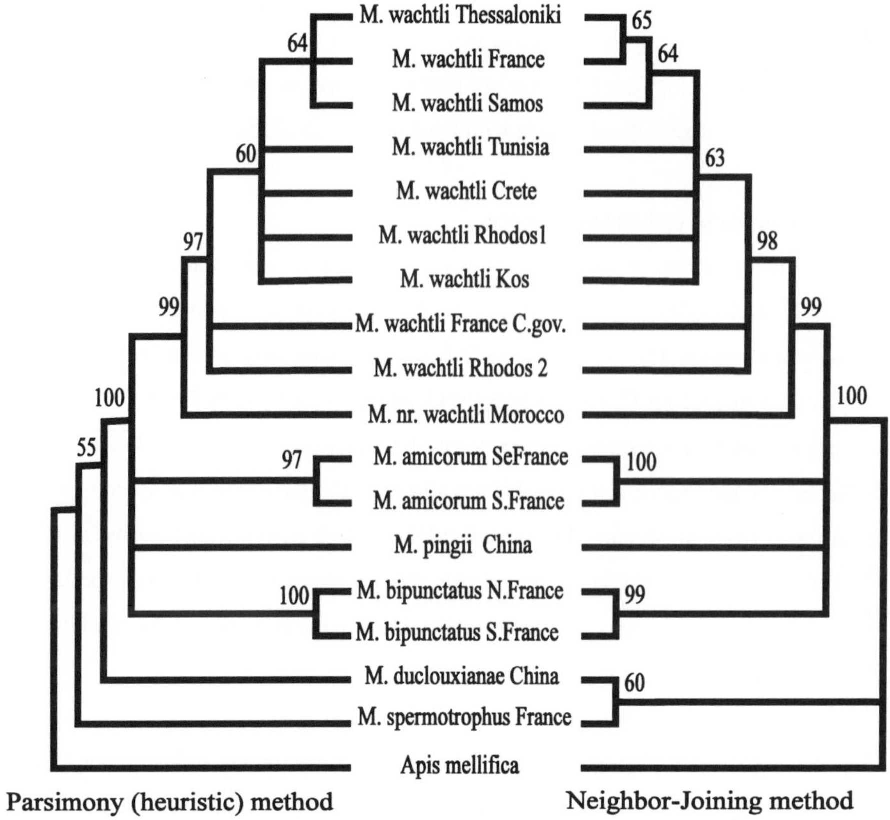

Figure 5. Phylogenetic trees of *Megastigmus* species attacking Cupressaceae based upon partial sequencing of the cytochrome b gene of mtDNA. Trees built using parsimony and neighbor-joining methods. Bootstrap procedure with 1000 iterations. *C. gov.*: Individuals from Cupressus *goveniana* (Le Rouet). S. France: southern France; N. France: northwestern France; SeFrance: southeastern France.

Hardy-Weinberg tests showed that the chalcid populations from Crete, Rhodos, Samos and Kos (i.e., from natural stands) were in equilibrium whereas these from mainland Greece, France, Tunisia, and Italy did not. Moroccan populations were in equilibrium only when we separated them into two groups on the basis of difference in emergence period. Fig. 6 shows the tree built from genetic distances between populations. Three population groups clearly individualized: (i) Crete, Kos, Rhodos, Samos, and mainland Greece but the populations from Crete also differed from the others whilst these from the three Dodecannese islands seemed genetically close; (ii) France, Italy and Tunisia, which were very close and characterized by a high homozygosity, including many females homozygous at the five loci; and, (iii), Morocco, which largely diverged from the others. The tree built from genetic distances between individuals gave similar results (Carcreff, 1996). Individuals from Tunisia, Italy and France were distinctly separated from these originating from the eastern Mediterranean basin but the Tunisian specimens were more variable than the other western chalcids.

Two independent populations, Crete and the Dodecannese islands (which probably also involved Turkey) thus seemed to have originated in the Eastern Mediterranean. Chalcid colonization of mainland Greece also appeared to be rather ancient and to proceed from population of both Crete and the eastern Aegean. An important bottleneck effect characterized the west Mediterranean populations. The genetic proximity to the Cretan populations suggested that these populations originated from the introduction of Cretan seeds by Ancient Greeks or Romans. With regard to the controversial native origin of the Makthar cypress stand in Tunisia, the seed chalcid may be a good marker for assuming the introduced origin of this stand. It must also be noticed that the two individuals attacking *C. goveniana* we analyzed at Le Rouet largely differed from the other French chalcids, and were genetically closer to the chalcid populations of the eastern Mediterranean.The capability of shifting to exotic cypresses may thus depend on chalcid genotype. This remains to be tested on a larger number of individuals attacking seeds of exotic species.

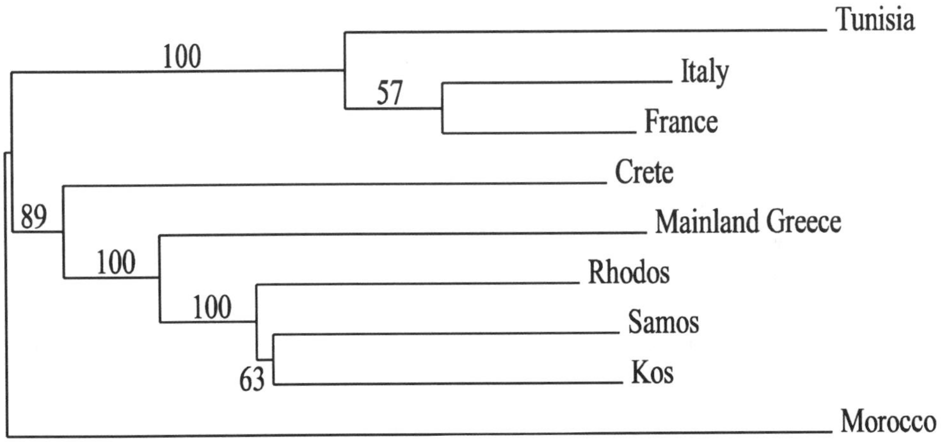

Figure 6. Genetic relationships between populations of cypress seed chalcids. Tree based upon distance between shared alleles (DSA). Bootstrap procedure with 2000 iterations.

Analysis of tree genetic variability vs. chalcid variability

Allozyme studies of Greek populations of *Cupressus sempervirens* showed a similar differentiation into three groups: Crete, the eastern Aegean islands, and mainland Greece (Papageourgiou *et al.*, 1994). Thus, the chalcid diversity clearly reflects that of the tree.

CONCLUSION

Studying the genetic diversity of a specialized insect pest is likely to give relevant information about the host history and evolution. We may assume that the first cypresses planted in the west Mediterranean, in France as well as in Italy, originated from Crete. The long-term and continuous introduction of cypresses in continental Greece results in a higher diversity of chalcids. The presumed native stand of Makthar in Tunisia probably originated from an introduction of seeds from Crete. The occurrence of a seed chalcid specific to the Moroccan cypress is a witness of the sharing of the range of Mediterranean Cypress into three species during glaciation.

ACKNOWLEDGEMENTS

We thank J.P. Raimbault, INRA Orléans, France, and Pan Yong- zhi, Southwest Forestry College, Kunming China, for the radiographic analyses. This work was funded by the European Union as part of the project AIR 3-CT- 93- 1675 "Cypress", and by the "Bureau des Ressources Génétiques" (France) as part of the project "Biodiversité et Ressources Génétiques".

REFERENCES

BAUMANN H., 1982. *Die grieschische Pflanzenwelt in Mythos, Kunst und Literatur*. München, Hirmer, 250 p.

BEN JAMAA M.L., ROQUES A., 1997. Survey of impact on seed cones of two species of Cupressaceae, *Cupressus sempervirens* L. and *Tetraclinis articulata* Mast. in Tunisia. *Proc. 6th Arabian Congress for Vegetal Protection*, Beyrouth, October 1997, in press.

BROWER A.V., 1994. Phylogeny of *Heliconius* inferred from mitochondrial DNA sequences (Lepidoptera: Nymphalidae). *Molecul.Phylog.Evol.*, 3, 159- 174.

ÇANAKCIOGLÜ H., 1959. Studies on insects which are injurious to the turkish forest tree seeds and control of some of the important species. *Orman Fakültesi Dergisi ser. A.*, 9, 126- 165.

CARCREFF E., 1996. *Relations phylétiques et caractérisation génétique de* Megastigmus wachtli *(Hym. Torymidae).* DEA Physiologie des Invertébrés, Univ. Paris VI, 45 p.

CARCREFF E., RASPLUS J.Y., ROQUES A., MONDOR G., VAUTRIN D., SOLIGNAC M., 1997. Isolation and characterization of microsatellite loci in the seed chalcid, *Megastigmus wachtli. Molec. Ecol.*, in press.

CHAKRABORTY R., JIN L., 1992. Heterozygote deficiency, population substructure and their implications in DNA fingerprinting. *Human genetics*, 88, 267-272.

CROZIER R.H., DOBRIC N., IMAI H.T., GRAUR D., CORNUET J.M., TAYLOR R.W., 1995. Mitochondrial -DNA sequence evidence on the phylogeny of Australian jack-jumper ants of the *Myrmica pilulosa* complex. *Molec. Phyl. Evolution*, 4, 20-30.

DOUGLAS O.C., WOLSTENHOLME D.R., 1985. The mitochondrial DNA molecule of *Drosophila yakuba*: Nucleotidic sequence, gene organisation and genetic code. *J. Molec. Evol.*, 22, 252- 271.

GADEK P.A., QUINN C.J., 1993. An analysis of relationships within the Cupressaceae *sensu stricto* based on rbcL sequences. *Ann. Missouri Bot. Garden*, 80, 581-586.

GUIDO M., BATTISTI A., ROQUES A,. 1995. A contribution to the study of cone and seed pests of the evergreen cypress (*Cupressus sempervirens* L.) in Italy. *Redia*, 78, 211- 227.

HEDLIN A. F., YATES H.O. III, CIBRIAN-TOVAR D., EBEL B.H., KOERBER T. W., MERKEL E.P., 1980. *Cone and seed insects of North American conifers*. Ottawa, Washington and Mexico: Can. For. Serv., USDA For. Serv, Secr. Agric. Recur. Hidraul., 122 p.

HIGGINS D.G., BLEASBY A.J., FUCHS R., 1992. Clustal V: Improved sofware for multiple sequence alignment. *Comput. Appl. Biosc.*, 8, 189- 191.

KIMURA M., 1980. A simple method for estimating evolutionary rate of base substitutions through comparative studies of nucleotide sequences. *J. Molec. Evol.*, 16, 111- 120.

KUMAR S., TAMURA K., NEI M., 1993. *MEGA: molecular evolutionary genetics analysis, version 1.01.* University Park, Pensylvania State Univ..

NEI M., 1978. Estimation of average heterozygoty and genetic distances from a small number of individuals. *Genetics*, 89, 583-590

NEI M., TAJIMA F., 1985. Evolutionary change of restriction clivage sites and phylogenetic inferences for man and apes. *Molec. Biol. Evol.*, 2, 189- 205.

PAPAGEORGIOU A.C.., PANETSOS K.P., HATTEMER H.H., 1994. Genetic differentiation of natural Mediterranean cypress (*Cupressus sempervirens* L.) populations in Greece. *For. Gen.*, 1(1), 1-12.

RAYMOND. M., ROUSSET F., 1995. GENEPOP (version 1.2.): a population genetics software for exact tests and eucumenicism. *J. Hered.*, 86, 248-249.

ROQUES A., RAIMBAULT J. P., 1986. Cycle biologique et répartition de *Megastigmus wachtli* (Stein) (Hymenoptera, Torymidae), chalcidien ravageur des graines de cyprès dans le Bassin méditerranéen. *J. Appl. Entomol.*, 101, 370-381.

ROQUES A. , SUN J. H., PAN Y.Z., ZHANG X.D., 1995. Contribution to the knowledge of seed chalcids, *Megastigmus* spp. (Hymenoptera: Torymidae) in China, with the description of a new species. *Mitt. Schweiz. Entomol. Gesell.*, 68, 211-223.

ROQUES A., ROUX G., MARKALAS S., 1997. Entomofauna of seed cones of evergreen cypress, *Cupressus sempervirens*, in natural stands of the eastern Aegean region. *Proc. 5th Intern. Conf. Cone and Seed Insects IUFRO Working Party (WP S7.03-01).* Padova, Padova Univ., in press.

ROUX G., ROQUES A., 1996. Biochemical genetic differentiation among seed chalcid species of genus *Megastigmus* (Hym., Torymidae). *Experientia*, 52, 522-530

SAITOU N., NEI M. 1987. The neighbor-joining method: A new method for reconstructing phylogenetic trees. *Molecul. Biol. Evol.*, 4, 406-425.

SAMBROOK J., FRITSCH E.F., MANIATIS T., 1989. *Molecular Cloning: A Laboratory Manual.* Cold Spring Harbor Laboratory Press, New York.

SWOFFORD D.L., 1993. *PAUP version 3..1.1 Program and documentation.* Illinois Natural History Museum, Champagne.

TURGEON J.J., ROQUES A., DE GROOT P., 1994. Insect Fauna of Coniferous Seed Cones. Diversity, Host-Plant Interactions, and Management. *Ann. Rev. Entomol.*, 39, 179-212.

VIDAKOVI M., 1991. Conifers: morphology and variation. Zagreb: Grafi ki zavod Hrvastke.

XU Z.H., HE J.H., 1995. [Notes on species of phytophagous group of *Megastigmus* (Hymenoptera: Torymidae) in China] (in Chinese with English summary). *Entomotaxonomia*, 17, 4, 243- 253.

Physiology and Genetics of Tree-Phytophage Interactions
Gujan (France), August 31 - September 5, 1997
Ed. INRA, Paris, 1999 (Les Colloques, n°90)

Traumatic resin duct formation in Norway spruce (*Picea abies* (L.) Karst.) after wounding or infection with a bark beetle-associated blue-stain fungus, *Ceratocystis polonica* Siem.

E. CHRISTIANSEN[1], V.R. FRANCESHI[2], N.E. NAGY[1], T. KREKLING[3], A.A. BERRYMAN[4], P. KROKENE[1], H. SOLHEIM[1]

[1] *Norwegian Forest Research Institute, N-1432 Ås, Norway*
[2] *Botany Department, Washington State University, Pullman, WA 99164, USA*
[3] *LAK-EM, Agricultural University of Norway, N-1432 Ås, Norway*
[4] *Entomology Department, Washington State University, Pullman, WA 99164, USA*

RESUME

Norway spruce trees, exposed to sub-lethal attacks by the bark beetle *Ips typographus*, form distinct necrotic and resin-soaked reaction zones in the bark and outer sapwood within which the beetles and their associated fungi are enveloped and arrested. In these trees a ring of axial resin ducts regularly form in the stem xylem. These ducts are included in a false annual ring with narrow tracheids. A similar ring of resin ducts is seen in trees artificially administered a sub-lethal inoculation dose of the blue-stain fungus *Ceratocystis polonic*ı, a pathogenic associate of *I. typographus*. Here we report preliminary studies on the development of traumatic axial ducts in stems of Norway spruce after beetle and fungus invasion, and some cytochemical aspects related to the formation of phenolics and terpenes. We suggest that traumatic resin ducts furnish the reaction zones with materials toxic to both beetles and fungi, and that increased numbers of ducts may render trees more resistant to attack.

INTRODUCTION

Bark beetles may transfer a multitude of microorganisms to their host trees, including blue-stain fungi, some of which are important pathogens (Reid *et al.*, 1967) (Berryman, 1969; Berryman, 1972). The spruce bark beetle *Ips typographus* L. infects Norway spruce (*Picea abies* (L.) Karst.) with *Ceratocystis polonica* (Siem.) C. Moreau, a fungus capable of killing healthy trees when inoculated under the bark in adequate doses (Horntvedt *et al.*, 1983) (Christiansen, 1985b). Here, a true mutualistic relationship exists; the fungus being carried to new hosts, and the beetle being aided in its tree-killing.

Combined beetle-fungus attacks, as well as wounding and infection of the bark in general, are counteracted by the trees' defense mechanisms. Resinous material, pre-formed or produced by induced reactions, play an important role. When a resin reservoir (e.g. a resin blister or duct) is opened up by a beetle's boring activity an almost immediate flow of constitutive resin occurs (Berryman, 1972). A small number of "pioneer" beetles may be repelled or arrested by this flow of "primary" resin and the attack brought to an end. Massive attacks overwhelm this defense paving the way for gallery excavation, during which the beetles disseminate fungal spores. As demonstrated for *I. typographus*, and *C. polonica* (Furniss *et al.*, 1990) and other systems, the beetles carry fungal spores both externally and internally. Upon spore germination hyphae will penetrate phloem, cambium, and sapwood if not checked by other defenses of the tree.

When pioneer beetles have gained a first foothold, but the number of attacks is not overly high, an induced reaction starts: necrotic areas develop in tissues adjacent to the site of infection and are gradually impregnated with resinous materials. Within these reaction zones the pathogen may be enveloped and rendered harmless to the tree (Reid *et al.*, 1967; Berryman, 1972; Christiansen, 1985a). The resin of the reaction zones is termed "secondary", inferring that it originates from sources other than reservoirs in the bark and wood.

The induced defense reaction in Norway spruce takes several weeks to fully develop (Christiansen and Solheim, unpublished data), and therefore it cannot prevent *I. typographus* mass attacks, which are completed in a couple of days when temperatures are high enough for flight and beetles are abundant. However, under Scandinavian field conditions where periods of cool weather often slow down attack rates and gallery construction, the induced defense reaction may be a significant obstacle as long the "Threshold of Successful Attack" (Thalenhorst, 1958) is not reached. Also, when the local beetle population is low, the reaction will contribute to the suppression of the beetles and the protection of the forest.

In Norway spruce, reaction zone resin apparently holds non-volatile fungistatic substances that are not present in the preformed resin (Solheim, 1991). This could, e.g., be phenolic substances or high-molecular terpenes. Phenols and tannins from the phloem parenchyma cells of Norway spruce might be released into the reaction zones (Franceschi *et al.*, Submitted). Moreover, resistance to *C. polonica* could be influenced by the ability of the trees to activate a particular pathway of phenolic synthesis (Brignolas *et al.*, 1995).

Constitutive resin in Norway spruce is stored in a system of ducts in the bark, axial ducts in the wood, and radial ducts in the phloem and xylem. Resistance to *C. polonica* is closely correlated to the resin concentration of the reactions zones, which is as high as 30-40% of the fresh weight in trees that successfully defend themselves (Christiansen, 1985a). The origin of such considerable quantities of resin has not been clarified. Some of it is possibly produced by dying parenchyma and callus cells inside the zone, but it seems likely an import from areas outside the zone seems likely. Existing resin systems in the bark and wood may contribute, assuming that upon wounding a signal goes to the epithelial cells lining the ducts to secrete more material. Another possible resin source is the traumatic ducts in the sapwood. The formation of such ducts is reported in several cases where conifers have survived bark beetle attacks or artificial fungal infection (Berryman, 1969) (Christiansen and Solheim, 1990; Christiansen and Fjone, 1993; Kytø *et al.*, 1996; Solheim and Safranyik, 1997.) Traumatic resin ducts are known to be formed after wounding

(Bannan, 1936; Nylinder, 1951), and are also observed in leader shoots of *Picea glauca* (Mönch) Voss that are resistant to *Pissodes strobi* Peck attack (Alfaro, 1995).

To elucidate the question of resin origin we have undertaken a study of the resin duct system in Norway spruce, using clonal trees. Here we report some preliminary results of this study, which deals with both the normal ducts and traumatic ducts formed after wounding and fungus infection.

MATERIAL AND METHODS

Twenty-five year old spruce trees growing in Ås, Norway, were used for the studies of normal resin ducts and of the developmental features of traumatic resin duct formation after fungal inoculation or sterile wounding with a cork-borer. Bark and wood samples taken 0, 6, 12, and 36 days after wounding or fungal infection were studied using light microscopy (LM), transmission electron microscopy (TEM), and scanning electron microscopy (SEM). Preparation of specimens for light and electron microscopy was as described in Franceschi et al. (1997).

RESULTS AND DISCUSSION

Normal Resin Duct System in Norway spruce

Relatively large axial resin ducts can be found in the outer part of the bark between the periderm and the oldest layer of secondary phloem (Figure 1). These are the resin ducts that were formed in a circumferential ring in the cortex of the primary stem, and they appear to persist for at least 25 years. These axial ducts in older trees typically have 2-3 layers of small tabular cells surrounding a well defined circular or oval lumen, as seen in cross section. The epithelial cells surrounding the lumen are living cells as indicated by nuclei and cytoplasmic contents. These axial resin ducts remain functional due to the manner in which the periderm is formed in young Norway spruce trees, which is from a subepidermal cell. This allows for periderm formation without destruction of the original cortex of the primary stem.

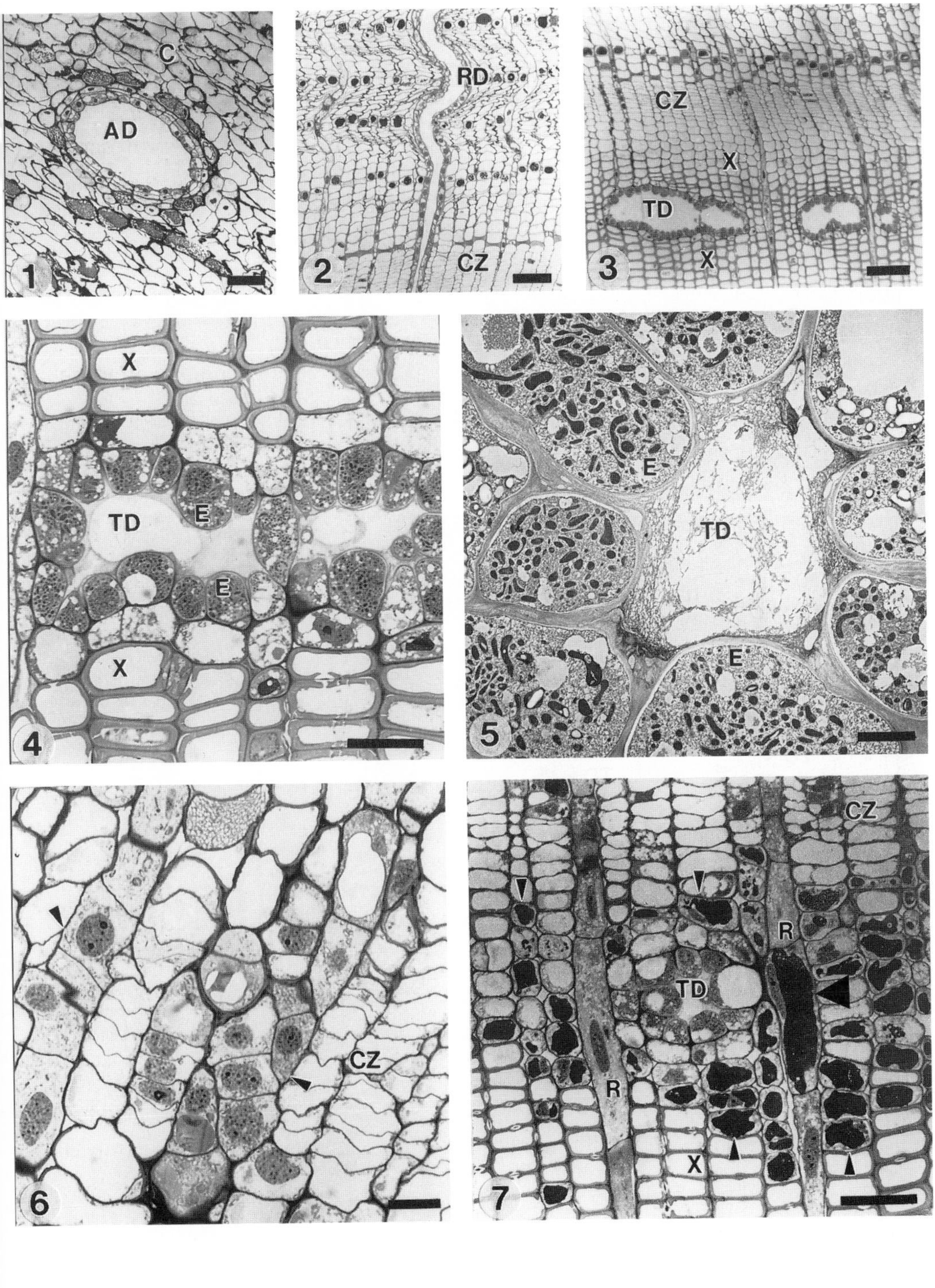
C
AD
1
RD
CZ
2
CZ
X
TD
X
3
X
TD
E
E
X
4
E
TD
E
5
CZ
6
CZ
R
TD
R
X
7

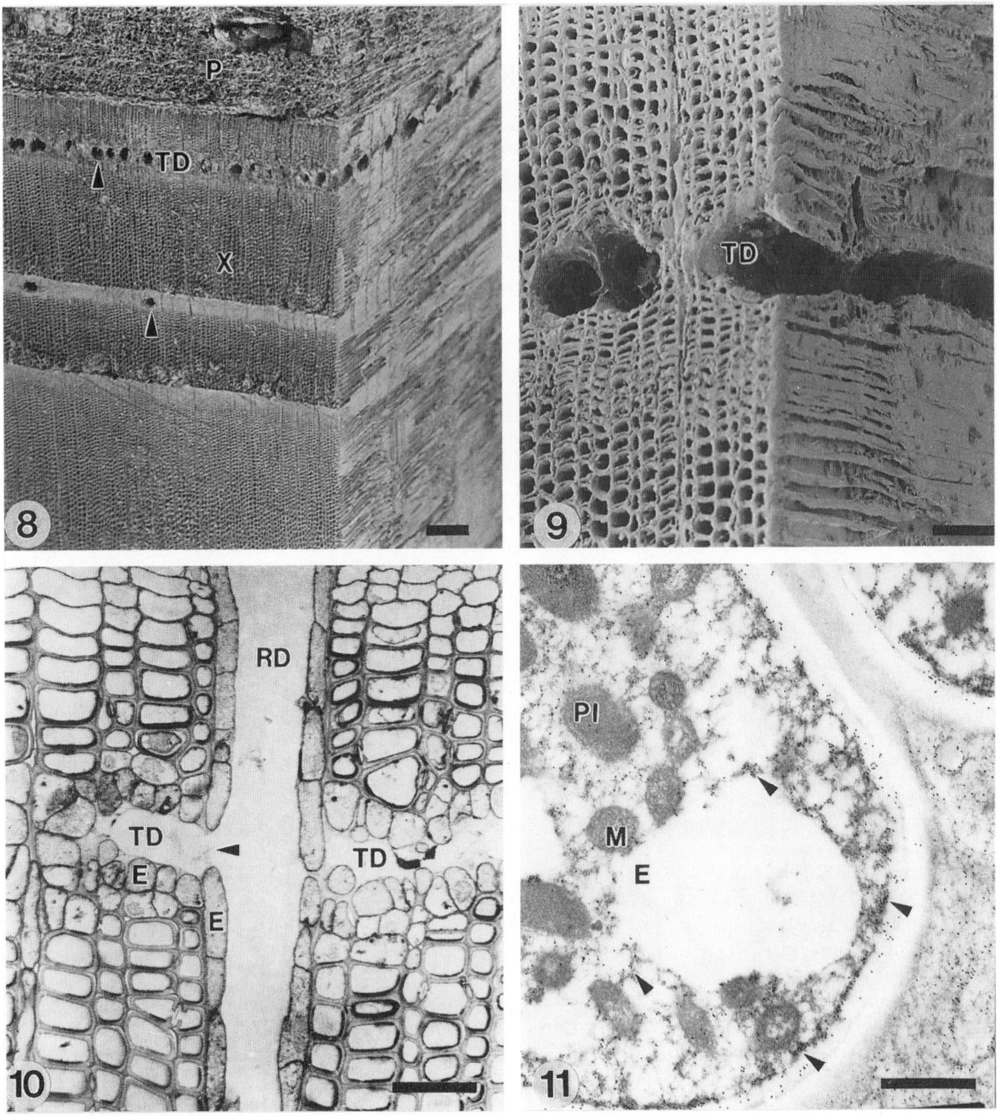
P
TD
X
8
TD
9
RD
TD
TD
E
E
10
PI
M
E
11

FIGURE LEGENDS

Fig. 1. Light microscopy (LM) cross-section through an axial resin duct (AD) in the original cortex of a 25 year old stem (C, cortical cells). x75, bar = 100µm.

Fig. 2. LM cross-section, through a cambial zone (CZ) and about 4 years of secondary phloem, showing a radial resin duct (RD). x75, bar = 100µm.

Fig. 3. LM cross-section through xylem (X), cambial zone (CZ) and mature traumatic resin ducts (TD), 36 days after wounding. x75, bar = 100µm.

Fig. 4. LM cross-section of mature traumatic resin ducts (TD), with cytoplasmic-rich epithelial cells (E) surrounded by newly formed xylem (X). x290, bar = 50µm.

Fig. 5. Transmission electron micrograph (TEM) of a mature traumatic duct (TD). Most of the dense bodies in the epithelial cells (E) are plastids. A flocculent material can be seen in the lumen of the duct. x2040, bar = 5µm.

Fig. 6. LM cross-section showing an early stage of traumatic resin duct formation (6 days after wounding). Cells of the rays in the cambial zone (CZ) have undergone divisions to form cluster of cells (arrows). x463, bar = 20µm.

Fig. 7. LM cross-section showing an intermediate stage (18 days) of traumatic resin duct (TD) formation. The ducts are surrounded by cells derived from the original cambial zone, which have accumulated phenolic bodies (arrows). Even some ray cells (R) have developed phenolic bodies (large arrow). The cambial zone (CZ) has become reorganized above the TD region, while xylem (X) is differentiating around the ducts. x290, bar = 50µm.

Fig. 8. Scanning electron micrograph (SEM) showing three annual rings of xylem (X) and the inner phloem (P). Whereas the innermost xylem rings have no axial ducts, the next has two ducts in the latewood (arrow), last year's xylem has a false annual ring with numerous traumatic ducts (TD, arrow). x36, bar = 200µm.

Fig. 9. SEM of three traumatic ducts (TD), one of which is cut through radially to show its extension in axial direction. x220, bar = 50µm.

Fig. 10. LM intersection of mature radial ray resin duct (RD) and traumatic ducts (TD) demonstrating an interconnection between the two systems (arrow). The interconnecting regions are lined by epithelial cells (E). x290, bar = 50µm.

Fig. 11. TEM showing immunocytochemical localization of PAL (phenylalanine ammonia lyase, a key enzyme in phenol biosynthesis), in mature traumatic duct epithelial cells (E). PAL is present at high levels, as indicated by black dots (arrows), in the cytosol and along the plasma membrane. Unlabelled plastids (Pl) and mitochondria (M) are also seen. x16.000, bar = 1µm.

The radial resin ducts are formed from the rays and occur primarily in the bark, but individual radial ducts may span from sapwood into the older layers of secondary phloem (Figure 2). The lumen of the radial ducts increases in size in the older parts of the bark, and can be quite extensive. The epithelial cells lining the resin ducts are small, compact cells with the further distinguishing characteristics of being densely cytoplasmic with little or no vacuole, enriched in plastids, and having numerous lipid bodies within the cytoplasm.

Axial resin ducts of the xylem can be observed in the earliest stages of secondary xylem formation after a vascular cambium has been fully formed in the first year of stem development. The ducts are scattered throughout the xylem and are often, but not always, found in association with ray parenchyma in the stem cross sections examined. They are formed prior to xylem differentiation just below the active cambial zone and usually have a single layer of epithelial cells, most of which develop thick lignified walls as they age. Axial resin ducts in the xylem appear randomly throughout many years of growth in the trees we have sampled.

Development of Traumatic Resin Ducts

Mature traumatic ducts were formed by 36 days after inoculation and in cross sections through stem samples they could clearly be seen as a line of densely stained structures embedded in the newly formed sapwood (Figure 3). The dense staining of these structures is due to the specialized epithelial cells lining the ducts, which are densely cytoplasmic, and contain numerous plastids compared to other cell types in the stem (Figures 4 and 5). Radial resin ducts are lined by the same cell type. Resin could be seen within the lumen of the mature traumatic ducts both on the LM and TEM level (Figures 4, 5).

The first signs of traumatic duct formation were seen within 6 to 12 days of inoculation or wounding. The early stages of development consist of swelling and rapid division of ray parenchyma and undifferentiated cells of the cambial zone (Figure 6). Some of these cells begin to organize into a layer of cells which will become epithelial cells, while many of the cells surrounding them begin to fill with polyphenolic substances (Figure 7). The cambial zone is re-established above this and gives rise to more cells which will differentiate into xylem. The polyphenol-containing cells surrounding the developing epithelium loose their phenolic contents and most will eventually differentiate into tracheids (Figure 8).

The mature traumatic ducts formed after bark beetle attack or artificial inoculation occur in false annual rings of the xylem where tracheidal lumens are temporarily reduced (Figures 9 and 10). Extensive LM and SEM examination indicate that they form rather complex structures with lumens of varying lengths. However, the ducts in a particular axial file may be made of a series of shorter ducts that are sealed at either end rather than continuous along a large length of stem. Often the continuity of the ducts in an axial file appear to be disrupted by radial rays, most of which do not contain resin ducts. However, a few examples of connection of the axial traumatic resin duct system and the radial resin duct system have been observed (Figure 10). Further studies will determine if most of the radial resin ducts are actually connected with the traumatic duct system, which would seem logical for enhanced resin flow in beetle-attacked regions of the bark.

The observation that during early stages of traumatic resin duct formation many of the cells in the region accumulate polyphenols, is quite novel. Equally important is the fact that these phenolic compounds disappear as the cells differentiate into tracheary elements. The compounds must be released into the general region of the traumatic ducts and may account for the "browning" that is seen in wood discs where traumatic duct formation is prominent. This may enhance the resistance of the newly formed sapwood to fungal infection, a matter which deserves further study. Related to this is the observation that PAL, an important enzyme in the phenolic synthesis pathway, is abundant in the cells of the region where traumatic ducts are developing, as demonstrated by immunocytochemical analysis (Figure 11). PAL label was also found in developing and mature secretory epithelial cells of the traumatic ducts, even though these cells did not accumulate polyphenolic bodies nor formed a lignified cell wall during the time span of this study. It is interesting to speculate that perhaps the traumatic ducts are producing resin that also has phenolic compounds incorporated into it. As yet, we have no analytical data at this time to support this hypothesis but further biochemical analysis is planned.

One interesting possibility is that the formation of traumatic resin ducts following an unsuccessful bark beetle attack may render spruce trees more resistant to later assaults since traumatic ducts have been formed and more resin hence is available for defense. In addition, the possibility exists that resin from traumatic ducts might contain substances that are more toxic or fungistatic than the resin of normal ducts, as indicated by our observation of phenolic substances in cells lining the former.

ACKNOWLEDGEMENT

This study was funded by grant number 104023/110 from the Research Council of Norway, which supported an international scientific research effort on conifer defense mechanisms (CONDEF group), and by a Fulbright scholarship to N. Nagy. Part of the work was conducted in the Unit for Electron Microscopy, (LAK-EM), Agricultural University of Norway, and the Electron Microscopy Center, Washington State University.

REFERENCES

ALFARO R.I., 1995. An induced defence reation in white spruce to attack by the white pine weevil, *Pissodes strobi*. *Can. J. For. Res.*, 25, 1725-1730.

BANNAN M.W., 1936. Vertical resin ducts in the secondary wood of the Abietineae. *New Phytologist*, 35, 11-46.

BERRYMAN A.A., 1969. Responses of *Abies grandis* to attack by *Scolytus ventralis* (Coleoptera: Scolytidae). *Can. Ent.*, 101, 1033-1041.

BERRYMAN A.A., 1972. Resistance of conifers to invasion by bark beetle-fungus associations. *BioScience*, 22, 598-602.

BRIGNOLAS F., LACROIX B., LIEUTIER F., SAUVARD D., DROUET A., CLAUDOT A.C., YART A., BERRYMAN A.A., CHRISTIANSEN E., 1995. Induced responses in phenolic metabolism in two Norway spruce clones after wounding and inoculation with *Ophiostoma polonicum*, a bark beetle-associated fungus. *Plant Physiol.*, 109, 821-827.

CHRISTIANSEN E., 1985a. *Ceratocystis polonica* inoculated in Norway spruce: Blue-staining in relation to inoculum density, resinosis, and tree growth. *Eur. J. For. Pathol.*, 15, 160-167.

CHRISTIANSEN E., 1985b. *Ips/Ceratocystis*-infection of Norway spruce: what is a deadly dosage? *Z. ang. Ent.*, 99, 6-11.

CHRISTIANSEN E., FJONE G., 1993. Pruning enhances the susceptibility of *Picea abies* to infection by the bark beetle-transmitted blue-stain fungus, *Ophiostoma polonicum*. *Scand. J. For. Res.*, 8, 235-245.

CHRISTIANSEN E., SOLHEIM H., 1990. The bark beetle-associated blue-stain fungus *Ophiostoma polonicum* can kill various spruces and Douglas fir. *Eur. J. For. Path.*, 20, 436-446.

FRANCESCHI V.R., KREKLING T., BERRYMAN A.A., CHRISTIANSEN E., Submitted. Specialized phloem parenchyma cells in Norway spruce are an important site of defense reactions. *American Journal of Botany*.

FURNISS M.M., SOLHEIM H., CHRISTIANSEN E., 1990. Transmission of blue-stain fungi by *Ips typographus* (Coleoptera: Scolytidae) in Norway spruce. *Ann. Entomol. Soc. Am.*, 83, 712-716.

HORNTVEDT R., CHRISTIANSEN E., SOLHEIM H., WANG S., 1983. Artificial inoculation with *Ips typographus*-associated blue-*stain fungi can kill healthy Norway spruce trees. Medd. Nor. Inst. Skogforskning*, 38, 1-20.

KYTØ M., NIEMELA P., ANNILA E., 1996. Vitality and bark beetle resistance of fertilized Norway spruce. *For. Ecol. Manage.*, 84, 149-157.

NYLINDER P., 1951. Om patologiska hartskanaler (On pathological resin canals). *Medd. Stat. Skogsforskningsinstitut,* 40, 1-12.

REID R.W., WHITNEY H.S., WATSON J.A., 1967. Reactions of lodgepole pine to attack by *Dendroctonus ponderosae* Hopkins and blue stain fungi. *Can. J. Bot.*, 45, 1115-1126.

SOLHEIM H., 1991. Oxygen deficiency and spruce resin inhibition of growth of fungi associated with *Ips typographus. Mycol. Res.*, 95, 1387-1392.

SOLHEIM H., SAFRANYIK L., 1997, in press. Pathogenicity of the spruce beetle associated blue-stain fungi, *Ceratocystis rufipenni* and *Leptographium abietinum*, to Sitka spruce. *Can. J. For. Res.*

THALENHORST W., 1958. Grundzuge der Populationdynamik des grossen Fichtenborkenkafers *Ips typographus* L. *SchrReihe forstl. Fak. Univ. Göttingen*, 21, 1-126.

Physiology and Genetics of Tree-Phytophage Interactions
Gujan (France), August 31 - September 5, 1997
Ed. INRA, Paris, 1999 (Les Colloques, n°90)

Histological observations on the interaction between *Leptographium wingfieldii* Morelet and *Pinus sylvestris* L.

E. BOIS, F. LIEUTIER

INRA, Station de Zoologie Forestière, Ardon
45160, Olivet, France

RESUME

Two Scots pine clones were chosen with respect to their susceptibility to *Leptographium wingfieldii*, a fungus associated with *Tomicus piniperda*. In response to inoculation of sterile malt-agar or fungus, a callus region and a wound periderm took place. After fungal inoculation, the parenchyma cells and ray cells were deformed and emptied of their contents. Moreover, after a fungal inoculation, a "substance" appeared in and between the sieve cells. All the modifications after inoculations were faster and more important in the resistant clone than in the susceptible one and there were much more fungal hyphae in the phloem of the suceptible clone than in the phloem of the resistant one.

INTRODUCTION

Phloem induced reactions play a basic role in conifer resistance to attacks by bark beetles and their associated fungi (Berryman, 1972; Christiansen *et al.*, 1987; Långström *et al.*, 1992; Raffa and Kleipzig, 1992; Lieutier, 1993). These reactions take place in longitudinal elliptical reaction zones surrounding each point of attack, and involve dramatic changes in concentrations of secondary metabolites such as terpenes and phenols (Shrimpton, 1973; Raffa and Berryman, 1982; Delorme and Lieutier, 1990; Brignolas *et al.*, 1995 a; Lieutier *et al.*, 1996 a). In the case of a small number of attacks, these reactions are generally effective and stop the aggressors. In case of mass attacks, however, they can become ineffective, the aggressors succeed in killing the tree and establishing their populations. Conifers' resistance to bark beetles attacks is measured by the maximum density of attacks (threshold of attack density) that a tree is able to contain before being overcome (Mulock and Christiansen, 1986; Christiansen *et al.*, 1987). Fungi introduced by the beetles into their galleries stimulate the tree reaction induced by the boring insect (Lieutier, 1993; Lieutier *et al.*, 1995), thus lowering the threshold of attack density (Berryman, 1972; Christiansen *et al.*, 1987). Mass inoculations with beetle-associated fungi are commonly used to evaluate a trees' resistance level, thus defining a threshold of inoculum density (Horntvedt *et al.*, 1983; Solheim *et al.*, 1993).

This study is a part of a program aiming at understanding the mechanisms involved in the induced response of Scots pine phloem (*pinus sylvestris*) phloem to aggression. In previous studies, we have observed the phenolic response of the Scots pine, and we have proposed some resistance markers (Lieutier *et al.*, 1996 a; Bois and Lieutier, 1997). In this present study, we wanted to observe anatomical mechanisms involved in the induced response of Scots pine phloem to aggression.

Previuos histological studies, have demonstrated that after septic or aseptic inoculations, various conifers showed a wound response (Reid *et al.*, 1967; Wong and Berryman, 1977; Mullick, 1977; Shrimpton, 1978), and finally, the fungus was compartimentalized in the reaction zone (Shigo, 1984). Moreover, the death of the phloem cells in advance of the fungus spread, and the synthesis of secondary resin linked to phloem parenchyma and ray parenchyma have been also observed (Wong and Berryman, 1977; Cheniclet *et al.*, 1988; Lieutier and Berryman, 1988), after various aggressions. However, the Scots pine anatomy was never observed after inoculation of blue-stained fungus associated to bark beetles.

The objectives of the present study were to describe the anatomical changes in the phloem of Scots pine that are susceptible or resistant to mass inoculations with *L. wingfieldii*, a fungus associated with *T. piniperda*. This fungus does not seem to play an important role in the establishment of *T. piniperda* populations in Scots pine, probably due to its low frequency and abundance on the beetles (Lieutier *et al.*, 1995). However, it can kill healthy Scots pines after mass inoculations (Solheim and Långström, 1991; Solheim *et al.*, 1993), and is an excellent tool to study the response of Scots pine phloem to aggressors (Långström *et al.* 1992; Lieutier *et al.*, 1996 b). Moreover, we wanted to describe the phloem anatomy, and the fungal pathway in the phloem.

MATERIALS AND METHODS

Screening the resistance level of Scots pine clones.

In April 1994, 18 Scots pine clones were tested for their susceptibility to infection by *L. wingfieldii.* The trees originating from the natural Haguenau provenance (Bas-Rhin, France) had been grafted in 1985, and cultivated in the nursery of INRA (Orléans, France). Two healthy ramets of each clone were mass inoculated at a density of 400 inoculation m^{-2} on a 1 m section of the stem at about breast height. Inoculations were done with two-week-old sporulating cultures growing on malt agar using a cork-borer technique (Wright, 1933). Bark plugs were removed with a 5 mm cork borer and a calibrated disc (5 mm diameter) of cultures were introduced into the tree in cambium-deep holes, and the holes were closed with the bark plugs. Three months later, the trees were felled. The inoculated stem sections were brought to the laboratory where three thin discs were taken, two at 15 cm from each end of the inoculated section and one in the middle. The extension of occluded sapwood (comprising blue-stained sapwood, desiccated but unstained sapwood, and resin impregnated sapwood), was delineated on the discs, quantified with a planimeter and expressed as a percentage of the total sapwood area. Clones were ranked according to the percentage of occluded sapwood, corresponding to a ranking according to tree's resistance level, with the most resistant clones having the lowest percentages of occluded sapwood (Christiansen and Berryman, 1995).

Sampling for histological study.

Based on the results from the screening experiment, one resistant and one susceptible clones were chosen. In March 1995, one healthy ramet of each clone received five inoculations of a malt agar culture of *L. wingfieldii* and five inoculations of sterile malt agar to serve as wounded controls. Three, 7, 14, 30 and 60 days after inoculations, the outer bark was removed around one inoculation point per treatment and per tree. In the lower part of the reaction zone, at 2 mm of the inoculation point, pieces of the reactional phloem were sampled for the histological study. At day 0 (the day of inoculation) and day 30, samples of unwounded phloem were also taken from each tree. Immediately after cutting, the samples were transferred into a fixation solution containing 5% glutaraldehyde and embedded in glycolmethacrylate (Gutman and Feucht, 1991). Semithin sections (2-10 µm) were cut on a Leitz microtome 1400 equipped with a carbide knife. Sections, 2 µm thick were stained with toluidine blue O, and with safranine o lugol, and the sections of 10 µm were stained with DMACA according to Gutmann and Feucht (1991) for the staining of flavan-3-ols.

The fungal density was estimated by quantifying the number of fungal sections in a reference cell (0.25 mm x 0.375 mm). Fourty-two repetitions were made by treatment, by tree and by date. The data were analyzed using SAS software (SAS Institute Inc. 1985, 1986, 1987). Treatments, dates and trees were tested by one way analysis of variance, and with Tukey test for multiple comparisons. All means were expressed with their confidence interval. Differences between means were taken into acount only when significant at the 95% level.

RESULTS

The percentage of occluded sapwood differed from one clone to another (fig. 1). A resistance gradient was thus obtained in which the extreme clone categories were chosen to the histological study. Clone 765 having a high percentage of occluded sapwood was chosen as the least resistant clones (called " susceptible " clone in the present study), while clones 874 having a low percentage of occluded sapwood was chosen as the most resistant clones (called " resistant " clone in the present study).

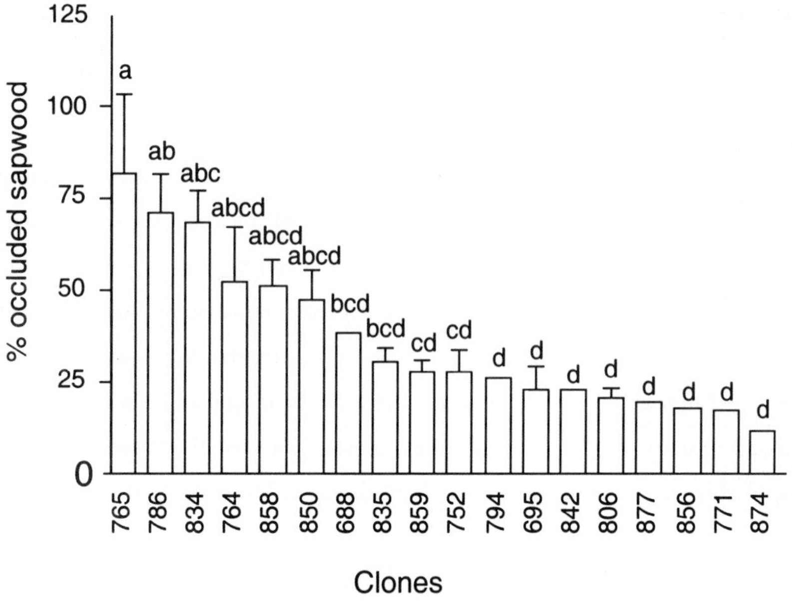

Figure 1: Percentage of occluded sapwood after mass inoculations with *L. wingfieldii* in different Scots pine clones. Values are means SD ± (n=2 for each sample). Values with the same letter did not differ significantly (P=0.05).

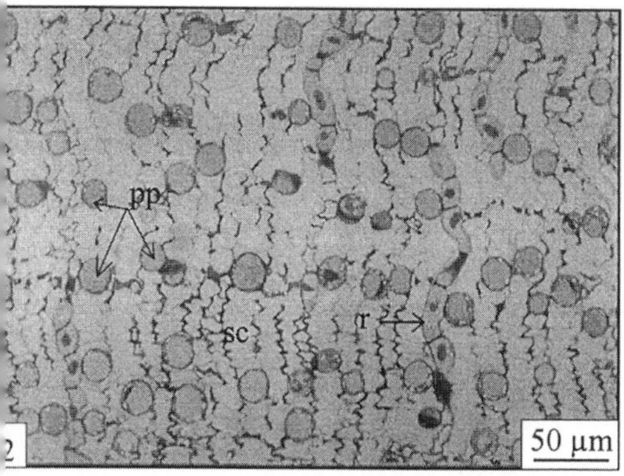

igure 2: Cross section of general anatomy of cots pine phloem. Blocks of sieve cells (sc) are eparated by row of phloem parenchyma (pp). 'arenchyma rays are uniseriate. Toluidine blue O.

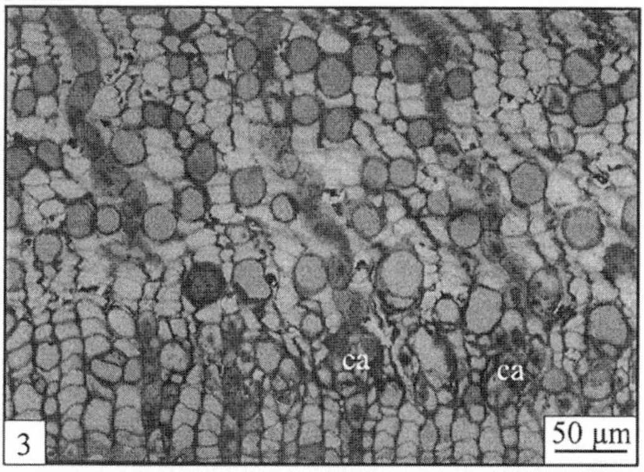

Figure 3: Cross section of the phloem after inoculations. A callus region (ca) took place near the cambial zone. Safranine O Lugol.

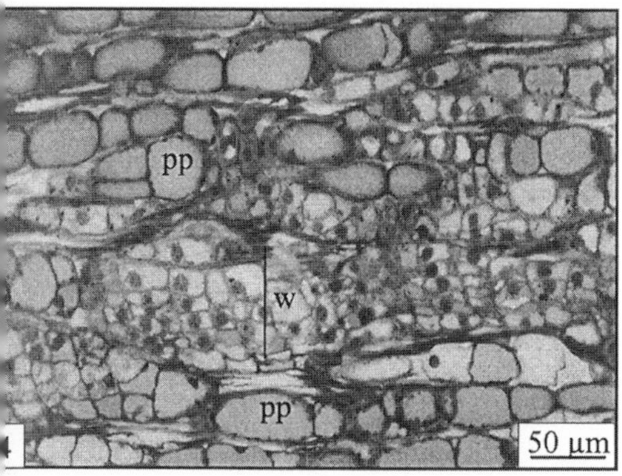

igure 4: Tangential section of the phloem after ıoculations. A wound periderm (w) took place ıd seemed to derive from the phloem arenchyma (pp). Safranine O Lugol.

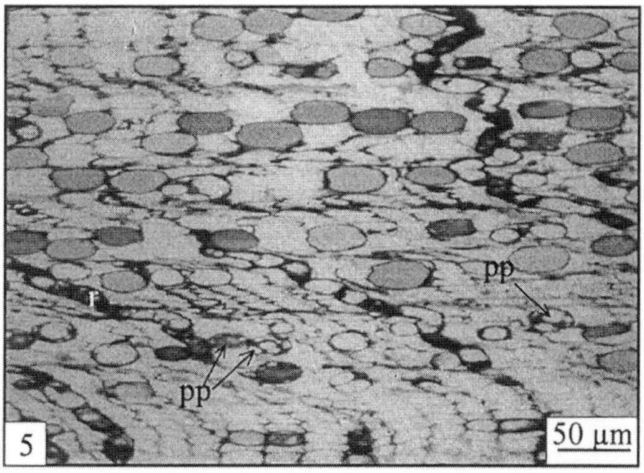

Figure 5: Phloem degeneration, 14 days after fungal inoculation. The parenchyma phloem (pp) and the ray parenchyma (r) seemed to degenerate and empty of their contents.. Toluidine blue O.

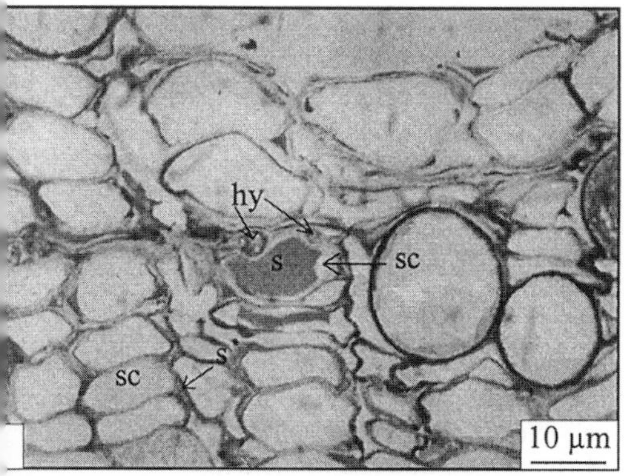

igure 6: Accumulation of a substance pink- ɔloured (s) in and between sieve cells (sc), with yphae (hy) in a sieve cell (sc). Toluidine blue O.

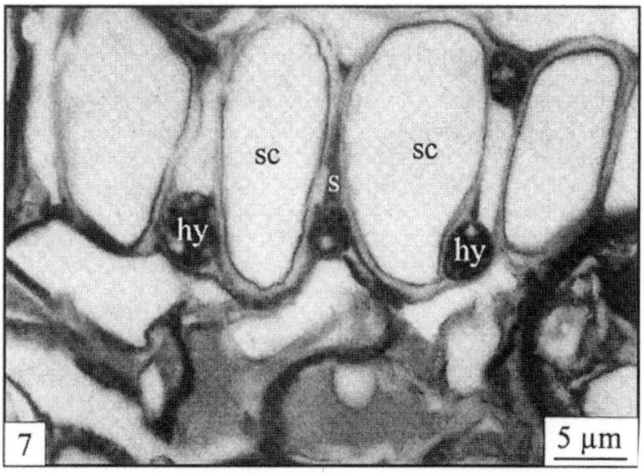

Figure 7: Cross section of fungal hyphae (hy) between sieve cells (sc). The substance pink- coloured (s) was between sieve cells. Toluidine blue O.

The secondary phloem of Scots pine was made up of three major types of cells : sieve cells, radial ray parenchyma, and phloem parenchyma (fig 2). In ray parenchyma and in phloem parenchyma, phenolic compounds (flavan-3-ols) were stained in blue by DMACA. No differences were observed between the two trees.

After fungal or sterile malt-agar inoculation, the young ray cells of the cambial zone divided and enlarged to form a callus region (fig. 3). Moreover, In the oldest phloem, the phloem parenchyma cells seemed to divide to form a wound periderm (fig. 4). All these anatomical changes occured in both trees, but sooner after sterile inoculation than after fungal inoculation, and sooner in the resistant tree than in the suceptible one. After fungal inoculation, the phloem parenchyma cells and the ray parenchyma cells were deformed and progressively emptied of their contents (Fig. 5). These changes began 7 days after fungal inoculations and were amplified with time. They seemed quicker and sooner in the resistant tree than in the suceptible one. Moreover, a substance pink-coloured with toluidine blue O occured in and between sieve cells, after fungal inoculations (fig. 6).

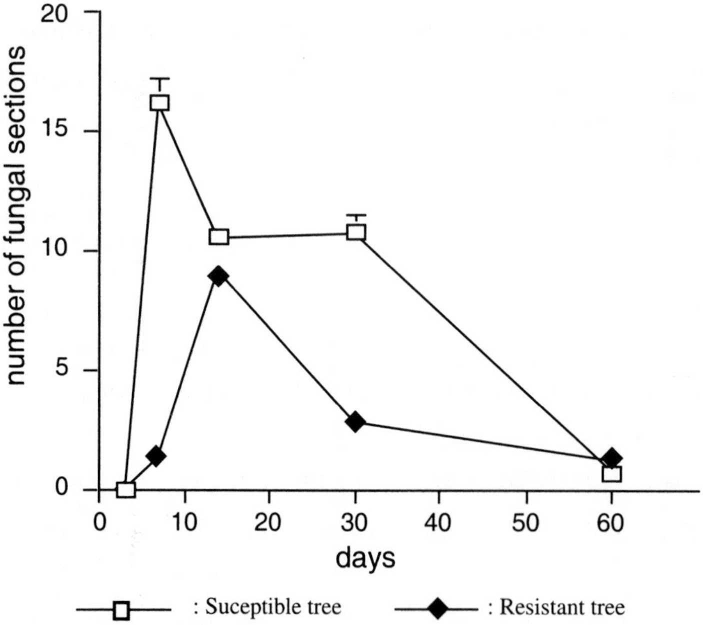

Figure 8: Number of fungal sections by cell reference, after inoculation of *L. wingfieldii* in Scots pine phloem of tree which differed in their susceptibility to *L. wingfieldii*. Values are means ± SD (n=42 for each sample). Significant differences are indicated in the text.

In both tree, fungal hyphae was found in and between sieve cells (fig 6, 7), sometimes in ray parenchyma and in phloem parenchyma. The hyphae grew in the phloem by sieve area and through cell walls. Seven days after inoculation, the fungal hyphae was present in the phloem of the two trees (fig. 8). The maximum of fungal sections was reached 7 days after inoculations in the susceptible tree and 14 days after inoculation in the resistant one. Progressively the fungal sections decreased. Moreover, the number of fungal sections in the phloem after inoculation was always significantly higher in the susceptible tree than in the resistant one, except 60 days after fungal inoculation.

DISCUSSION

Response of the tree

A callus and a wound periderm took place in the phloem after fungal or sterile inoculation, but they appeared belatedly after these aggressions. Such changes have already been observed after wound alone, or after fungus or insect attacks in various trees (Mullick, 1977; Shigo, 1984), and their late appearance have already been observed on *Abies grandis* (Wong and Berryman, 1977) and on *Pinus contorta* (Reid *et al.*, 1967; Shrimpton, 1978). The presence of the fungus in the wound delayed the formation of the callus and the wound periderm. Such a difference in timing has been observed on *Prunus persica* (Biggs, 1984; Wisniewski *et al.*, 1984). Biggs (1984) hypothesized that the presence of the fungus was associated with inhibited differentiation of living tissues.

The phloem degeneration which emptied progressively of its contents has already been observed in phloem of *Abies grandis* after fungal inoculation (Wong and Berryman, 1977) and in phloem of *Pinus ponderosa*, *P. contorta* and *P. monticola* after various inoculations (Lieutier and Berryman, 1988). In the present study, since this degeneration occured onlly after fungal inoculation, it seemed linked to the interaction between *L. wingfieldii* and the phloem. According to Wong and Berryman (1977), Berryman (1988) and Lieutier (1993), the death of cells in advance of the fungal spread was not caused directly by hyphal penetration, but may be attributed to response of adjacent cells to stimuli orignating from damaged cells and fungal metabolites. Moreover, a substance which was pink-coloured by toluidine blue accumulated after fungal inoculation. Such an accumulation has been observed after inoculation of *Verticicladiella* sp on *Pinus pinaster* (Cheniclet *et al.*, 1988). It could result from the enzymatic activity when the fungus penetrated the walls, but it may also result from the phenolic degradation since in culture *O. minus* secreted phenoloxydases (Rosch *et al.*, 1969), or to the cellular modification in response of the infection.

Finally, the induced response of Scots pine phloem after wounding could be focused on the compartimentalization of the decay due to the formation of barrier zones. These phenomenon would not depend on the fungus presence, but on the tree itself. However, when the fungus was present other changes occured, and the fungus was confined by the removal of nutrients and the phloem degeneration. The fungal growth decreased, the reaction zone extension stopped and the compartimentalization occured (Wong and Berryman, 1977; Berryman, 1988; Lieutier, 1993).

Differences between trees

In the two trees, the host responses to wounding and pathogen infection were basically similar differing only in timing and intensity of response. The resistant tree reacted quicker and sooner than the susceptible one. Moreover, the density of fungal sections was higher in the susceptible tree, than in the resistant one. In accordance with previous study on phenolic response of Scots pine phloem (Bois and Lieutier, 1997), the speed and the intensity of the changes after inoculations seemed to play an important role in the resistance of Scots pine phloem to bark beetles and their associated fungi.

REFERENCES

BERRYMAN A.A., 1972. Resistance of conifers to invasion by bark beetle fungus associations. *BioScience.*, 22, 598-601.

BERRYMAN A.A., 1988. Towards a unified theory of plant defense. *In* Mattson W.J., Levieux J., Bernard-Dagan C. (Eds.) *Mechanisms of woody plant defenses against insects*, Springer-verlag. p.37-55.

BIGGS A.R., 1984. Boundary-zone formation in peach bark in response to wounds and Cytospora leucostoma infection. *Can. J. Bot.*, 62, 2814-2821.

BOIS E., LIEUTIER F., 1997. Phenolic response of Scots pine clones to inoculation with *Leptographium wingfieldii*, a fungus associated with *Tomicus piniperda*

BRIGNOLAS F., LIEUTIER F., SAUVARD D., YART A., DROUET A., CLAUDOT A.C., 1995 a. Changes in soluble phenol content of Norway spruce (*Picea abies* Karst) phloem in response to wounding and inoculation with *Ophiostoma polonicum. Eur. J. For. Path.*, 25, 253-265.

CHENICLET C., BERNARD-DAGAN C., PAULY G. 1988. Terpene byosynthesis under pathological conditions. *In* Mattson W.J., Levieux J., Bernard-Dagan C. (Eds.) *Mechanisms of woody plant defenses against insects*, Springer-verlag. p. 117-137.

CHRISTIANSEN E., BERRYMAN A.A., 1995. Norway spruce clones vary widely in their susceptibility to a bark beetle-transmitted blue-stain fungus. In Hain F.P., Salom S.M., Payne T.L., and Raffa K.F. (eds) *Behavior, population dynamics and control of forest insects*, Proceeding of the IUFRO working party S2.07-06 Maui, Hawaii, February 1994. Ohio State University Press, Columbus, Ohio, 152-153.

CHRISTIANSEN E., WARING R.H., BERRYMAN A.A., 1987. Resistance of conifers to bark beetle attack: Searching for general relationships. *Forest Ecol. Manage.*, 22, 89-106.

DELORME L., LIEUTIER F., 1990. Monoterpene composition of the preformed and induced resins of Scots pine, and their effect on bark beetles and associated fungi. *Eur. J. Forest Pathol.*, 20, 304-316.

GUTMANN M., FEUCHT W., 1991. A new method for selective localization of flavan-3-ols in plant tissues involving glycolmethacrylate embedding and microwave irradaition. *Histochemistry,* 96, 83-86.

HORNTVEDT R., CHRISTIANSEN E., SOLHEIM H. WANG S., 1983. Artificial inoculation with *Ips typographus*-associated blue-stain fungi can kill healthy Norway spruce trees. *Medd. Nor. Inst. Skogforsk.*, 38, 1-20.

LÅNGSTRÖM B., HELLQVIST C., ERICSSON A., GREF R., 1992. Induced defence reaction in Scots pine following stem attacks by *Tomicus piniperda. Ecography*, 15, 318-327.

LIEUTIER F., 1993. Induced defence reaction of conifers to bark beetles and their associated *Ophiostoma* species. In *Ceratocystis and Ophiostoma. Taxonomy, ecology, and pathogenicity*, Wingfield M.J. Seifert K.A. and Webber J.F. Saint Paul., ed., APS Press, 225-233.

LIEUTIER F., BERRYMAN A.A., 1988. Preliminary histological investigations of the defense reactions of three pines to *Ceratocystis clavigera* and two chemical elicitors. *Can. J. For. Res.*, 18, 1243-1247.

LIEUTIER F., GARCIA J., YART A., ROMARY P., 1995. Wound reactions of Scots pine (*Pinus sylvestris* L.) to attacks by *Tomicus piniperda* L. and *Ips sexdentatus* Boern. (Coleoptera : Scolytidae). *J. Appl. Ent.*, 119, 591-600.

LIEUTIER F., SAUVARD D., BRIGNOLAS F., PICRON V., YART A., BASTIEN C., JAY-ALLEMAND C., 1996 a. Changes in phenolic metabolites of Scots pine phloem induced by *Ophiostoma brunneo-cilatum*, a bark-beetle-associated fungus. *Eur. J. For. Path.*, 26, 145-148.

LIEUTIER F., LÅNGSTRÖM B., SOLHEIM H., HELLQVIST C., YART A., 1996 b. Genetic and phenotypic variation in induced reaction of Scots pine (*Pinus sylvestris* L.) to *Leptographium wingfieldii*: Reaction zone length and fungal growth. In Mattson W.J. Niemelä P., ed., *Mechanisms of woody plant defences against herbivores*, Proceedings of the IUFRO conference for Working Party S2.05-06, Maui, Hawaii, 166-177.

MULLICK D., 1977. The non-specific nature of defense in bark and wood during wounding, insect and pathogen attack. *Recent Adv. phytochem.*, 2, 395-441.

MULOCK P., CHRISTIANSEN E., 1986. The threshold of successful attack by *Ips typographus* on *Picea abies* : a field experiment. *For. Ecol. Manage.*, 14, 125-132.

RAFFA K.F., BERRYMAN A.A., 1982. Accumulation of monoterpenes and associated volatiles following inoculation of grand fir with a fungus transmitted by the fir engraver, *Scolytus ventralis* (Coleoptera: Scolytidae). *Can. Entomol.*, 114, 797-810.

RAFFA K.F., KLEIPZIG K.D., 1992. Tree defence mechanisms against fungi associated with insects. In *Defence mechanisms of woody plants against fungi.* Blanchette R.A. and Biggs A.R., ed., Berlin: Springer-Verlag, 354-389.

REID R.W., WHITNEY H.S., WATTSON J.A., 1967. Reactions of lodgepole pine to attack by *Dendroctonus* ponderosae Hopkins and blue stain fungi. *Can. J. Bot.*, 45, 1115-1126.

SHIGO A.L., 1984. Compartimentalization: aconceptual framwork for understanding how trees grow and defend themselves. *Ann. Rev. Phytopathol.*, 22, 189-214.

SHRIMPTON D.M., 1973 Extractives associated with the wound response of lodgepole pine attacked by the mountain pine beetle and associated microorganismes. *Can. J. Bot.*, 51, 527-534.

SHRIMPTON D.M., 1978. Resistance of lodgepole pine to muntain pine beetle infestation. In: Berryman AA., Amman G.D., Stark R.W., Kibbe D.L. (Ed.): *Theory and practice of mountain pine beetle management in lodgepole pine forest*, College of For. ressources, Univ. Idaho, Moscow. p.64-76.

SOLHEIM H., Långström B., 1991. Blue-stain fungi associated with *Tomicus piniperda* in Sweden and preliminary observations on their pathogenicity. *Ann. Sc. For.*, 48, 149-156.

SOLHEIM H., LÅNGSTRÖM B., HELLQVIST C., 1993. Pathogenicity of blue-stain fungi *Leptographium wingfieldii* and *Ophiostoma minus* to Scots pine: effect of tree pruning and inoculum density. *Can. J. For. Res.*, 23, 1438-1443.

WISNIEWSKI M., BOGLE A.L., WILSON C.L., 1984. Histopathology of canker development on peach trees after inoculatuion with Cytospora leucostoma. *Can. J. Bot.*, 62, 2804-2813.

WONG B.L., BERRYMAN A.A., 1977. Host resistance to the fir engraver beetle. 3. Lesion development and containment of infection by resisatnt *Abies grandis* inoculated with *Trichosporium symbioticum. Can. J. Bot.*, 55, 2358-2365.

WRIGHT E., 1933. A cork borer method for inoculating trees. *Phytopathology*, 23, 487-488.

Physiology and Genetics of Tree-Phytophage Interactions
Gujan (France), August 31 - September 5, 1997
Ed. INRA, Paris, 1999 (Les Colloques, n°90)

Relative amounts and enantiomeric compositions of monoterpene hydrocarbons in *Pinus yunnanensis* Fr. and *Pinus sylvestris* L.

A.-K. BORG-KARLSON[1], M. PERSSON[1], Å. CHRISTIANSSON[1], J. FÄLDT[1],
B. LÅNGSTRÖM[2], L. LI[3], H. LIU[3], N. ZHOU[3], AND F. LIEUTIER[4]

[1] Royal Institute of Technology, Department of Chemistry, Organic Chemistry, S-100 44 Stockholm, Sweden;
[2] Department of Entomology, Swedish University of Agricultural Sciences, P.O. Box 7044, S-75007 Uppsala, Sweden;
[3] Yunnan Academy of Forest Sciences, Heliongtan, Kunming, 650204, Yunnan, P.R. China
[4] Institut National de la Recherche Agronomique, INRA, Centre de Recherches d'Orléans, Station de Zoologie Forestière, Ardon, 45160 Olivet, France

RESUME

The Yunnan pine, *P. yunnanensis,* is heavily attacked and often killed by the pine shoot beetle *Tomicus piniperda* in certain parts in the Yunnan province of South West China. In Europe the insect species normally causes mild damage, mainly growth losses, in Scots pine *P. sylvestris*. In order to identify significant components in the host-insect relationships, characteristic for the two pine species, the monoterpene fractions of 27 *P. sylvestris* and 17 *P. yunnanensis* trees were analysed. Cross sections containing both xylem and phloem of one year old twigs and increment cores of trunk xylem were extracted in hexane and analysed by a two dimensional GC and a GC-MS. The relative amounts of 21 monoterpene hydrocarbons, including enantiomers were determined.

Large variations were found in the relative amounts, as well as in enantiomeric compositions of the monoterpene hydrocarbons, both within and among the trees of the two species. Two chemotypes, separated by the relative amounts of (–)-β–pinene, were found in *P. yunnanensis*. In the cross section of the twig (–)-β- and (+)–α–pinene were the main monoterpenes followed by (–)–α–pinene, (–)-β-phellandrene and myrcene. The relative amounts of (–)–α–pinene and (+)-α-pinene were higher in twigs of *P. yunnanensis* than in *P. sylvestris.* In the trunk xylem the relative amounts of (+)-α-pinene and (+)-3-carene dominated. In the trunk xylem, the enantiomeric compositions of (–)–α–pinene displayed a much wider range (8-95%) in *P. yunnanensis* than in *P. sylvestris* (3-30%). In the twigs, the enantiomeric compositions of the five chiral monoterpenes analysed showed a similar pattern between the two pine species.

INTRODUCTION

The common pine shoot beetle, *Tomicus piniperda* (L.) (Coleoptera: Scolytidae) is a major pest insect in pine forests in Europe and in Asia. In Europe, it mainly attacks Scots pine, *Pinus sylvestris* L., but seldom kill healthy trees (Långström & Hellqvist 1993, and references therein). In Scandinavia, it may cause substantial growth losses by its shoot feeding behaviour (Långström & Hellqvist 1991). In southwestern China, however, forests consisting of Yunnan pine, *P. yunnanensis* (Fr.) have been severely attacked and often killed by *T. piniperda* (Wang *et al.* 1987; Ye 1991, Li *et al.* 1993). It has been observed that the beetles are selectively attracted to, and feed on, the shoots of certain trees within a forest stand (Ye & Lieutier 1997). In Sweden, no such aggregation to certain trees has been observed, but the beetles clearly prefer the upper part of the crown (Långström 1980).

In an attempt to study the host finding mechanisms and its possible chemical basis (primary attraction, Lanne *et al.* 1987) in *T. piniperda,* we decided to sample non-attacked and attacked shoots from trees with different degree of attack. In this paper, we present the analyses of the fractions containing monoterpene hydrocarbons in *P. yunnanensis*, and compare them to our results on *P. sylvestris.*

MATERIAL AND METHODS

Biological samples

The samples of *P. sylvestris* were taken from selected plus trees (i.e. phenotypically superior individuals) of a number of provenances originating from the northern part of Sweden to the middle of Europe. The trees of *P. yunnanensis* were growing in the Yunnan province of South West China, and were selected due to the degree of shoot attack (26-83%) of *T. piniperda.* Cross sections containing both the xylem and the phloem of shoots from current year, and increment cores of the trunk xylem were extracted in 1 ml of hexane (pa Merck). Samples were taken 100 mm from the base of the shoots of both healthy and infested shoots on the same tree. The cross sections from the infested shoots were taken in the healthy parts 2 cm from the entrance hole made by the insect. Extracts were made in field and transported to the laboratory where they were kept at -18 °C before analyses.

Chemical analyses

The monoterpene fractions (constituting the 24 monoterpenes shown in Fig. 1.) of 27 *P. sylvestris* and 17 *P. yunnanensis* trees were analysed. *P. sylvestris* samples were filtered through a plug (0.2g) of SiO_2.The hexane extracts were analysed by GC and GC-MS.

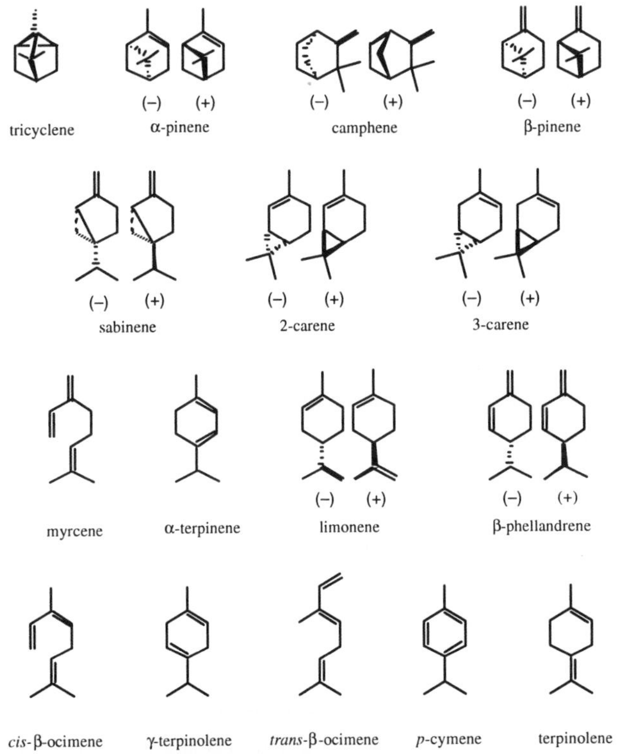

Figure 1 Structures of the monoterpene hydrocarbons present in the monoterpene fraction analysed. Due to the minute amounts of sabinene, 2-carene and 3-carene present in the *P. yunnanensis* samples, no determination of the enantiomeric compositions were made for these constituents. (+)-3-Carene was the only enantiomer present in *P. sylvestris*.

Relative amounts of the monoterpene hydrocarbon constituents and the enantiomeric compositions of the five major chiral monoterpenes (α-pinene, camphene, β-pinene, limonene, β-phellandrene) were determined by the use of a two-dimensional Varian 3400 GC system (Borg-Karlson *et al.* 1993). A DB-WAX column (J&W Scientific; 30 m, 0.25 mm i.d., 0.25μm film thickness) was used in the first GC for the non-chiral separations of the monoterpene hydrocarbons with the following temperature programme: 40 °C (1 min) followed by 3° min^{-1} up to 110° followed by 10° min^{-1} up to 200°C. Terpinolene was eluted after 16 min. Small amounts of α–phellandrene, possibly present in the samples, were not separated from myrcene under the conditions used. In the second GC, a Cyclodex-B, permethyl-β–cyclodextrin/DB1701, fused silica capillary column (J&W Scientific; 30 m, 0.25 mm i.d., 0.25 μm film thickness) was used for the analysis of the chiral monoterpene hydrocarbons. The temperature programme was 55 °C (11 min) followed by 1° min^{-1} up to 75 °C. The constituents of the monoterpene fractions were identified on a Finnigan instrument SSQ 7000, connected with a Varian 3400 GC, using a DB-WAX column (J&W Scientific; 30 m, 0.25 mm i.d., 0.25 μm film thickness). The temperature programme was 40 °C (1 min) followed by 3° min^{-1} up to 110° followed by 10° min^{-1} up to 200 °C. Separation method for 3-carene is referred in Borg-Karlson *et al.* (1993). Monoterpene enantiomers were identified by means of GC retention times, using naturally occurring or synthetic reference compounds (Borg-Karlson *et al.* 1993). Data are presented in terms of *relative amounts* of the 21 monoterpene hydrocarbons identified in *P. yunnanensis.* The enantiomers of five chiral monoterpene hydrocarbons are included as separate as well as in terms of *enantiomeric compositions* {area of (–)-enantiomer peak divided by the sum of areas of (–)- and (+)-enantiomer peaks, in percent}.

Multivariate data analyses

GC data were evaluated by multivariate data analysis using the programme CODEX[R] vers. 2.6 (Chemometric Optimization and Design for Experimenters, a product from SumIT System AB, Box 1936, S-171 19 Solna, Sweden) which was installed as an add-in module to Microsoft Excel[R]. The data were subjected to PC and PLS analyses (for references see Persson *et al.* 1996). Raw data were normalized to 100% and treated in accordance with the procedure used in an earlier investigation on *P. sylvestris* (Persson *et al.* 1996). The PCA plots visualize the data structures. The closer two trees are found in a plot, the more similar are their monoterpene compositions. The corresponding loading plots give information about the importance of each constituent for making up the model. Each variable was scaled to unit variance (autoscaling). The number of significant components was determined by cross-validation (Sjödin *et al.* 1995). A component was judged to be significant, when CSV/SD was < 0.95.

RESULTS

Large variations were found, both within and among the trees of both pine species, in the relative amounts of the monoterpenes (Figures 2a and 2b) as well as in the enantiomeric composition of the chiral monoterpenes (Figures 3a and 3b). Two chemotypes, separated by the relative amounts of (–)-β–pinene, were found in *P. yunnanensis.* In addition, one tree with large amounts of 3-carene was analysed.

Twig

The samples of *P. yunnanensis* contained either high percentage of (–)-β–pinene or (–)-α–pinene plus (+)-α–pinene (Fig. 2a). The relative amounts of both (–)-α–pinene and (+)-α–pinene were higher in some of the samples of *P. yunnanensis* than in the samples of *P. sylvestris.* (+)-3-Carene was the main component in the majority of *P. sylvestris* trees. However, certain chemotype with a low (+)-3-carene and high (–)-limonene content was found among *P. sylvestris* trees originating from the northern part of Sweden.

The enantiomeric compositions of all five chiral monoterpenes analysed showed a similar pattern between the two pine species (Figure 3a).

Trunk xylem

A striking difference between the two species, was found among the samples of xylem of the trunk (Fig 2b): *P. yunnanensis* showed a much wider range, in relative amounts, of (–)-α–pinene (5-90%), than in *P. sylvestris* (3-30%). (+)-3-Carene was almost exclusively found in *P. sylvestris* while a group of *P. yunnanensis* trees contained high amounts of (–)-β–pinene.

The enantiomeric compositions of α–pinene in the trunk xylem had a much wider range (8-95%) in *P. yunnanensis* than in *P. sylvestris* (3-30%) (Figure 3b). A similar distribution was found for camphene.

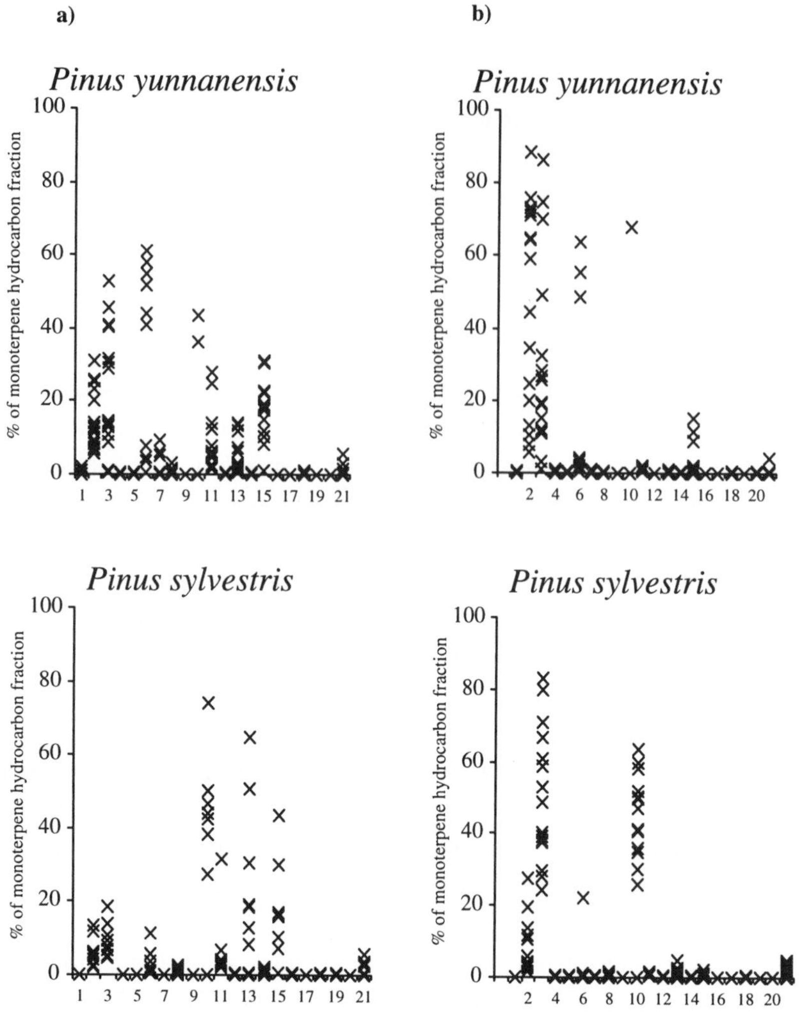

Figure 2 Variation in relative amounts for each monoterpene in the two pine species. The monoterpene hydrocarbon fraction in hexane extracts of two different tissues from *P. yunnanensis* and *P. sylvestris* were analysed by two-dimensional GC and GC-MS. The relative amounts of 21 monoterpenes including enantiomers of five chiral monoterpenes are shown here: 1) tricyclene, 2) (–)-α-pinene, 3) (+)-α-pinene, 4) (–)-camphene, 5) (+)-camphene, 6) (–)-β-pinene, 7) (+)-β-pinene, 8) sabinene, 9) 2-carene, 10) 3-carene, 11) myrcene, 12) α-terpinene, 13) (–)-limonene, 14) (+)-limonene, 15) (–)-β-phellandrene, 16) (+)-β-phellandrene, 17) *cis*-β-ocimene, 18) γ-terpinene, 19) *trans*-β-ocimene, 20) *p*-cymene, 21) terpinolene.

a) Variation in relative amounts for each monoterpene originating from the cross section of one year old twig containing both xylem and phloem. In the upper diagram 8 *P. yunnanensis* trees are presented by two crosses per tree (one healthy shoot and one infested, if present). The lower diagram shows 10 *P. sylvestris* trees presented by one cross per tree.

b) Variation in relative amounts for each monoterpene originating from the increment cores of trunk xylem of 17 *P yunnanensis* trees and 17 *P. sylvestris* trees, all represented by one cross per tree.

Note: the *P. sylvestris* trees analysed in Figure 2a) are not the same trees as in Figure 2b) but the 8 *P. yunnanensis* trees in Figure 2a) are among the 17 individuals presented in Figure 2b).

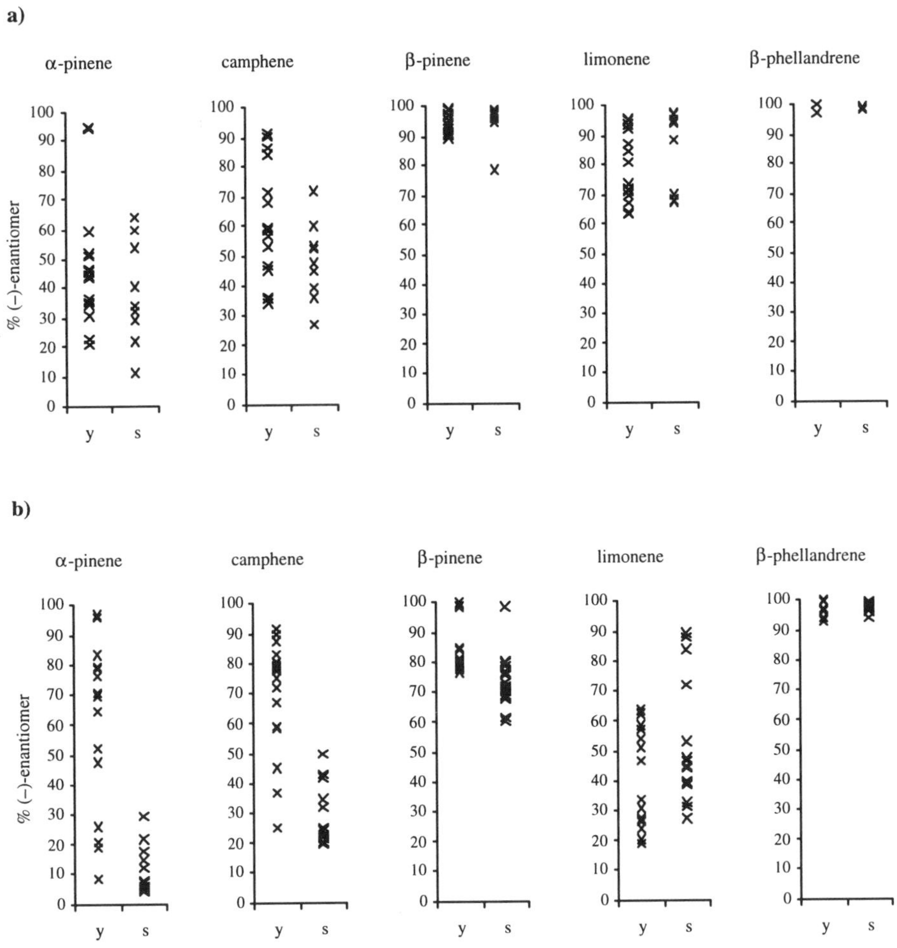

Figure 3 Variation in enantiomeric composition. The differences between *P. yunnanensis (y)* and *P. sylvestris (s)* in enantiomeric compositions of five chiral monoterpenes are shown here. The same trees and tissues as described in Fig 2.

a) Cross section of twig b) Trunk xylem

Multivariate data analyses

Figure 4 presents a PC-plot made from 100% normalized GC-data, including 21 integrated peaks, from the cross section of *P. yunnanensis* and *P. sylvestris* twigs. The groups are formed mainly due to high amount of (+)-3-carene (among others in the left part in the p-plot) or high amounts of (–)-α-pinene and (–)-camphene according to the corresponding loading plot. The PC-analysis resulted in this model having one significant component (as judged by cross validation) explaining 33% of the variance in the data.

No obvious relation was found between monoterpene composition in the trunk xylem and degree of attack in the shoots on the pines from Yunnan judged by PLS analysis not shown here.

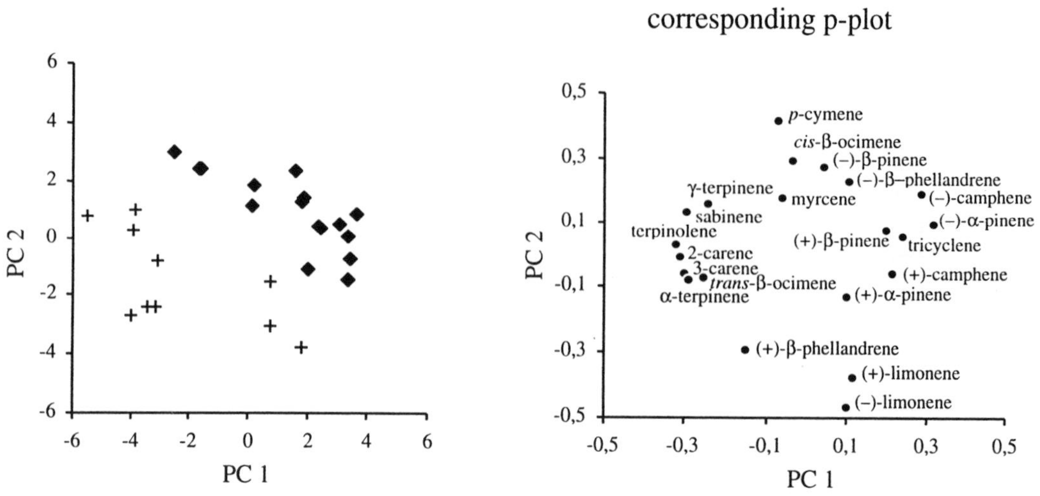

Figure 4 Principal Component (PC)-plot based on relative amounts of monoterpenes in samples of cross section of twigs (the same samples as in Fig. 2a). The crosses marks the *P. sylvestris* and the filled rombs *P. yunnanensis*. A PC-analysis including 21 integrated GC-peaks resulted in a model having one significant component explaining 33% variance in the data.

DISCUSSION

The variation of monoterpene hydrocarbons in different tissues among and within trees has earlier been shown in *Picea abies* (Borg-Karlson *et al.* 1993, Persson *et al.* 1993) in *P. sylvestris* (Yasdani *et al.* 1985, 1986; Sjödin 1996) and in four pine species from Cuba (Valterová *et al.* 1995). A similar distribution of the enantiomeric composition of (–)-α-pinene present in the trunk xylem of *P. yunnanensis* (8-95%) have also been found in the oleoresin of *P. maestrensis* (5-91%) from Cuba (Valterová *et al.* 1995).

The observed large differences of the relative amounts of monoterpene hydrocarbons among *P. yunnanensis*, could explain the observed differences in attack by *T. piniperda*. However with the limited number of samples there was no obvious correlation between insect attack and monoterpene composition. It still remains to be shown that beetles discriminate between trees with different terpene composition. In *Pinus caribaea* growing in Cuba, significant differences in the monoterpene pattern have been found between trees attacked and not attacked by the moth *Dioryctria horneana* (Valterová *et al.* 1995).

When comparing the cross sections of the twigs, the enantiomeric composition of α-pinene showed a similar distribution between the two species, indicating host odour similarity. The relative amounts of both enantiomers of α-pinene were, however, much larger in *P. yunnanenis*. If the enantiomers of α-pinene act as key compounds for *T. piniperda* in host selection, a larger amount of α-pinene may explain the higher frequence of attack in *P. yunnanensis* than in *P. sylvestris*.

(–)–α–Pinene has been effectively used for monitoring of *T. piniperda* in Sweden (Schroeder 1987, Byers *et al.* 1985.). The combination of (–)–α–pinene and ethanol increased trap catches up to a certain amount of ethanol (Byers *et al.* 1985). When a too high concentration of ethanol was used a repellent effect was noted. Up to now, there are no experimental data indicating enantioselectivity in long distance attraction of *T. piniperda*. However, the differences found in the relative amounts of (-)-α–pinene may have an effect on the primary attraction. (–)-Limonene was present in high amounts in some of the *P. sylvestris* trees but was generally low in the *P. yunnanensis* trees analysed. Addition of (–)-limonene to baits has been shown to effectively reduce trap catches of the pine weevil (Nordlander 1990, 1991) in field tests. The effects of (–)-limonene, separately and in combination with other host compounds, in reducing the attack by *T. piniperda* would be of interest to test in future bioassays.

ACKNOWLEDGEMENTS

Dr Inger Ekberg selected the *P. sylvestris* plus trees used in this study and Mrs Liang Chang acted as interpreter. This project has been financially supported by The Carl Trygger Foundation, the Swedish Council for Forestry and Agricultural Research and the INCO-DC EU-programme EC 18 CT 960057 fall name “For Protec China”.

REFERENCES

BORG-KARLSON A.-K., LINDSTRÖM M., PERSSON M., NORIN T. AND VALTEROVÁ I. 1993. Enantiomeric composition of monoterpene hydrocarbons in different tissues of Norway spruce *Picea abies* (L.) Karst. A multidimensional gas chromatography study. *Acta Chemica Scandinavica*, 47, 138-144.

BYERS J. A., LANNE B. S., LÖFQVIST J. SCHLYTER F., AND BERGSTRÖM G. 1985. Olfactory recognition of host-tree susceptibility by pine shoot beetles. *Naturwissenchaften*, 72, 324.

LANNE B.S., SCHLYTER F., BYERS J., LÖFQVIST J., LEUFVÉN A., BERGSTRÖM G., VAN DER PERS J., UNELIUS R., BAECKTRÖM P., NORIN T. 1987. Differences in attraction to semiochemicals present in sympatric pine shoot beetles *Tomicus piniperda*, and *T. minor*. *J. Chem. Ecol.*, 13, (5), 1045-1066.

LI L.S., WANG H.L., CHAI X.S., WANG Y.X., SHU N.B., AND YANG D.S. 1993.Study on the biological characteristics of *Tomicus piniperda* and its damage. *Forest Research* 6, 14-20.

LÅNGSTRÖM B., 1980. Distribution of pine shoot beetle attacks within the crown of Scots pine, *Studia Forestalia Suecica*, 154, 1-25.

LÅNGSTRÖM B. 1983. Life cycles and shoot feeding of the pine shoot beetles. *Studia Forestalia Suecica*, 163, 1-29.

LÅNGSTRÖM B. AND HELLQVIST C. 1991. Shoot damage and growth losses following three years of *Tomicus*-attacks in Scots pine stands close to a timber storage site. *Silva Fennica,* 25, (3), 133-145.

LÅNGSTRÖM B. 1993, Scots pine susceptibility to attack by *Tomicus piniperda* (L) as related to pruning date and attack density. *Ann. Sci. For.*, 50, 101-117.

LÅNGSTRÖM B. AND HELLQVIST C. 1993. Induced and spontaneous attacks by *Tomicus piniperda* and *T. minor* on young Scots pine trees: tree mortality and beetle performance. *J. appl. Ent.* 115. 25-36.

NORDLANDER G. 1991 Host finding in the pine weevil *Hylobius abietis* effects of conifer volatiles and added limonene..*Entomol.Exp. Appl.* 59, 229.

NORDLANDER G. 1990. Limonene inhibits attraction to α-pinene in the pine weevils *Hylobius abietis* and *H. pinastri. J. Chem. Ecol.* 16: 1307-1320.

PERSSON M., SJÖDIN K., BORG-KARLSON A.-K., NORIN T., AND EKBERG I. 1996. Relative amounts and enantiomeric compositions of monoterpenes in different tissues of *Picea abies Phytochemistry*, 42, (5), 1289-1297.

SJÖDIN K., PERSSON M., BORG-KARLSON A.-K., AND NORIN T. 1996. Enantiomeric compositions of monoterpene hydrocarbons in different tissues of four individuals of *Pinus sylvestris. Phytochemistry*, 41, (2), 439-445.

SCHROEDER L.M., 1988. Attraction of the bark beetle *Tomicus piniperda* and some other bark- and wood living beetles to host volatiles α-pinene and ethanol. *Entomol. Exp. appl.*, 46, 203-210.

VALTEROVÁ I., SJÖDIN K., VRKOC J., AND NORIN T. 1995. Contents and enantiomeric compositions of monoterpene hydrocarbons from four *Pinus* species growing in Cuba. comparison of trees unattacked and attacked by *Dioryctria horneana. Biochem. Syst. Ecol.* 23, (1), 1-15.

WANG H.L., CHEN S.W. WU Y. AND PU M.G. 1987. Preliminary studies on the bionomics and management of the pine bark beetle (*Blastophagus piniperda* L.) in Kunming district, China. *Journal of Southwest Forestry College* 2, 33-42.

YE H. 1991. On the bionomy of *Tomicus piniperda* (L.) (Col., Scolytidae) in the Kunming region of China. *J. appl. Ent.* 112, 366-369.

YAZDANI R., NILSSON J.-E., AND ERICSSON T. 1985. Geographical variation in the relative proportion of monoterpenes in cortical oleoresin of *Pinus sylvestris* in Sweden. *Silvae Genetica,* 34, 201-208.

YAZDANI R. AND NILSSON J.-E. 1986. Cortical monoterpene variation in natural populations of *Pinus sylvestris* in Sweden. *Scand. J. For. Res.* 1, 85-93.

YE H., AND LIEUTIER F. 1997. Shoot aggregation by *Tomicus piniperda* L. (Coleoptera: Scolytidae) in southwestern China. *Ann. Sci. For.*, 54, 635-641.

Physiology and Genetics of Tree-Phytophage Interactions
Gujan (France), August 31 - September 5, 1997
Ed. INRA, Paris, 1999 (Les Colloques, n°90)

Differences in palatability of *Fraxinus excelsior* L., for the vole, *Microtus arvalis* ,and the scale, *Pseudochermes fraxini* L.

L.G. MORAAL[1], P.W. GOEDHART [2]

[1]*Institute for Forestry and Nature Research (IBN-DLO),*
PO Box 23, NL-6700 AA Wageningen, The Netherlands.

[2]*Centre for Biometry Wageningen (CPRO-DLO),*
PO Box 16, NL-6700 AA Wageningen, The Netherlands.

RESUME

In wintertime, when population densities are high and food is scarce, small rodents, such as voles, consume the bark of young trees. As a result, the trees may die. In choice-tests with the common vole, *Microtus arvalis* , we observed significant differences in palatability of the bark of individual trees of *Fraxinus excelsior.* Also a bark-sucking insect, the ash scale, *Pseudochermes fraxini,* seems to respond to an antifeedant in the bark. The bark of a progeny which was infested by the insect was preferred in choice-tests with voles. There is some evidence that these effects are related to differences in the concentrations of bitter tasting coumarin derivatives in the bark. These findings might be of interest for genetical improvement in order to select resistant trees..

INTRODUCTION

In recent years, severe vole damage on trees over large areas has been observed in The Netherlands. In 1991, some 50 ha of poplar plantations, planted under the set-aside scheme, were destroyed by the common vole, *Microtus arvalis* (Moraal, 1993). This is due to planting of trees on formerly agricultural land. Weeds grow abundantly on these rich soils, creating an ideal habitat for voles, leading to high population densities. In wintertime when food is scarce, the voles use the bark of the young trees as an alternative food source. The trees may die as a result of girdling the bark of the stems or gnawing the roots. Vole damage can be prevented by using poison, or by making their habitat unsuitable by weed control, or by protecting the trees with chemical deterrents or plastic guards (Davies and Pepper, 1989, 1990; Moraal, 1993). These methods, however, are either too expensive for application on a large scale, or undesirable for the environment.

Another possibility for protection is the use of resistant trees (Wink, 1988). Tree species vary greatly in their palatability to mammals such as hares and voles (Pigott, 1985). It is well known that bitter tasting secondary metabolites like tannins or phenolic glycosides in the bark, often determine these differences in palatability (Bryant et al., 1991; Tahvanainen et al., 1985). Browsers also select among genotypes within the same species such as *Pinus*, *Picea*, *Salix* and *Betula* (Gill, 1992; Rousi et al., 1990; Tahvanainen et al., 1985).

As far as we know, palatability differences for *Fraxinus excelsior*, with respect to bark consumption by mammals, have never been reported before.

For years, we have observed that rabbits showed a clear preference for the bark of certain *Fraxinus excelsior* clones. We tested therefore several provenances and progenies of Fraxinus *excelsior* with voles to detect tree resistance. Vole resistant trees may also be resistant against bark feeding by sheep, rabbits, hares, and deer.

MATERIALS AND METHODS

Trees

In 1986, a test site for a genetic trial was established at Windesheim in The Netherlands with two-year old *Fraxinus excelsior* trees. In the trial, 67 selections (progenies and provenances) were tested for growth, health, and quality. Of each selection, 25 trees were planted. The trial mainly contains indigenous Dutch ashes and some foreign provenances from Germany, Switzerland and Rumania. For the vole choice-tests, we selected 32 selection numbers (table 1).

We collected one-year old twigs of three individual trees (further called a,b,c) for each of the 32 selection numbers. These twigs were collected in February 1994 and immediately stored at -30o C, until used in choice-tests and for chemical analysis of the bark.

Voles

Adult and subadult common voles, *Microtus arvalis*, were obtained from the wild and caged in an unheated laboratory. They were kept individually in cages with hay and maintained on a diet of a standard laboratory mouse feed (RMH-B; Hope Farms, Woerden, The Netherlands) and carrots. One day before each experiment all food, except the hay for shelter, was removed.

Choice-tests with voles

So-called multiple choice-tests or cafeteria-tests were carried out to determine relative differences in palatability among the one-year old twigs of *Fraxinus* selections. In each choice-test, 10 separately caged voles were used. Each vole was simultaneously offered four, 10-cm long twigs, from different selections. Except the hay for shelter, there was no other food in the cage, so the voles were forced to eat from the bark of the twigs. After 42 h, the consumed bark area was measured in square centimeters, according to Rousi et al. (1990). The measured areas were transformed to ranks and Friedman's rank test was used to assess differences in palatability between the twigs. This test is performed by means of a randomised blocks analysis of variance on the ranks, in which the voles play the role of the block, see Conover (1980). The standard error of differences of the ANOVA can then be used to compare individual genotypes. In this way, relative differences of four twigs can be measured. However, absolute differences cannot be measured by means of choice-tests. A twig of medium palatability will possibly not be consumed when it is offered with twigs of good palatability, but it will be eaten when offered with unpalatable twigs. Because we were only interested in finding some arbitrary palatable and non-palatable twigs, this was not considered to be a major drawback of the method.ow

Experiment 1

A first experiment was carried out to identify some palatable and non-palatable trees with which we could experiment further. In 8 experiments, all the 'a' individuals of 32 *Fraxinus excelsior* selection numbers (table 1) were tested in choice-tests. The allocation of these 32 selections over the 8 experiments was done at random since we had no prior knowledge. The same allocation was used to test the 'b' and 'c' individuals in 16 further experiments.

Table 1. *Fraxinus excelsior* progenies and provenances as used in choice-tests with the common vole *Microtus arvalis*.

Selection nr.	Identification	Selection nr.	Identification
progenies:		403	Echteld-01 NL
1718	Altena NL	468	Ede-01 NL
2718	Westhof's Glorie NL	475	,,
4718	unknown	477	,,
5218	Beesd NL	480	,,
5518	Bunnik NL	488	,,
6018	Ophemert NL	*provenances:*	
6118	Bruchem NL	269	Germany
240	Utrecht NL	270	,,
273	St. Geertruid NL	507	,,
349	Echteld-01 NL	511	,,
352	,,	516	Switzerland
367	,,	517	Rumania
370	,,	518	Germany
375	,,	519	Echteld-01 NL
389	,,	520	Domen-3 NL
400	,,	521	Domen-1 NL

For genetical improvement it is important to know if palatability or non-palatability is a stable hereditary factor within a certain *Fraxinus* selection. Therefore, from the first experiment, four apparently palatable selections (269, 370, 517, 519) and four non-palatable selections (270, 468, 475, 518) were chosen with which an additional experiment was conducted. These selections were tested in two choice-tests, with 15 voles each. Instead of offering twigs from the same tree, as we did in the first experiment, twigs of 15 different individual trees were used.

Experiment 2

During several years, we observed heavy infestations by the ash scale, *Pseudochermes fraxini*, in some 15-year old ash stands in one of the new polders in the province of Flevoland. These insects completely cover the stem, causing cracks in the bark. We noticed that a certain ash progeny, SVH 71, was heavily infested, while another progeny, NR 123, of the same age in the same stand, was hardly infested. We hypothesised that the insects might respond to the same secondary plant metabolites as voles. Therefore, we collected one-year old twigs of infested and non-infested trees. In a choice-test with 18 voles we offered each vole one twig of an infested and one of a non-infested tree. The percentage consumed bark of the heavily infested progeny, in relation to the total amount of consumed bark, was analysed by logistic regression using quasi-likelihood (McCullagh and Nelder, 1989). When there is no difference between the progenies, this percentage should equal 50.

Chemical analysis of the bark

We submitted palatable trees (269b, 389c and 511a) and non-palatable trees (468c, 518b and 1718a) to our laboratory for the identification of the responsible secondary plant metabolite. From the literature it is known that the bark of *Fraxinus* may contain high concentrations of bitter tasting coumarin derivatives (Berenbaum, 1991; Gaedcke, 1993; Hegnauer, 1969; Murray et al., 1982). The chemical analysis was focused to find differences in concentrations of coumarin between palatable and non-palatable bark. For this analysis, the bark was removed, cut in small pieces and extracted with alcohol. This extract was analysed once with UV fluorescence

Table 2. Results of Experiment 1. Each line shows the results of one choice-test. Test numbers 1-24 denote the 24 choice-tests, while A and B denote the two additional choice-tests. The standard error of differences of the ranks (s.e.d. rank) can be used for comparing individual genotypes within a line. Genotypes with a common letter are not significantly different at p=0.05.

Test nr.	*Fraxinus* genotypes used in test				Mean bark consumption (cm^2)				Mean rank (common letters not significantly different)				s.e.d. rank
1	5218a	349a	6118a	367a	3.43	0.83	2.58	1.30	3.55 y	2.00 x	2.70 xy	1.75 x	0.47
2	5218b	349b	6118b	367b	0.32	0.69	3.19	1.19	1.95 x	2.20 x	3.30 y	2.55 xy	0.54
3	5218c	349c	6118c	367c	4.16	2.08	3.11	2.51	2.60 x	1.95 x	2.90 x	2.55 x	0.57
4	352a	519a	403a	507a	2.41	1.38	3.47	0.60	3.10 y	2.40 xy	3.05 y	1.45 x	0.48
5	352b	519b	403b	507b	1.18	3.74	0.57	0.58	2.25 x	3.80 y	1.70 x	2.25 x	0.43
6	352c	519c	403c	507c	3.18	6.92	1.37	4.25	2.30 y	3.65 z	1.35 x	2.70 y	0.40
7	370a	6018a	2718a	521a	3.06	1.52	3.05	1.35	2.89 x	2.11 x	2.44 x	2.56 x	0.63
8	370b	6018b	2718b	521b	17.20	14.34	5.07	4.68	3.55 y	3.05 y	1.60 x	1.80 x	0.40
9	370c	6018c	2718c	521c	13.34	11.17	13.43	9.70	2.60 x	2.40 x	2.80 x	2.20 x	0.53
10	480a	477a	4718a	273a	2.71	1.18	2.23	5.91	2.43 x	1.64 x	2.21 x	3.71 y	0.54
11	480b	477b	4718b	273b	1.43	0.87	9.98	0.81	2.60 xy	2.30 x	3.30 y	1.80 x	0.41
12	480c	477c	4718c	273c	3.18	11.58	10.69	13.14	1.80 x	2.95 y	2.30 xy	2.95 y	0.55
13	270a	488a	240a	400a	0.34	2.16	3.17	3.18	1.62 x	2.00 xy	3.00 yz	3.38 z	0.53
14	270b	488b	240b	400b	0.23	2.40	0.32	1.49	2.25 x	3.35 y	2.45 x	1.95 x	0.42
15	270c	488c	240c	400c	3.68	8.33	23.67	21.09	1.25 x	1.95 y	3.55 z	3.25 z	0.24
16	518a	520a	517a	269a	2.45	2.43	10.69	5.82	1.75 x	1.95 xy	3.50 z	2.80 yz	0.43
17	518b	520b	517b	269b	0.22	2.63	5.17	12.92	1.45 x	2.00 x	2.85 y	3.70 z	0.39
18	518c	520c	517c	269c	4.87	19.38	18.56	14.77	1.20 x	3.20 y	2.95 y	2.65 y	0.40
19	511a	1718a	468a	389a	5.80	0.31	0.90	1.86	3.80 z	1.40 x	1.95 x	2.85 y	0.35
20	511b	1718b	468b	389b	0.31	1.94	0.13	1.95	2.30 xy	2.75 yz	1.90 x	3.05 z	0.35
21	511c	1718c	468c	389c	7.38	21.79	3.24	24.83	1.90 x	3.30 y	1.30 x	3.50 y	0.29
22	5518a	375a	516a	475a	0.09	0.45	1.68	0.50	1.72 x	2.33 xy	3.33 y	2.61 xy	0.52
23	5518b	375b	516b	475b	4.08	5.43	0.83	0.21	3.00 y	3.00 y	2.35 xy	1.65 x	0.36
24	5518c	375c	516c	475c	7.00	15.50	17.26	4.03	2.05 x	3.20 y	3.30 y	1.45 x	0.39
A	270	269	517	468	2.64	4.60	4.16	2.29	2.37 x	2.67 x	2.93 x	2.03 x	0.46
B	518	519	370	475	5.21	4.81	12.49	5.14	2.30 x	2.20 x	2.97 x	2.53 x	0.47

spectro-photometrical methods and compared with scopoletin as a reference for measuring the sum of coumarin derivatives. Most natural coumarins show a fluorescence when irradiated with UV light (365 nm). Further information on methods for detection and isolation of coumarin derivatives can be found in Gaedcke (1993) and Murray et al. (1982).

RESULTS

Choice-tests with voles

Experiment 1

The results of the 24 choice-tests are given in table 2. The results of these single tests can be compared within each line. Sometimes a large variation for the a, b and c individuals was noticed; see for example test numbers 19, 20 and 21. Also note that the ordering of the genotypes with respect to mean consumption is not necessarily equivalent to the ordering with respect to mean ranks. This can be caused, for example, by an abnormally high consumption of a specific genotype by one mouse only, which can result in a large mean consumption for that genotype, without a corresponding high mean rank. Nevertheless we have observed statistically significant differences ($p<0.05$) in palatability for individual trees in 19 of the 24 choice-tests. Furthermore the a, b and c genotypes showed some consistency in non-palatability for the *Fraxinus* selection-numbers 270, 468, 518 and 475, while the selection-numbers 269, 517, 519 and 370 appeared to be palatable. These 8 numbers have been used for the additional tests A and B.

In the additional tests A and B, we found a tendency for palatable and non-palatable progenies but we did not find significant differences (table 2). However, our method of statistical testing was a classical and not a highly discriminative one. Correlative chemical analysis of the bark would produce more precise and reliable data. Within the present project, comprehensive chemical analysis could not be included.

Experiment 2

The bark of trees which was infested by the insect was more consumed by the

Table 3. Contents of coumarin derivatives in the bark of *Fraxinus excelsior*, in relation with the palatability for voles (bark samples of size one).

Fraxinus-genotype	Palatability	Coumarin (mg/kg bark)
518b	non-palatable	0.445
468c	non-palatable	0.394
1718a	non-palatable	0.203
389c	palatable	0.075
269b	palatable	0.017
511a	palatable	0.006

voles than the bark of non-infested trees. The mean percentage of consumed bark of the infested trees was found to be 71.5 % and this was significantly different from 50 % at p=0.012.

Chemical analysis of the bark

From the 24 choice-tests (table 2), the 3 tests with the largest differences in consumed bark area were selected. The extremes in palatability and non-palatability within these tests were subjected to a chemical analysis of the bark (table 3).

Table 3 shows very large differences in the concentration of coumarin in the bark. These differences in palatable and non-palatable twigs are significant (two sample t-test on log scale; p=0.022). The results indicate that the observed differences in palatability among the individual trees are caused by a natural variation in the concentration of coumarin derivatives in the bark.

DISCUSSION

Coumarins and their derivatives, being natural secondary plant metabolites, are widely distributed in many plant families. On arthropods they may have allomonal effects: feeding deterrence, growth reduction, and toxicity. In contrast with insect herbivores, the interactions between vertebrate herbivores and coumarin-containing plants have not been well studied (Berenbaum, 1991). It is known that the bark of *Fraxinus excelsior* trees contains several bitter tasting coumarin derivatives such as Isofraxidin, Aesculin, Aesculetin, Scopoletin, Fraxin, Fraxinol, Fraxetin, Fraxidin and Isofraxidin (Berenbaum, 1991; Gaedcke, 1993; Hegnauer, 1969; Murray et al., 1982).

Studies in Scandinavia clearly show that susceptibility of trees to vole damage has a genetic basis. Consistent differences in susceptibility of provenances or families of Norway spruce (Hagman, 1973), lodgepole pine (Hansson, 1985), birch (Rousi et al., 1990) have been reported. Differences in provenance susceptibility are apparently unrelated to growth rate, so fast growing, vole resistant varieties can be found (Rousi, 1988, 1989). On the long term, it is not profitable to select trees only for fast and straight growth. In general, little attention is paid to tree-resistance against pests and diseases. However, selection for and improvement of endogenous pest resistance in trees is advantageous. It can reduce pest damage and the cost of pest control (Wink, 1988).

Within our preliminary studies, the bark of individual *Fraxinus excelsior* trees have shown a strong and significant variation in feeding deterrence, against the vole *Microtus arvalis* and the bark-sucking insect *Pseudochermes fraxini*. We also found a corresponding variation in the concentrations of bitter tasting coumarin derivatives. Although we found a tendency for palatability differences between progenies of Fraxinus excelsior, we did not find significant differences. The lack of significance might be due to a large variability between individual trees within a progeny, which would necessitate experiments with larger numbers of voles. As an alternative, chemical analysis of the bark would possibly reveal significant differences in concentrations of coumarin between progenies. However, within this project, comprehensive chemical analysis could not be included.

Further, chemical analysis of vole and insect resistant and non-resistant trees is necessary for the identification of the precise coumarin derivative which might be responsible for the antifeedant properties. These findings are of interest for future genetic improvement, in order to select resistant ash trees to prevent damage by voles and bark-sucking insects as well as sheep, rabbits and hares.

ACKNOWLEDGEMENTS

This work was granted by the EU project AIR3-CT-920134 'Alternative Agricultural Land-use with Fast Growing Trees'. The authors wish to thank the following persons: A.F.M. Olsthoorn (IBN-DLO), for his suggestions during the experiments and reading of the manuscript; B.H. Kroes, Department of Pharmacognosy, Utrecht University for information on the coumarins; E.M. de Ruiter and J.T. Verbunt (IBN-DLO), for the chemical analysis.

REFERENCES

BERENBAUM M.R. 1991. Coumarins. In: ROSENTHAL G.A., BERENBAUM M.R. (eds.), *Herbivores: their interactions with secondary plant metabolites*, Volume 1, The chemical participants. Academic Press, San Diego, 468 p.

BRYANT J.P., PROVENZA F.D., PASTOR J., REICHARDT P.B., CLAUSEN T.D., DU TOIT J.T., 1991. Interactions between woody plants and browsing mammals mediated by secondary metabolites. *Ann. Rev. Ecol. Syst.* 22: 431-446.

CONOVER W.J., 1980. *Practical nonparametric statistics*, second edition. John Wiley & Sons, New York. 493 p.

DAVIES R.J., PEPPER H.W., 1989. The influence of small plastic guards, tree-shelters and weed control on damage to young broadleaved trees by field voles (*Microtus agrestis*). *Journal of Environmental Management,* 28: 117-125.

DAVIES R.J., PEPPER H.W., 1990. Protecting trees from field voles. *Arboriculture Research Note.* Forest Research Station, Farnham, Alice Holt Lodge. 3 p.

GILL R.M.A., 1992. A review of damage by mammals in north temperate forests. 2. Small mammals. *Forestry* 65 (3): 279-308.

GAEDCKE F., 1993. Fraxinus. In: *Hagers Handbuch der pharmazeutischen* Praxis. Band 5: 188-200 (eds. HÄNSEL R. et al.) Springer Verlag, Berlin.

HAGMAN M., 1973. Differences in resistance to voles in provenances of Norway spruce (*Picea abies* L. Karst). *IUFRO Working Party on Norway spruce provenances.* Biri, Norway, p. 40.

HANSSON L., 1985. Damage by wildlife, especially small rodents, to North American *Pinus contorta* provenances introduced into Sweden. *Canadian Journal Forest Research* 15: 1167-1171.

HEGNAUER R., 1969. *Chemotaxonomie der Pflanzen.* Band 5. Birkhauser Verlag, Basel, 506 p.

MCCULLAGH P., NELDER J.A., 1989. *Generalized linear models.* Second edition. London, Chapman and Hall. 599 p.

MORAAL L.G., 1993. Prevention of vole damage on trees: a review of literature. *IBN Research Report 93/7.* 14 p.

MURRAY R.D.H., MENDEZ J., BROWN S.A., 1982. *The natural coumarins: occurrence, chemistry and biochemistry.* Wiley and sons, Chicester. 702 p.

PIGOTT C.D., 1985. Selective damage to tree-seedlings by bank voles (*Clethrionomys glareolus*). *Oecologia* 67: 367-371.

ROUSI M., 1988. Resistance breeding against voles in birch: possibilities for increasing resistance by provenance transfers. *EPPO bulletin* 18: 257-263.

ROUSI M., 1989. Susceptibility of winter dormant *Pinus sylvestris* families to vole damage. *Scandinavian Journal Forest Research* 4: 149-161.

ROUSI M., HENTTONEN H., KAIKUSALO A., 1990. Resistance of birch (*Betula pendula* and *B. platyphylla*) seedlots to vole (*Microtus agrestis*) damage. *Scandinavian Journal Forest Research* 5: 427-436.

TAHVANAINEN J., HELLE E., JULKUNEN-TIITTO R., LAVOLA A., 1985. Phenolic compounds of willow bark as deterrent against feeding by mountain hare. *Oecologia* 65: 319-323.

WINK M., 1988. Plant breeding: importance of plant secondary metabolites for protection against pathogens and herbivores. *Theoretical and Applied Genetics* 75: 225-233.

Physiology and Genetics of Tree-Phytophage Interactions
Gujan (France), August 31 - September 5, 1997
Ed. INRA, Paris, 1999 (Les Colloques, n°90)

Climatic adaptedness of conifers and susceptibility to damage by mammalian herbivores - a case study of *Microtus* voles and Norway spruce (*Picea abies* (L.) Karst.) origins

M. ROUSI, H. SIKANEN

The Finnish Forest Research Institute, Punkaharju Research Station
Finlandiantie 18, FIN-58450 Punkaharju, Finland

RESUME

During the cyclic peak years *Microtus*-voles may cause considerable damage to forest tree plantations in boreal forests. We assessed vole damage in 39 Norway spruce provenance experiments established in Finland during a thirteen year period, 1958-1970. In total 280 177 seedlings were planted, and 6.5 % of them were damaged. Damage was serious in 11 experiments : 13 % of the seedlings of local origins and 23 % of the seedlings of southern origins were damaged. There was no clinal latitudinal trend in susceptibility of southern origins. The reasons for increased susceptibility of southern spruces and other conifers is discussed.

INTRODUCTION

Pleistocene glaciations had a drastic effect on the number of species of forest trees growing at northern latitudes. In Europe alone, some 58 species of trees became extinct (see Niemelä and Mattson, 1996), and at present in the Fennoscandinavian countries, for example, very few indigenous species are important for forestry. Due to the small number of species, several trials have been made in which exotics were planted in an attempt to increase the growth and productivity of forests in Europe as well as in Japan, the northernmost island of Hokkaido.

Spruce (*Picea abies*) is an example of a relative newcomer after the Pleistocene times. Geological investigations show that spruce reached western Finland only 1500 - 1000 years B.C. and that spruce has not yet reached western Norway by natural means. The use of various southern spruce origins has been quite widespread in Scandinavia, one of the reasons being that the late-starting southern trees are less prone to spring frosts that may damage local trees.

Transfer of tree species and origins to new growing sites may also lead to difficulties in their resistance to abiotic and biotic factors. In 1966, Japanese researchers reported that exotic trees are much more susceptible to vole (*Clethrionymus rufocanus bedfordiae*) damage than local are species and concluded that the reason for this was the lack of co-evolution between voles and exotic species (Takahashi and Nishiguchi 1966a).

In far northern Europe, vole densities are very high during the cyclic peak years, usually occurring at 3- to 4-yr intervals. These cycles are common in Finland, but no longer occur in more southern regions, such as southern Sweden and Estonia (e.g. Hanski et *al*., 1991). In areas where numbers of voles are low and non-cyclic, they cause negligible damage to forest plantations; but in areas where the numbers of voles reach high levels, they can cause considerable damage to forest plantations. Another aspect is the fact that voles and other mammals usually damage tree species used in practical forestry only during the winter.

We evaluated the vole damage in spruce experiments carried out in Finland during 1958 - 1970 to determine the level of damage in general and whether there are differences in susceptibility to such damage among provenances and whether these differences can be attributed to the latitude of the origin of the provenances. In addition, we surveyed the literature on vole and other mammal damage related to different origins of conifers to ascertain whether latitudinal patterns are involved in their resistance.

MATERIAL AND METHODS

Seed material and the experiments

Experiment 90 was planted in southern Finland (60°03'N) on 25-27 May 1959 using 4-year-old seedlings. The two southernmost origins were from Austria (47°45' and 48°35'N), two origins were from Poland (49°35', 52°45'N), and two from Germany (50°10', 51°45'N). The control was one Finnish origin (60°04'N). Randomized block design (RBD) was used : 4 replicate blocks, 625 seedlings/replicate block/origin on an area of 42.5 x 42.5 m (planting distance 1.7 x 1.7 m). A total of 17 500 seedlings (7 origins x 4 replicate blocks x 625 seedlings) were planted. Seedlings in one replicate block were dead due to abiotic reasons (excessive ground moisture) ; therefore we used only 3 replicate blocks for calculations. Vole damage was assessed in 1962.

Experiment 143 was planted in southern Finland (60°30'N) in May 1959 using 4-year-old seedlings. The exotic origins were the same as in Exp. 90 (only the southernmost origin was lacking), but the local controls were from 60°21' and 60° 29'N. Four replicate blocks, 400 seedlings/replicate block/origin were planted on an area of 20 x 20 m (planting distance 2 x 2 m). A total of 11 200 seedlings were planted (7 origins, 4 blocks x 400 seedlings). Vole damage was assessed in 1962.

Experiment 146 was planted in southern Finland (60°27'N) in the spring of 1959, using 4-year-old seedlings. A total of seven origins and provenances were planted : one origin from Austria (47°38'N), one from Poland (49°35'N), three origins and provenances from Germany (50°25' - 51°45'N) and two local origins from southern Finland (60°21' and 60°29'N). RBD was used : 3-5 replicate blocks, 114-340 seedlings/replicate block/origin ; planting distance was 2 x 2 m. Vole damage was assessed on 6075 seedlings in 1963.

Experiment 147 was planted in southern Finland (60°52'N) in the spring of 1958, using 4-year-old seedlings. The dead seedlings were replaced in 1959 from the same nursery stock. A total of 6 origins were planted, but one (local) origin had only two replicate blocks and that origin was rejected. Local origins were from 61°02', 61°05' and 61° N ; the two exotic origins were from Austria (47° 38'N) and from Germany (51°40'N). RBD was used: 5 replicate blocks, 400 - 2000 seedlings/replicate block/origin; planting distance was 2 x 2 m. A total of 8122 seedlings were assessed for damage in 1963.

Experiment 148 was planted in southern Finland (60°26'N) in 1958 using 3-year-old seedlings. There were three provenances from Austria (47°45', 48°00', 48°12'N), one from Poland (52° 45'N), one from Germany (50°25'N) and four local origins. 2 replicate blocks, 400 seedlings/replicate block/origin were planted on an area of 40 x 40m (planting distance 2 x 2 m). A total of 7158 seedlings were assessed for vole damage in 1963.

Experiment 171 was planted on 28 May 1962 in southern Finland (60°03'N). A total of 27 origins and provenances were planted, one provenance from Switzerland (46°30'N), seven origins from Austria (47°23' - 48°40'N), five origins from Slovakia (48°40' - 49°27'N), eight origins and provenances from Germany (48°57' - 50°35'N), three from Poland (49°35' - 52°45'N), one origins from Belarussia (53°30'N), one provenance from Russia (58°00'N) and one of local origin (60°21'N). RBD was used, 6 replicate blocks, 90 seedlings/replicate block/origin on an area of 18 x 20 m (planting distance 2 x 2 m). A total of 14 549 seedlings were assessed for vole damage in 1966.

Experiment 191 was planted on 24 May 1961 in southern Finland (61°31'N) using 4-year-old seedlings. Two origins were planted: a local and an origin from Belarussia (53°30'N). RBD was used : 2 replicate blocks, 540 seedlings/replicate block/origin at different planting distances. A total of 5512 seedlings were assessed for vole damage in 1966.

Experiment 194 was planted June 9, 1962, in southern Finland (61°56'N) using 5-year-old seedlings. A total of 18 origins and provenances were planted. Three origins and provenances from Switzerland (46°30' - 40'N), seven origins from Austria (47°00 - 48°40'N), one origin from the Czech Republic (48°40'N), four origins and provenances from Germany (48°57' - 50°36'N) two origins from Poland (49°35', 52°45'N) and one of local origin (61°06'N). RBD was used : 5 replicate blocks, 86 seedlings/replicate block/origin on an area of 20 x 20 m (planting distance 2 x 2m). A total of 8539 seedlings were assessed for vole damage in 1970.

Experiment 217 was planted in southern Finland (61° 48'N) on 2 June in 1964 using 4-year-old seedlings. Of the 26 origins, the southernmost was from Romania (47° 20'N), four were from Slovakia (49°00' - 49°15'N) and 17 from Germany (50° 25'N - 50°44' N), four origins from southern Finland (60°21', 60°40', 61° 30 and 61°41'N). RBD was used : 6 replicate blocks/origin, 25 seedlings/origin/replicate at 10 x 10 m area (planting distance 2 x 2 m). A total of 3900 seedlings were assessed for vole damage in 1970.

Experiment 237-4 was planted in southern Finland (61°12'N) on 11-13 Sept. 1967 using 4-year-old seedlings. Of the 17 origins, 13 were from Romania (45°35' - 48°12'N), one from Germany (51°40') and three from Finland (60°21', 61°22 and 63°41'N). RBD was used : 6 replicate blocks/origin, 49 seedlings/origin/replicate on an area of 14 x 14 m (planting distance 2 x 2m). A total of 4763 seedlings were assessed for vole damage in 1970.

Origins and provenances

Part of the seed material was obtained from the original growth site of a particular stand (=seed origin); in other cases seed came from a forest that was established earlier in Finland using exotic seeds (=provenance). In the case of provenances, then the seed produced may be the result of a crossing between exotic trees or a provenance hybrid between an exotic tree and local pollen. We calculated the results using the latitude of the original growth site of origins and provenances and the mean of the latitude of the original growing site of parent trees and their present growing site (= southern Finland). As there was also wide variation in the altitude of the original growing site of the trees, we paid attention to that variation.

Damage

The species of vole causing damage was not identified ; but on the bases of the type of damage, *Microtus agrestis* is, however, the most likely species. For calculations, we combined all the damage (severe and mild) and used only percentage-damaged seedlings of the total number of planted seedlings.

Even after transformations, the material was not normally distributed. Therefore we used Kruskall Wallis H-test and for pairwise comparisons, the Mann Whitney U-test.

RESULTS

During 1958-1970 a total of 95 several kind of experiments were established using 620 160 seedlings of spruces. Vole damage was observed in a total of 39 spruce experiments, and in those experiments all 280 177 seedlings were assessed for vole damage. Occasional damage was reported on the average of 6.5 % of all planted seedlings in those 39 experiments. Considerable damage was found in 11 provenance experiments. In these experiments a total of 18 190 seedlings , i.e. 20.2 %, were damaged. One experiment was a comparison between greenhouse and outdoor grown seedlings and was omitted from further calculations. Voles may also destroy practical plantations as indicated by heavy losses in two additional experiments which were established using local seedmaterial only (34% of 4116 and 15% of 4096 seedlings damaged).

In four of those ten provenance experiments there were no differences in susceptibility to voles among the planted origins and provenances (Figs 1a and 1b). In a comparison between local origins combined vs exotics combined there was no difference in two experiments (90 and 171). In Exp. 143 the difference was almost statistically significant (p=.086), but in seven experiments the difference was unequivocal (p<.0370). In general, origins from Switzerland, Austria, Germany, Poland, Romania and Belarussia were more susceptible: 23 % of those seedlings were damaged compared to 13 % seedlings of local origins. The only origin from Russia in this experimental series (58°N in exp. 171) seemed to be resistant (Fig. 1a).

There is no exact latitudinal pattern in the resistance of origins south of Finland (Figs 1a and 1b), and possible hybridization (exotics x southern Finnish pollen) had no clear effect on the results. Nor did the altitude of the original growing site affect this pattern.

DISCUSSION

In general, vole damage in the spruce experiments was not very significant during the 13-year period covered by this study. Local damage, however, can be substantial. This was usually due to the use of southern origins (Figs. 1a and 1b), but voles can clearly cause considerable damage also in plantations using local seedmaterial. Earlier Christiansen (1975) and Hansson

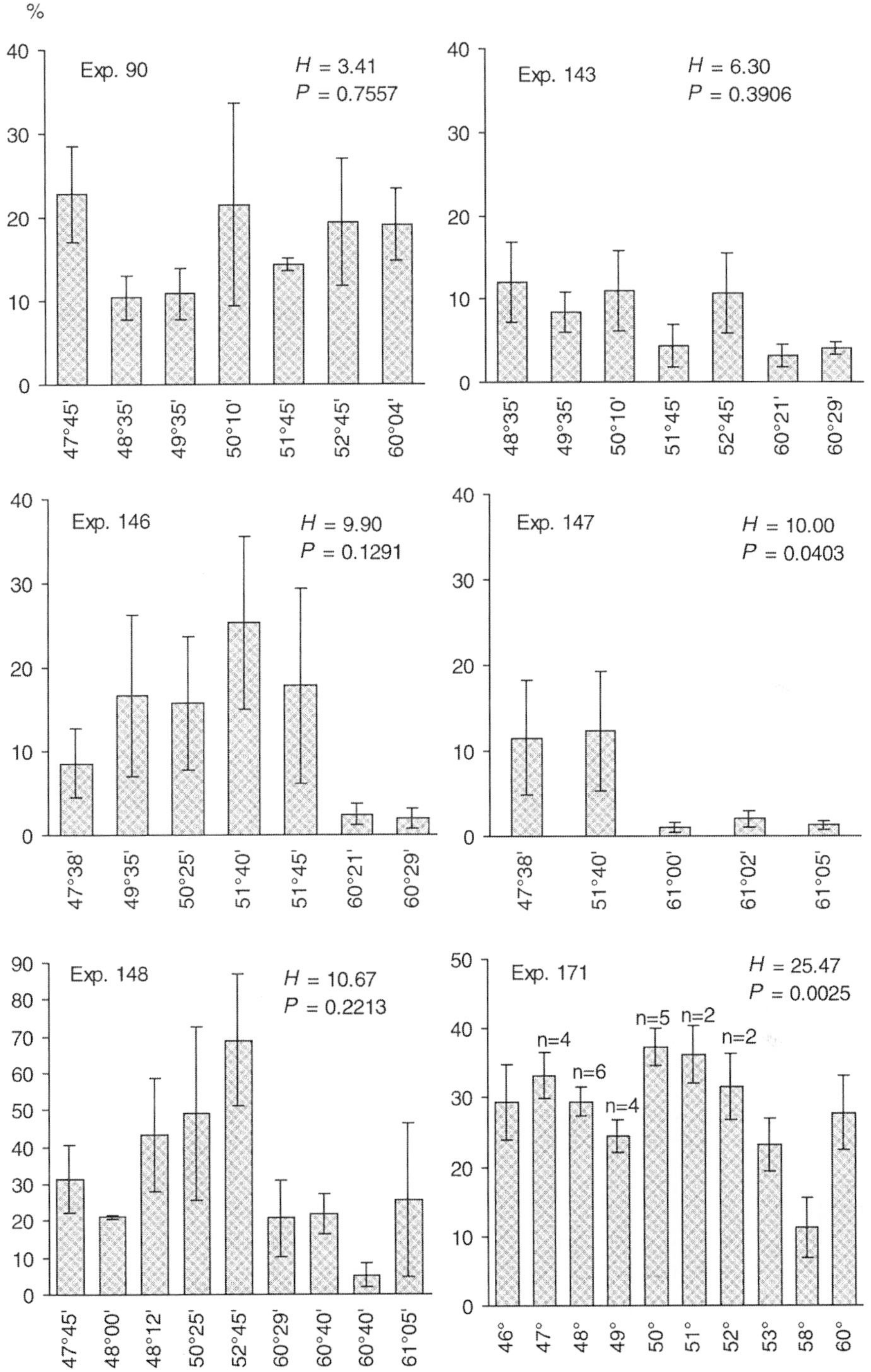

Figure 1a. Vole damage in spruce provenance experiments.
N indicates number of provenances from each latitude, n=1 if not otherwise stated.

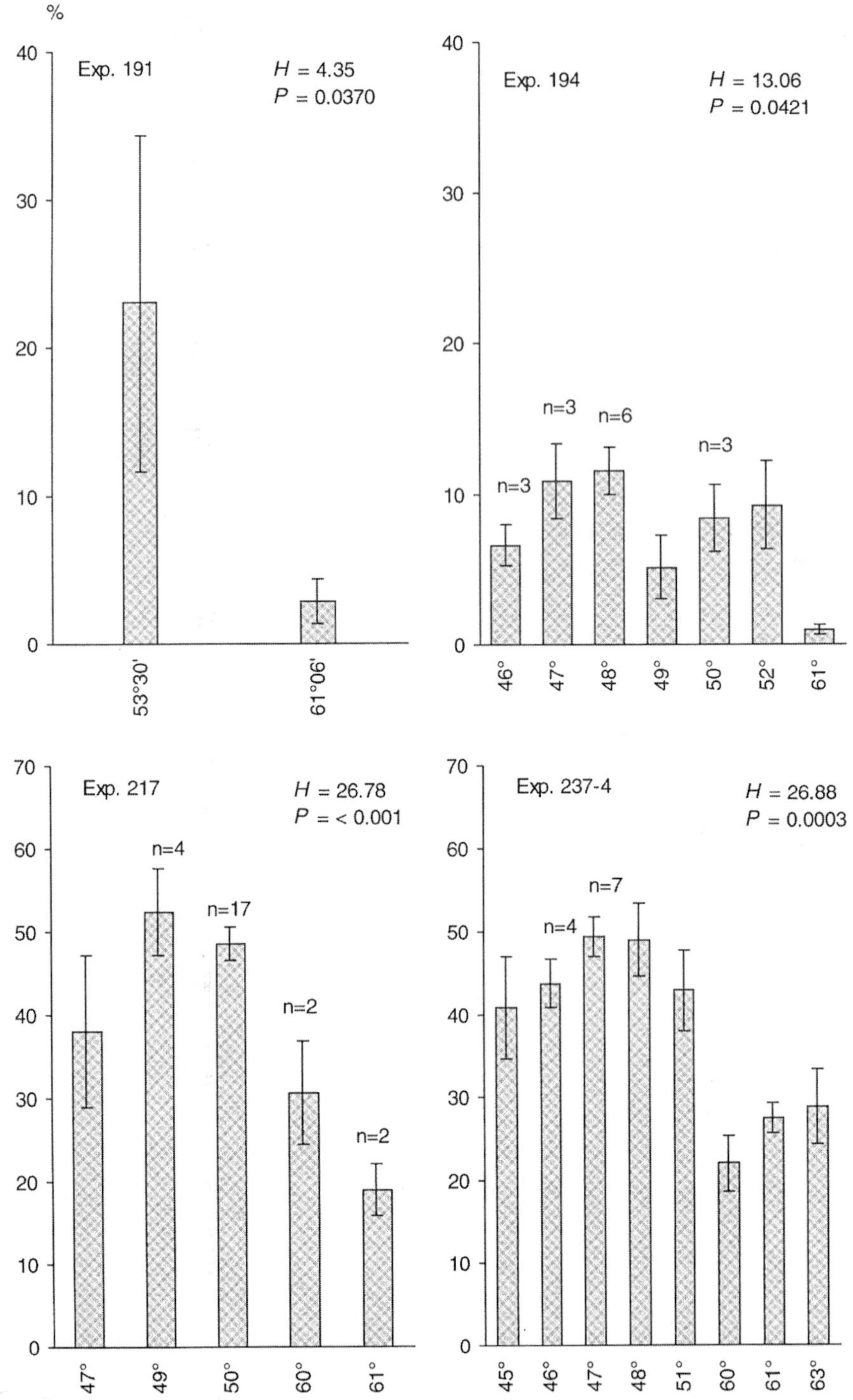

Figure 1b. Vole damage in spruce provenance experiments.
N indicates number of provenances from each latitude, n=1 if not otherwise stated.

(see Hansson, 1988) have also suggested the increased susceptibility of southern spruce origins, but their material was probably somewhat limited.

In other conifer species, increased susceptibility of southern species and origins of forest trees to voles has often been reported. For example, in the northern Island of Hokkaido in Japan, Takahashi and Nishiguchi (1966a) studied seedlings of six *Larix*-species, twelve *Pinus*-, eight *Picea*-, six *Abies*- and one *Pseudotsuga* species. Their conclusion was that it is impossible to find vole-resistant trees in a region far from the natural habitat of *Clethrionymus*-voles.

Provenance experiments with lodgepole pine (*P. contorta*) have been planted in Finland and Sweden for a long time. Practical plantations in Sweden cover some 500 000 ha. The northernmost origins of lodgepole pine in Canada grow at a latitude of 63°N, while most of the plantations in Scandinavia occur at more northerly areas. In Scandinavian experiments it has been observed that the susceptibility of lodgepole pine to vole (*Microtus* species) damage is related to the geographic origin of each provenance. This was very obvious in northern Finland (Rousi, 1983a) and Sweden (Hansson, 1985). In general, voles clearly prefer lodgepole pine to Scots pine (10 % of 29 000 lodgepole pine saplings inspected were damaged, compared to 0.5 % of the 14 000 Scots pines inspected (Rousi, 1983a). Susceptibility of lodgepole pine twigs to moose damage also seems to be related to latitude of the origin; more northern origins seem to be more resistant (Rosvall & Friberg, 1989). Still, Hansson (1985) found that moose and vole each attacked different provenances of lodgepole pine.

In Scots pine, there seems to be a slight negative correlation between the timing of bud set and susceptibility to vole damage : seedlings which grow longer in the autumn seem to be more susceptible to damage (Rousi, 1989). Also the susceptibility of pine twig to browsing by moose is related to latitude of the pine origin: in two provenance trials, moose preferred the same origins ; and in general, northern origins were less preferred than southern origins (Niemelä et al., 1989). It has also been postulated that the increase in hare damage in fertilized pines might be a due to disturbances in their winter-hardening (Rousi, 1983b).

In larch hybrids (*Larix gmelini* x *L. leptolepis*) Takahashi and Nishiguchi (1966b) found that autumn leaf colour was related to resistance to voles : larch-types that exhibited long growth periods (*L. leptolepis*-type) were more susceptible than *gmelini*-types of hybrids with a short growth period. The same phenomenon was also found in larch experiments in Finland : *L. sibirica* with a shorter growth period is more resistant than *L. decidua*. Resistance of hybrids and backcrosses of *L. sibirica* and *decidua* was related to needle colour: in late automn :the longer the growth period, the more susceptible are the seedlings.

For conifers in general, the species and origins that are adapted to a long growth period, (in particular exotic species and origins) show increased susceptibility to voles as well as to other mammals such as moose and hare. Consequently, physiological changes related to successful winter hardening lead to an increase in resistance. Thus an increase in resistance is probably a by-product of successful winter-hardening. Other genotype- and organ-specific mechanisms also have an affect on resistance differences among species, origins and genotypes of conifers.

Southern origins of Norway spruce have generally shown good survival and adaptedness to more northern conditions, e.g. saplings of present origins and provenances usually survived well and reached about the same height as local origins in southern Finland, at least as juvenile saplings (Hagman, 1980). However, in spruce as in other conifers increased susceptibility to mammal damage may be a sign of difficulties in winter-hardening process, difficulties which may also lead to increased susceptibility to pathogens and environmental hazards.

REFERENCES

CHRISTIANSEN E., 1975. Field rodent damage in Norway. *Ecol. Bull.* 19, 37-46.

HAGMAN M., 1980. Experiments with Norway spruce provenances in Finland. *Silva Fennica* 1, 32-39.

HANSKI I., HANSSON L., HENTTONEN H., 1991. Specialist predators, generalist predators, and the microtine rodent cycle. *J. Anim. Ecol.* 60, 353-367.

HANSSON L., 1985. Damage by wildlife, especially small rodents, to North American Pinus contorta provenances introduced into Sweden. *Can. J. For. Res.* 15, 1167-1171.

HANSSON L., 1988. Natural resistance of plants to pest rodents. *In :* Prakash, I. (Ed.) *Rodent pest management*, Boca Raton, CRC Press, pp. 391-397.

NIEMELÄ P., HAGMAN M., LEHTILÄ K., 1989. Relationship between Pinus sylvestris L. origin and browsing preference by moose in Finland. *Scand. J. For. Res.* 4, 239-246.

NIEMELÄ P., MATTSON W., 1996. The invasion of North American forests by European phytophagus insects. *BioScience* 46, 741-753.

ROSVALL O., FRIBERG G., 1989. Lodgepole pine and moose damages. Institutet för Skogsförbättring. Skogsträdsförädlingsinformation NR 4, 5 pp. (In Swedish with English summary).

ROUSI M., 1983a. Vole damage in tree species trials in northern Finland in the winter of 1981/82. *Folia Forestalia* 569, 10 pp (In Finnish with English summary).

ROUSI M., 1983b. Susceptibility of pine to mammalian herbivores in northern Finland. *Silva Fenn.*17(4), 301-312.

ROUSI M., 1989. Susceptibility of winter-dormant Pinus sylvestris families to vole damage. *Scand. J. For. Res.* 4, 149-161.

TAKAHASHI N., NISHIGUCHI C., 1966a. Studies on the resistance of forest trees to red-backed vole, *Clethrionymus rofocanus bedfordiae* (Thomas). (I) Relative feeding preference of the vole for seedlings of conifers under laboratory conditions. *Bull. Tokyo Univ. For.* 62,153-172 (In Japanese with English summary).

TAKAHASHI N., NISHIGUCHI C., 1966b. Studies on the resistance of forest trees to red-backed vole, *Clethrionymus rofocanus bedfordiae* (Thomas). (II) Relative feeding preference of the vole for seedlings of larch F_1-hybrids under laboratory conditions. *Bull. Tokyo Univ. For.* 62, 173-188 (In Japanese with English summary).

Physiology and Genetics of Tree-Phytophage Interactions
Gujan (France), August 31 - September 5, 1997
Ed. INRA, Paris, 1999 (Les Colloques, n°90)

Larval tunnels of *Phytobia betulae* Kang. in birch - a new trait for birch breeding?

T. YLIOJA, M ROUSI

Finnish Forest Research Institute, Punkaharju Research Station
FIN-58450 Punkaharju, Finland

RESUME

Long larval tunnels of *Phytobia betulae* Kang. (Diptera: Agromyzidae) are an economically important and aesthetic problem in birch wood. *Phytobia* has a unique life cycle, in which the host tree plays a vital role. Birch trees show large variation in their susceptibility to *Phytobia*. Fast growing trees are generally susceptible to *Phytobia* damage. We discuss the possibilities of using resistance breeding to decrease the loss in wood quality caused by *Phytobia*.

INTRODUCTION

Phytobia betulae Kang. (Diptera: Agromyzidae) is a very common insect in northern boreal forests. Its life-cycle is closely associated with white birches, in the Fennoscandian countries European white birch (*Betula pendula* Roth) and pubescent birch (*B. pubescens* Ehrh.) (Kangas, 1935; Hara, 1994). The larvae of *Phytobia* mine in the differentiating xylem, leaving empty larval tunnels in the newly-formed wood. The tunnels are subsequently filled by the tree with brown parenchyma tissue (Gregory and Wallner, 1979; Ylioja *et al.*, 1998a).

Birches are important tree species for the Finnish forest industries, and light-coloured birch wood is highly valued for furniture, flooring and decorative purposes. Dark brown larval tunnels of *Phytobia* are considered to be an aesthetic defect in birch veneer and sawn timber. Brown larval tunnels reduce the quality classification of the end product and the price of the raw material. A survey of 925 trees sampled in 42 different stands (pure birch stands and mixed stands with coniferous trees), indicated that only 4% of the butt logs were free of larval tunnels (Ylioja and Schulman, in prep.). Consequently, butt logs without stripes are a special quality of wood, and their price can be 2-3 times higher than the average price for birch butt logs.

Despite the economic importance of the problem, the life cycle of *Phytobia* is inadequately known and no methods for control of *Phytobia* are available. There is large variation in the amount of larval tunnels among birch trees within a stand. If these differences are genetically based, resistance breeding could be used to reduce the damage caused by *Phytobia*. Here we discuss our preliminary results concerning the resistance of birch to *Phytobia*.

LONG LARVAL TUNNELS

Phytobia betulae is univoltine (Kangas, 1935). In June, the female lays her eggs one at a time into young, rapidly-growing shoots situated in the upper part of the tree crown (Ylioja *et al.*, in prep). *Phytobia* larvae have three instars (Hanson and Benjamin, 1967; Hara, 1990). The larvae first mine from the canopy down towards the base of the stem. The tunnels are completed in August and can be up to 17 m long (Ylioja *et al.*, 1998a). Before the larvae exit the stem, they may mine back and forth in the roots and at the stem base, forming very wide tunnels near the stem base. The last instar, which is 15 - 20 mm long, exits through the bark either from the roots or at the stem base, forms a yellowish 4-5 mm long puparium and overwinters in the soil (Kangas, 1935; Ylioja *et al.*, 1998a). The tunnels are easily visible as so-called "pith flecks" in the annual rings in stem cross-sections, especially in the lower part of the stem. The susceptibility of a tree to *Phytobia* can be estimated by counting the annual pith flecks on disks taken from the stems.

TREE GENETICS AND ENVIRONMENT PLAY A ROLE IN RESISTANCE

In two field trials, 41 and 44 open-pollinated European white birch families differed in their susceptibility to *Phytobia*, as did eight or nine 4- and 6-year-old clones of the same species in three other trials. The frequency of pith flecks in the most susceptible families and clones was 2 - 4 times higher than that in the most resistant families and clones. Resistance and the growth rate were negatively correlated in all the field trials (Ylioja *et al.*, in prep; see also Ylioja *et al.*, 1995), and when the effect of tree growth was incorporated into the ANOVA models as a covariate it explained 50 – 80% of the variation in susceptibility. However, *Phytobia* numbers were not only explained by good growth, because family and clone still explained significant amounts (about 10%) of the variation in susceptibility.

Two fertilisation experiments were carried out in two successive years with 2-year-old clonal plantlets of *B. pendula* grown at three different nutrient levels (poor, moderately fertile and very fertile). The frequency of successful *Phytobia* infection was higher in the two most fertile levels in both experiments (Ylioja *et al.*, in prep.). Further experiments will reveal whether the effects of fertilisation on the primary and secondary metabolism of birch are important for *Phytobia* resistance, or whether the increase in susceptibility can be explained by increased growth (e.g. number of oviposition sites in the canopy) only.

BREEDING BIRCHES FOR *PHYTOBIA* RESISTANCE

The determination of susceptibility to *Phytobia* attack is destructive for trees. Oviposition does not leave any visible scars on the shoots, and therefore cannot be used to estimate *Phytobia* damage. The most accurate method for determining the resistance is to fell a tree and count the exact *Phytobia* populations that have survived in the tree within its lifetime (Ylioja *et al.*, 1998b). If one does not want to kill a tree, increment cores could be used to estimate the level of resistance in birch. Using increment cores, however, involves two serious problems: 1) birch is very susceptible to fungal infestation via any kind of bark wound, and 2) the method does not give a reliable estimate of the susceptibility, since the probability to hit a pith fleck (larval tunnel) is lower in the outer annual rings than in the inner ones. The latter problem could possibly be taken into account by estimating the probabilities at different ages from empirical data. In addition, several scores per tree would probably be needed for a reliable estimate.

The resistance of birch genotypes can be estimated from young trees since susceptible trees retain their susceptibility throughout their lifetime (Ylioja *et al.*, 1998b). Estimation of the quality of wood in the final cutting with respect to *Phytobia* damage can be done already at a relative young age, e.g. during first thinning in a progeny trial. Field trials can be used to estimate the susceptibility to *Phytobia* since infection is wide spread and is not localised within a field trial. If the progeny trials of birch were thinned in such a way that the spatial structure of a trial is kept uniform, the removed stems would easily provide an accurate estimate of the susceptibility to *Phytobia.*

The biology of *Phytobia* is not completely known, nor the chemical, physical and physiological resistance mechanisms related to female selection of a host plant or survival of larvae. The negative phenotypic correlation between resistance and growth is bad news for forest tree breeders and birch growers, because the genetic correlation between these two traits may also be negative. Our studies are limited, and it may therefore be possible to find genotypes whose resistance and good growth are not negatively correlated. In the future genetic markers may be useful to identify resistant trees.

REFERENCES

GREGORY R., WALLNER. W, 1979. Histological relationship of *Phytobia setosa* to *Acer saccharum. Canadian Journal of Botany* 57, 403-407.

HANSON J. B., BENJAMIN D. M., 1967. Biology of *Phytobia setosa*, a cambium miner of sugar maple. *Journal of Economic Entomology* 60, 1351-1355.

HARA H., 1994. Life history of *Phytobia betulae* which causes pith-flecks in the wood of Japanese white birch. *Transactions of the* Meeting *in Hokkaido Branch of the Japanese Forestry Society* 42, 162-162. (In Japanese).

KANGAS E., 1935. Die Braunfleckigkeit des Birkenholzes und ihr Urheber *Dendromyza* (Dizygomyza) *betulae* n. sp. Vorläufige Mitteilung. *Communicationes Instituti Forestalis Fenniae* 22(1), 1-31.

YLIOJA T., SCHULMAN E., ROUSI M., VELLING P., 1995. Susceptibility of white birch (*Betula* spp.) hybrids to *Phytobia* fly. Icelandic Agricultural *Sciences* 9, 125-133.

YLIOJA T., SARANPÄÄ P., Roininen H., ROUSI M., 1998a. Larval tunnels of *Phytobia betulae* (Diptera:Agromyzidae) in birch wood. *Journal of Economic Entomology* 91, 175-181.

YLIOJA, T., ROININEN H., AYRES M. P., ROUSI M., PRICE P. W., 1998b. Host-driven population dynamics in an herbivorous insect. *Submitted.*

Physiology and Genetics of Tree-Phytophage Interactions
Gujan (France), August 31 - September 5, 1997
Ed. INRA, Paris, 1999 (Les Colloques, n°90)

Comparison of different selection methods for the resistance to *Dioryctria sylvestrella* Ratz. (*Lepidoptera: Pyralidae*) in *Pinus pinaster* Ait.

H. JACTEL[1], M. KLEINHENTZ[1]; A. RAFFIN[2], P. MENASSIEU[1]

[1] *INRA, Laboratoire d'Entomologie Forestière, INRA, BP 45, 33611 GAZINET Cedex.*
[2] *INRA, Laboratoire d'Amélioration et Génétique des Arbres Forestiers, BP 45, 33611 GAZINET Cedex.*

RESUME

Fifteen-year-old Maritime pines from a full diallel mating design were studied for sensitivity to the stem borer *Dioryctria sylvestrella* and growth in 1994-1996. The family effect was significant and the genetic contribution of the parents almost entirely additive for both resistance and diameter. Tree susceptibility was positively and genetically correlated with tree diameter. Eleven-year-old Maritime pines from a clonal test consisting of full-sib families were studied for sensitivity to *D. sylvestrella*, growth and terpene composition of the oleoresin in 1994-1996. Infested trees contained significantly more terpinolene and the regression between percentage of attacked trees and mean proportion of terpinolene per family was significant. The proportion of terpinolene was not correlated with tree diameter. The family effect was significant for several terpenes including terpinolene. Direct and indirect selections using terpinolene as biochemical marker are compared regarding expected genetic gains for tree resistance and correlative genetic loss for tree growth, cost and optimal time for selecting genotypes.

INTRODUCTION

In Aquitaine, where one million hectares of Maritime pine stands are intensively managed (Merzeau, 1995), the stem borer *Dioryctria sylvestrella* has become the major insect pest (Jactel and Kleinhentz, 1997). Tree infestation by *D. sylvestrella* results from a primary attraction mediated by oleoresin components exuding from the stem bark. The response of the insect is both qualitative, depending from the terpene profile of the oleoresin, and quantitative, the amount of oleoresin release increasing with tree vigor and bark injuries (Jactel et al, 1996 a). Intensive management of Maritime pine stands involves low density planting, fertilizing and pruning and consequently increases tree susceptibility to the stem borer (Jactel et al, 1994; Jactel and Kleinhentz, 1997). Because chemical control is not realistic (the pest is hidden under the bark almost all over the year) and biological control is not efficient, selection of resistant varieties represents a promising alternative method of pest management. A Maritime pine breeding program has been developed by INRA since the 1960s (Baradat and Pastuszka, 1992), in which resistance to *D. sylvestrella* could be integrated. As a first approach, direct selection for resistance could be promoted. But since tree vigor and tree susceptibility are related, genetic gain in tree resistance may result in genetic loss in wood production. An indirect selection, using terpenes as biochemical markers, could also be used to avoid this drawback providing that terpene rates are sufficiently heritable, genetically correlated with tree resistance and not correlated with growth. The first objective of this paper is to compare relative efficiency of direct versus indirect selection for Maritime pine resistance to the stem borer. Due to tree species longevity, geneticists expect to characterize traits to be selected as soon as possible. Maritime pine tree infestation by *D. sylvestrella* begins in 6 to 8-year-old trees and increases until trees are 15 to 20-year-old. Then the reliability of direct selection may increase when delaying the choice of resistant genotypes. In opposite, the terpene profile of Maritime pine oleoresin is supposed to stabilize in 6 to 8-year-old trees (Baradat et al, 1972), allowing therefore early indirect selection. The second objective of this study is to compare the optimal time for selecting genotypes in direct and indirect selection for resistance to *D. sylvestrella*.

1. DIRECT SELECTION FOR THE RESISTANCE TO *DIORYCTRIA SYLVESTRELLA* IN *PINUS PINASTER*

MATERIAL AND METHODS

Plant material and measurements

Data were collected from a full diallel cross of Maritime pine comprising twelve parents. Among the 144 combinations, 29 were missing due to unsuccessful crosses (tabl. 1). The twelve parents were part of a "plus trees" collection phenotypically selected for the stem growth and straightness in the local provenance of the Landes de Gascogne. The crossing program was carried out in 1980 and the plants were transferred to a forest site in Cestas (Gironde) in 1982. This trial was laid out in 74 incomplete randomized blocks. Each family was repeated 4 to 15 times with line plots of 2 to 4 trees. In October 1994, all of the 3618 trees, 15-year-old, were sampled for *D. sylvestrella* infestation (scored as 0 or 1) and diameter at breast height (1.3 m). In May 1996, one tree per plot was pruned (1006 trees) to increase the natural infestation and, in October 1996, all of the 3618 trees, 17-year-old, were sampled again for *D. sylvestrella* infestation.

Table 1. Mating design (diallel) for the study of direct selection for resistance to *Dioryctria sylvestrella* (number of clones per family)

Father code Mother code	**0018**	**5309**	**3823**	**3820**	**1307**	**5101**	**1901**	**0214**	**1308**	**4701**	**0152**	**3821**
0018	9			25	30	21	29	53		25	33	37
5309				28	52	34	38	50	45	28	25	25
3823	27	30		32	23	22	34	26	30	28	34	42
3820	37	30		31	25	21	27	33	34	40		24
1307	45	51		25	25	27	27	41	30	28	18	34
5101		24		22	18	8			25	21	22	
1901	33	34		30	23	22	13	20	26	26	29	31
0214	29	44		16	37	16	24	28	21	23	28	44
1308	47	44		18	52	28	25	42	18	31	29	38
4701	38	34		34	41	38	33	35	33	32		32
0152	38					39	31	37				
3821	51	53		33	43	32	29	52	48	47	39	19

Estimation of genetic parameters

For each plot, *e.g.* each family replicate, were calculated the mean diameter (DBH) and the percentage of attacked trees (respectively DS94 and DS96 in 1994 and 1996). Analysis of variance, with random family and block effects, was carried out with the OPEP program (Baradat and Loustau, 1997). Self combinations were not considered. The coefficient of genetic prediction (CGP) was computed as a generalization of the heritability concept (Baradat and Labbé, 1995). Relative genetic gain estimates (%) in a trait were computed by multiplying the intensity of selection by the phenotypic coefficient of variation of the trait and the coefficient of genetic prediction (Baradat and Loustau, 1997).

RESULTS AND DISCUSSION

The family effect was highly significant for both resistance and diameter, which justifies the following genetic analyses (tabl. 2). As the block effect was highly significant in all of the traits, data were adjusted in further calculations. General combining ability (GCA) was highly significant and specific combining ability (SCA) was never significant for both diameter and susceptibility to *D. sylvestrella* (tabl. 3). Regarding these traits, the genetic contribution of the parents to their progeny is almost entirely additive.

Table 2. Analysis of variance for the percentage of infested trees in 1994 and 1996 (DS94 and DS96) and the diameter (DBH) in the diallel cross of Maritime pine.

Source	*d.f.*		**DS94**	**DS96**	**DBH**
Family	114	*Mean square*	0.058	0.081	185.38
(random)		*F test*	1.86	1.76	4.65
		Prob (%)	$< 10^{-3}$	$< 10^{-3}$	$< 10^{-3}$
Block	73	*Mean square*	0.055	0.089	139.61
(random)		*F test*	1.75	1.94	3.50
		Prob (%)	0.020	0.001	$< 10^{-3}$
Error	853	*Mean square*	0.031	0.046	398.91

There was no significant general reciprocal effect for the sensitivity to *D. sylvestrella*, indicating the absence of deviation from a mendelien process of transmission. The specific reciprocal effects were significant, perhaps resulting from environmental effects on several mother trees. They were included in the phenotypic variance, before the calculation of coefficient of genetic prediction.

Table 3. Analysis of the genetic effects for the percentage of infested trees in 1994 and 1996 (DS94 and DS96) and the diameter (DBH) in the diallel cross of Maritime pine.

Effect			**Traits**	
		DS94	**DS96**	**DBH**
mean		10.5 %	16.8 %	12.0 cm
GCA	F	5.64	7.20	16.55
General combining ability	*Prob (%)*	(0.001)	($< 10^{-3}$)	($< 10^{-3}$)
SCA	F	0.62	0.58	0.45
Specific combining ability	*Prob (%)*	(93.8)	(96.0)	(99.5)
GRE	F	0.89	1.11	2.52
General reciprocal effects	*Prob (%)*	(55.7)	(38.2)	(2.26)
SRE	F	1.85	1.65	2.10
Specific reciprocal effects	*Prob (%)*	(0.28)	(1.30)	(0.04)

The genetic correlations between susceptibility and tree diameter traits were positive (tabl. 4). The correlation level increases with tree age. Selection for tree resistance to *D. sylvestrella* would then negatively affect wood production. The genetic correlation may be due to a genetic linkage or more likely due to a pleïotropic effect, which would be consistent with the host selection model (Jactel *et al.*, 1994) (radial growth, hence bark cracking and tree attractiveness would depend on the same group of genes).

Table 4. Total (entirely additive) genetic correlations between diameter and susceptibility to *D. sylvestrella* in the diallel cross of Maritime pine.

	DS94	**DS96**
DS96	0.95	
DBH	0.55	0.74

Environmental correlations between tree susceptibility and tree diameter were positive (tabl. 5). Because tree infestation by *D. sylvestrella* is favored by tree vigor, environmental conditions that are usually considered to largely affect the expression of tree radial growth might indirectly affect the expression of tree sensibility.

Table 5. Environmental (upper half) and phenotypic (lower half) correlations between diameter and susceptibility to *D. sylvestrella* in the diallel cross of Maritime pine.

	DS94	**DS96**	**DBH**
DS94	1	0.85	0.31
DS96	0.86	1	0.35
DBH	0.33	0.39	1

Coefficient of genetic prediction estimates were quite low (tabl. 6). The heritability of diameter is consistent with current values estimated in *Pinus* species (Costa *et al.*, 1996; Dieters, 1996) which are below 0.1-0.3. In a previous study based on factorial crosses, heritability estimates of Maritime pine resistance to *D. sylvestrella* ranged from 0.07 to 0.09 (Baradat and Marpeau., 1988).

Table 6. Coefficients of genetic prediction *sensu stricto* (%), heritability in the diagonal.

	DS94	**DS96**	**DBH**
DS94	0.08		
DS96	0.08	0.09	
DBH	0.06	0.08	0.13

In spite of low heritabilities, important relative genetic gains could be obtained in Maritime pine resistance to *D. sylvestrella,* especially in mean family level selection (tabl. 7), due to the phenotypic coefficients of variation (respectively 2.32 and 1.68 in DS94 and DS96). However the associated genetic loss in tree diameter ranged from 3 to 11% (6 to 22% in volume at constant height). The expected genetic gain when selecting resistant trees in 1996 would have been lower than when selecting in 1994 because of a lower phenotypic coefficient of variation of DS96 due to the effects of age and pruning on tree attractiveness.

Table 7. Expected genetic gain (relative %) when selecting on resistance to *D. sylvestrella* and correlative genetic loss in tree diameter according to the type and date of selection.

	Mass selection			**Mean family level selection**		
selection rate	*5 %*	*10 %*	*50 %*	*5 %*	*10%*	*50 %*
gain when selecting on **DS94**	37.8	32.1	14.6	95.2	80.9	36.8
gain when selecting on **DS96**	31.5	26.8	12.2	76.6	65.2	29.7
loss in **DBH** / selecting on **DS94**	- 3.0	- 2.6	- 1.2	- 8.2	- 7.0	- 3.1
loss in **DBH** / selecting on **DS96**	- 4.4	- 3.7	- 1.7	- 11.0	- 9.3	- 4.2

Because tree infestation by *D. sylvestrella* was twice recorded, the risk of selecting genotypes in families unattacked in 1994 but attacked in 1996 could be assessed. To simulate a selection strategy, families were arranged first in increasing order of infestation level in 1994 and in decreasing order of mean diameter. A second arrangement was realized using increasing infestation level in 1996 and decreasing mean diameter. Among the 115 families tested in the diallel, the best 6, 11 and 58 families were respectively chosen in the two arrangements to reproduce selection rates of respectively 5%, 10% and 50%. The expected genetic gain estimates were computed as the relative difference between the mean infestation level of the best families and the average infestation level in 1996. Then the loss of genetic gain was calculated as the difference between the estimates resulting from the two arrangements (tabl. 8). Anticipating the selection of resistance to *D. sylvestrella* for only two years may result in a loss in expected genetic gain varying from 10 to 20 %. Despite a slightly lower potential of genetic gain, it seems to be well advised to postpone the date of selection, waiting for a more achieved expression of the susceptibility to *D. sylvestrella*. Pruning trees would represent an effective way to speed up this process.

Table 8. Loss of expected genetic gain estimates (relative %) in resistance to *Dioryctria sylvestrella* if genotypes were chosen in the families with the higher mean diameter and lower infestation level in 1994 instead of their infestation level in 1996.

Selection rate	Number of selected families	Gain estimate (%) in 96 according to DS94[1]	Gain estimate (%) in 96 according to DS96[2]	Loss in gain estimate (%)
5 %	6	78.9	96.3	17.4
10 %	11	79.8	91.1	11.3
50 %	58	37.8	47.3	9.5

[1] [(mean DS96 of the top 6, 11 or 58 families in 94) – (mean DS96 of 115 families)] / [mean DS96 of 115 families]

[2] [(mean DS96 of the top 6, 11, or 58 families in 96) – (mean DS96 of 115 families)] / [mean DS96 of 115 families]

2. INDIRECT SELECTION FOR THE RESISTANCE TO *DIORYCTRIA SYLVESTRELLA* IN *PINUS PINASTER*

MATERIAL AND METHODS

Plant material and measurements

Data were collected from a Maritime pine clonal test consisting of 18 full sib families (tabl. 9) from nineteen unrelated parents of the local provenance of the Landes de Gascogne, and located in Cestas (Gironde, France). Two to five trees per family were cloned 3 to 6 times by grafting in 1983. In October 1994, a total of 227 trees, 11-year-old, were chosen from all of the 18 families and assessed for *D. sylvestrella* infestation (scored as 0 or 1), diameter at breast height and oleoresin composition. In October 1996, the same 227 trees, 13-year-old, were sampled again for *D. sylvestrella* infestation and diameter. The relative percentage of mono- and sesquiterpenes was calculated from the summation of all recorded terpene peaks from gas chromatograms. Only 10 terpenes with relative proportions higher than 0.1% were used throughout the study: α-pinene, camphene, β-pinene, myrcene, limonene, terpinolene, longipinene, longifolene, β-caryophyllene and α-humulene.

Table 9. Mating design for the study of indirect selection for resistance to *Dioryctria sylvestrella* (in bold, number of clones per family; in italic, number of trees per family)

Father code Mother code	0003	0004	0007	0011	0125	0205	0221	1312	5101
0054		**4** 22	**3** *11*		**3** *14*	**3** *10*	**3** *15*		
0123	**3** *12*		**3** *11*						
0133								**2** *5*	
0159							**2** *7*		
0222		**2** *11*	**3** ***12***						
0286								**4** *14*	**5** *15*
1301				**3** *14*					
3102		**2** *7*							
4321			**5** 20	**2** *10*					
5302			**5** ***18***						

Statistical analyses were carried out with SAS Software (SAS Institute, 1996). Analyses of variance of percentage variables were computed with the arcsin√x transformation (Dagnelie, 1973). Non-parametric analyses of variance (Wilcoxon test, SAS procedure NPAR1WAY) were used for oleoresin composition data which are proportions of n terpenes

with the constraint $\sum_{1}^{n} p_i = 1$

Estimation of genetic parameters

Due to the relationships between families and to low number of clones per family, the observed variances are probably underestimated, and the estimates of genetic parameters are only given as a first approximation in this test. The following model with random effects was used to estimate variances of terpene proportions, tree vigor and tree susceptibility to *D. sylvestrella*: $X_{ijk} = \mu + F_i + I/F_{ik} + e_{ijk}$, where F_i represents the effect due to family i ($1 \leq i \leq n$, variance σ^2_{FS}), I/F_{ik} is the effect due to tree k within family i ($1 \leq k \leq p$, variance σ^2_W) and e_{ijk} is the residual effect that results from the environment ($1 \leq j \leq c$, variance σ^2_E). Variances between family ($\sigma^2_{FS}=1/pc[CM_{FS}-CM_W]$), within families ($\sigma^2_W=1/c[CM_W-CM_E]$), and environmental variance ($\sigma^2_E=CM_E$), were estimated only when both individual and family effects were significant. Families were assumed to be independent full-sib families. Between and within variance were decomposed in additive and dominance variance as following: $\sigma^2_{FS} = \frac{1}{2}\sigma^2_A + \frac{1}{4}\sigma^2_D$ and $\sigma^2_W = \frac{1}{2}\sigma^2_A + \frac{3}{4}\sigma^2_{D6}$. Then the narrow sense heritability was calculated as following: $h^2_{ss} = (3\sigma^2_{FS} - \sigma^2_W) / (\sigma^2_{FS} + \sigma^2_W + \sigma^2_E)$.

Pearson correlation coefficients between terpenes proportion, traits of tree vigor and infestation rate by *D. sylvestrella*, were computed at the family mean level. These correlation values yield an approximate estimate of the genetic correlation coefficients (Roff, 1995).

RESULTS AND DISCUSSION

Susceptibility to *D. sylvestrella* infestation in relation to vigor and terpene composition of wood oleoresin

In 1994, 16.6 % of the trees were infested and 19.7 % in 1996. The diameter at breast height of infested trees was significantly higher (t test, P=0.005 in 1994 and P<0.0001 in 1996) than the diameter of uninfested trees (13.6 cm and 12.1 cm in 1994, 17.8 cm and 16.0 cm in 1996). These results are consistent with previous studies (Jactel et al, 1994) in which large diameter was shown to increase *D. sylvestrella* rate of infestation. The terpene composition of oleoresin did not differ qualitatively between infested and uninfested trees but infested trees in 1994 exhibited significantly more terpinolene (respectively 0.25% in unattacked trees and 0.48 % in attacked trees, Wilcoxon test, Prob>Z=0.035).

Among the 10 terpenes present in the oleoresin, only the mean proportion of terpinolene was significantly correlated with the percentage of infested trees in 1994 per family (n=18, r=0.54, P=0.02) (tabl. 10). The percentage of attacked trees per family, in 1994 and 1996, significantly increased with the mean tree diameter (n=18, respectively r=0.47, P=0.05 and r=0.56, P=0.02). There was no significant correlation between the mean proportion of terpinolene and the mean diameter. In a previous study, Jactel et al. (1996a) showed that a profile consisting of 6 terpenes - including terpinolene- could be used to discriminate between the two types of trees. Wright et al. (1975) have also related the resistance of southern Scots pine varieties to *D. zimmermani* (Grote) to low levels of δ3-carene and terpinolene. In Douglas-fir, Rappaport et al. (1995) found positive statistical correlations between Douglas-fir seed chalcid damage and emissions of limonene, myrcene and terpinolene. The lack of significant correlation between infestation rate in 1996 and mean proportion of terpinolene per family may be due to tree growth. It is assumed that tree attraction depends on the emission of a sufficient amount of attractant which depends on both terpinolene proportion in the resin and the amount of resin exudation which is favored by stem bark cracking. When trees grow older, the diameter and the bark cracking increases but the terpinolene proportion remains unchanged. Then some trees, with medium proportion of terpinolene, may reach progressively the attraction threshold as growing larger.

Table 10: Pearson correlation coefficients at the mean family level among traits of tree vigor, terpenes and tree susceptibility to *D. sylvestrella*. (* significant to α=0.05;**: significant to α=0.01)

	API	CAM	BPI	MYR	LIM	TPL	LGP	LGF	BCA	AHU	D94	D96	DS94
CAM	0.89**												
BPI	-0.97**	-0.82**											
MYR	-0.12	-0.11	0.14										
LIM	-0.47	-0.42	0.42	0.66**									
TPL	0.18	0.45	-0.17	-0.02	-0.005								
LGP	-0.32	-0.40	0.17	-0.07	-0.0.3	-0.49*							
LGF	-0.28	-0.38	0.13	-0.07	-0.005	-0.48*	0.99**						
BCA	-0.30	-0.44	0.12	-0.19	0.26	0.16	0.0002	0.006					
AHU	-0.21	-0.24	0.12	0.14	0.20	0.31	-0.27	-0.30	0.70**				
D94	-0.50*	-0.27	0.51*	0.24	0.43	0.17	0.04	0.03	0.02	-0.15			
D96	-0.51*	-0.27	0.51*	0.24	0.43	0.17	0.04	0.03	0.02	-0.25	0.98**		
DS94	-0.21	0.002	0.24	-0.18	-0.10	**0.54***	-0.10	-0.11	0.04	0.04	**0.48***		
DS96	-0.33	-0.11	0.34	0.03	-0.03	0.44	0.07	0.06	-0.05	-0.01		**0.56***	0.94**

API α-pinene, CAM camphene, BPI β-pinene, MYR myrcene, LIM limonene, TPL terpinolene, LGP longipinene, LGF longifolene, BCA β-caryophyllene, AHU α-humulene, D94 diameter in 1994, D96 diameter in 1996, DS94 *D. sylvestrella* infestation in 1994, DS96 *D. sylvestrella* infestation in 1996.

Heritabilities and genetic correlations of vigor, terpenes, and resistance

Narrow sense heritabilities and an approximation of genetic correlations were estimated using all of the 227 trees. Because tree susceptibility to *D. sylvestrella* has to be estimated using a percentage of attacked trees, the number of sampled clones was too low to calculate the within family effect, hence preventing heritability calculation for this trait. Analysis of variance (GLM) indicated significant differences among families and individuals for 8 out of 10 terpenes and for diameter in 1994 (tabl. 11). Estimates of heritabilities for terpenes varied from 0.05 (β-pinene) to 0.58 (limonene). The heritability of tree diameter in 1994 was 0.18 which is consistent with the value obtained in the diallel. Except for β-caryophyllene, the genetic expression of terpene composition was poorly affected by environmental factors. These results are similar to those obtained in the cortical tissues of *P. pinaster* (Baradat et al., 1972, 1975; Marpeau et al., 1975, 1983; Baradat et Marpeau, 1988), *Pinus taeda* (Squillace et al., 1980) and *Pinus sylvestris* (Yazdani et al., 1985), where the relative amount of some terpenes has been found to show simple monogenic inheritance.

Table 11: Probability associated with F test for family and individual effects. Estimates of additive genetic variance (AGV), dominance genetic variance (DGV), micro-environmental variance (EV) and narrow-sense family heritability (h^2) of terpenes and tree diameter

Terpene	Probability associated with F test		Estimates of genetic parameters			
	Family effects	Individual effects	AGV	DGV	EV	h^2_{FS}
α-pinene	0.0239	0.0001	0.0011	0.007	0.0012	0.12
camphene	0.0939	0.0027				
β-pinene	0.0333	0.0001	0.0004	0.0064	0.0012	0.05
myrcene	0.0879	0.0001				
limonene	0.0015	0.0001	$4.4\ 10^{-6}$	$2\ 10^{-6}$	$0.5\ 10^{-6}$	0.64
terpinolene	0.0126	0.0001	$1.5\ 10^{-6}$	$4.1\ 10^{-6}$	$0.67\ 10^{-6}$	0.24
longipinene	0.0157	0.0001	$0.29\ 10^{-6}$	$1.1\ 10^{-6}$	$0.54\ 10^{-6}$	0.15
longifolene	0.0114	0.0001	0.00007	0.00014	0.00002	0.30
β-caryophyllene	0.0141	0.0001	0.00009	0.00009	0.00015	0.27
α-humulene	0.0032	0.0001	$2.4\ 10^{-6}$	$1.3\ 10^{-6}$	$1.2\ 10^{-6}$	0.49
diameter 1994	0.0403	0.0064	10.22	5.28	57.61	0.18
diameter 1996	0.1019	0.0044				

Genetic gains in direct and indirect selection for resistance to *D. sylvestrella*

The genetic parameters estimations obtained in the clonal test for terpinolene proportion (heritability and correlation with susceptibility to *D. sylvestrella*) were used to compute expected gains in the previous diallel test, when using indirect selection and according to the following formula (Fins et al, 1992): $\Delta G = i.Corr(TPL, DS94).h_{TPL}.h_{DS94}.V_{DS94.}$ with i = selection intensity, h = square root of heritability, CV = phenotypic coefficient of variation. Genetic gain estimates in indirect selection could be then compared with genetic gains estimated in direct selection (tabl. 12).

Table 12. Expected genetic gain estimates (relative %) in resistance to *D. sylvestrella*, in the diallel.

	Direct mass selection			Indirect mass selection		
selection rate	*5 %*	*10 %*	*50 %*	*5 %*	*10 %*	*50 %*
DS94	37.8	32.1	14.6	34.8	29.6	13.5
DS96	31.5	26.8	12.2	27.3	23.2	10.6

Using the same selection intensity, indirect selection is more efficient (ΔG indirect > ΔG direct) if $Corr^2(trait\ 1, trait2).h^2_{trait2} > h^2_{trait1}$ (Gallais, 1990). Here, with a higher heritability for terpinolene as compared to DS94 or DS96 (respectively 0.24 in the clonal test, 0.08 and 0.09 in the diallel test) and a positive correlation between terpinolene and tree resistance (r(TPL, DS94)=0.54*; r(TPL, DS96)=0.44), expected gains are similar for the two types of selection.

From a practical point of view, the benefit of indirect selection is greater if the associated trait can be more easily measured. In this particular case, it is far quicker to evaluate trees for *D. sylvestrella* attack than to collect oleoresin and calculate the terpinolene proportion. But using terpinolene as biochemical marker in indirect selection offers two important advantages. First, because the terpene profile of the oleoresin is stabilized in about 6 to 8-year-old trees (Baradat et al., 1972), the terpinolene proportion could be used much earlier than attack rates to select resistant trees. Secondly, terpinolene is not correlated with diameter and thus the risk of genetic loss in tree volume associated with indirect selection is highly reduced.

CONCLUSIONS

Using direct selection, high genetic gains in Maritime pine resistance to *D. sylvestrella* could be obtained with a rather important loss in tree volume. But the main limit of this first strategy would be the time of selection. Because the expression of tree susceptibility depends on natural infestation and increases with age, breeders would have to delay selection of genotypes after 15 years. Using indirect selection based on trees with low proportion of terpinolene in the resin, the same genetic gains in resistance to *D. sylvestrella* could be obtained. No genetic loss in tree growth would be induced and the time of selection would be much earlier, on 6 to 8-year-old trees. The main limit of this second strategy would be the cost of the assessment which involves oleoresin collection and gas chromatography analysis. Perhaps the more convenient strategy would be to combine indirect and direct selection. For instance, breeders could select genotypes according to the volume and the presence of *D. sylvestrella* attacks at 11-12 years and then assess terpinolene proportion in the few pre-selected trees for the final selection at 15-16 years.

REFERENCES

BARADAT P. and DESPREZ-LOUSTAU M.L,. 1997. Analyse diallèle et intégration de la sensibilité à la rouille courbeuse dans le programme d'amélioration du pin maritime. *Ann. Sci. For.* 54, 83-106.

BARADAT P. and LABBE T., 1995. Opep. Un logiciel intégré pour l'amélioration des plantes pérennes. *Traitement statistique des essais de sélection*. Ed. Cirad, Montpellier, 303-330.

BARADAT P. and MARPEAU-BEZARD A., 1988. *Le pin maritime Pinus pinaster Ait. Biologie et génétique des terpènes pour la connaissance et l'amélioration de l'espèce*. Doctorat thesis N°953, Université de Bordeaux, France, 444 pp.

BARADAT P. and PASTUSZKA P., 1992. Le pin maritime. In *Amélioration des espèces végétales cultivées*. Edited by A. Gallais and H. Bannerot. Institut national de la recherche agronomique, Paris. pp 695-709.

BARADAT P., BERNARD-DAGAN C. and PAULY G., 1975. Les terpènes du pin maritime: aspects biologiques et génétiques. III. Hérédité de la teneur en myrcène. *Ann. Sci. Forest.* **31**(1): 29-54.

BARADAT P., BERNARD-DAGAN C., FILLON C., MARPEAU A. and PAULY G., 1972: Les terpènes du pin maritime: aspects biologiques et génétiques. II. Hérédité de la teneur en monoterpènes. *Ann. Sci. Forest.* 29(3): 307-334.

COSTA P. and DUREL C.E., 1996. Time trends in genetic control over height and diameter in maritime pine. *Can. J. For. Res.* 26:

DAGNELIE P., 1973. *Théorie et méthodes statistiques*. Presses agronomiques de Gembloux Editeur, Gembloux, Belgique. 463pp.

DIETERS M.J.J., 1996. Genetic parameters for Slash pine (*Pinus elliottii*) grown in sout-east Queensland, Australia: growth, stem straightness and crown defects. *Forest Genet.* 3, 27-36.

FINS L., FRIEDMAN S.T., and BROTSCHOL J.V., 1992. *Handbook of quantitative forest genetics*. Kluwer Academic Publishers, The Nederlands, 403 p.

GALLAIS, A. 1980. *Théorie de la sélection en amélioration des plantes*. Collection Sciences Agronomiques. Masson Ed. Paris, 588 p.

ILLY G., 1966. Recherches sur l'amélioration génétique du pin maritime. *Ann. Sci. For.* 23, 757-948

JACTEL H., MENASSIEU P. and Raise G., 1994. Infestation dynamics of *Dioryctria sylvestrella* (Ratz.) (*Lepidoptera: Pyralidae*) in pruned maritime pine (*Pinus pinaster* Ait). *For. Ecol. Manage.* 67: 11-22.

JACTEL H., MENASSIEU P., RAISE G. and BURBAN C., 1996a. Sensitivity of pruned Maritime pine (*Pinus pinaster* Ait) to *Dioryctria sylvestrella* (Ratz.) (*Lepidoptera: Pyralidae*) in relation to tree vigour and date of pruning. *J. Appl. Entomol.* 120:153-157.

JACTEL H., KLEINHENTZ M., MARPEAU-BEZARD A., MARION-POLL F., MENASSIEU P. and BURBAN C., 1996b: Terpene variations in Maritime pine constitutive oleoresin related to host tree selection by *Dioryctria sylvestrella* Ratz. (*Lepidoptera: Pyralidae*). *J. Chem. Ecol.* 22 (5): 1037-1050.

JACTEL H., KLEINHENTZ M., 1997. Intensive sylvicultural practices increase the risk of infestation by *Dioryctria sylvestrella* (Ratz.) (*Lepidoptera: Pyralidae*), the Maritime pine stem borer. *In*: J.C. Grégoire, A.M. Liebhold, F.M. Stephen, K.R. Day and S.M. Salom (Ed.): *Proceedings: Integrating cultural tactics into the management of bark beetles and reforestation pests.* USDA Forest Service General Technical Report NE-236, p.177-190.

MARPEAU A., BARADAT P. and BERNARD-DAGAN C., 1975. Les terpènes du pin maritime: aspects biologiques et génétiques. IV. Hérédité de la teneur en deux sesquiterpènes: le longifolène et le β-caryophyllène. *Ann. Sci. Forest.* 32 (4): 185-203.

MERZEAU D., 1995. Le pin maritime en France. *Forêt Entreprise*, 105: 28-30.

RAPPAPORT N.G., JENKINS M.K. and ROQUES A., 1995. Cone and foliage volatiles from douglas-fir and european larch: relationship to attack by cone and seed insects. *In Proceedings of the Fourth. IUFRO Cone and Seed Insects Conference*, Beijing, China, 1992, Ed G.L. De Barr.

ROFF A.D., 1995. The estimation of genetic correlations from phenotypic correlations: a test of Cheverud's conjecture. *Heredity* 74, 481-490.

SAS Institute, 1996. *SAS User's Guide: Statistics*, Version 5. SAS Institute, Cary, North Carolina.

SQUILLACE A.E., WELLS O.O. and ROCKWOOD O., 1980. Inheritance of monoterpene composition in cortical oleoresin of Loblolly pine. *Silvae Genetica* 29 (3-4): 141-152.

WRIGHT J.W., WILSON L.F. and BRIGHT J.N., 1975. Genetic variation in resistance of Scotch pine to Zimmerman Pine Moth. *Great Lakes Entomol.* 8: 231-236.

YAZDANI R., NILSSON J.E. and ERICSSON T., 1985. Geographical variation in the relative proportion of monoterpenes in cortical oleoresin of *Pinus sylvestris* in Sweden. *Silvae Genetica* 34 (6): 201-208.

Chapter 2

Biology and Variability of Aggressor Populations

Physiology and Genetics of Tree-Phytophage Interactions
Gujan (France), August 31 - September 5, 1997
Ed. INRA, Paris, 1999 (Les Colloques, n°90)

Measuring shifts in forest pathogen populations

E.E. WHITE[1], D. J. MORRISON[1], BB. KINLOCH JR.[2], R.D. WESTFALL[2], M.A. GITZENDANNER,[2] B.M. FOORD[1] AND G.E. DUPPER[2]

[1]*Canadian Forest Service, Pacific Forestry Centre, 506 West Burnside Road., Victoria, B.C., Canada V8Z 1M5*

[2]*Institute of Forest Genetics, Pacific Southwest Experiment Station, Box 245, Berkeley, Ca., USA 94701*

RESUME

The genetics of trees and phytophagous organisms converge at their interactions, producing resistance or susceptibility. In insect and disease interactions, resistance is the product of two sets of genes, those of the host and the pest. Knowledge of the genetics of both is necessary to understand the interaction. Genetic analysis of pathogens has been hindered when morphological differences are limited, as with some obligate parasites, or when morphological structures are rarely produced, as with some fungal fruiting structures. DNA analysis provides a profitable addition to the analysis of pathogen genetics, mating system, and population and species genetic diversity. This report reviews examples of our use of DNA analysis in studies of the genetics of two diseases, *Armillaria* root rot and white pine blister rust.

The study of *Armillaria* used variation in the ribosomal DNA region of the fungus to compare species genetic diversity. Genetic studies of *Cronartium ribicola*, causal agent of white pine blister rust, used this and other molecular markers and examined mating system and population structure. In both cases, the results provided information which was difficult or impossible to obtain on the basis of morphology alone.

In the *Armillaria* study, the ribosomal DNA marker provided a rapid, convenient species diagnostic. Epidemiological analysis requires species differentiation since only one of the four species commonly occurring in the study area is pathogenic. A large number of cultures generated by studies of *Armillaria* species distribution in British Columbia were identified with the diagnostic much more quickly and accurately than with conventional mating tests. For *Cronartium ribicola*, the results showed the pathogen is heterothallic, highly outcrossing and in genetic equilibrium. The demonstration of virtually uninhibited outcrossing has profound implications for the stability of tree resistance, because of the recombinational potential in the pathogen to generate races with multiple forms of virulence.

Major differences in the patterns of variability of DNA markers in the two fungi reflect major differences in their life cycles and modes of infection. Low variation in the DNA of Armillaria is consistent with reproductive isolation and vegetative spread. In *Armillaria*, reproductive isolation appears to have fixed the neutral markers used to differentiate the pathogenic species. In contrast, relatively high within-population variation in DNA markers occurs in *C. ribicola*, which is highly out-breeding and infects by spores.

INTRODUCTION

Mechanisms of resistance in trees are intimately linked to mechanisms of attack by insects or diseases. A resistant phenotype in a tree is the expression of two genotypes, those of the host and the pest. Therefore shifts in the genetic make-up of pathogen populations can have devastating results on their hosts. Uniformity for the Texas-type mitochondrial genome in corn (*Zea mays*) varieties widely planted in the early seventies led to a catastrophic pandemic of a race of corn blight (*Helminthosporium maydis*) pathogenic to plants with this mitochondrial genome (Miller and Koeppe, 1984). Changes in the genetic structure of the pathogen causing Dutch elm disease (*Ophiostoma ulmi*) resulted in new outbreaks of the disease in the 1980s (Brasier, 1988). Monitoring changes in genetic diversity of pathogen populations can help to evaluate reasons for epidemiological patterns and assess the probable outcomes of control strategies.

Classical genetic techniques have provided many fruitful insights into the varied mating systems of fungi and into their population structures. However, for some pathogens, classical morphological or nutritional mutants are limited. For example, in some root disease fungi, fruiting structures are rarely produced and hyphal characteristics are limited. For other pathogens, such as obligate biotrophs like *C. ribicola*, morphological characters are limited to spore types, and nutritional testing is difficult. DNA markers provide many more characteristics with which to examine the biology and population structure of tree pathogens.

DNA markers can be used to monitor population differentiation, or changes in population genetic structure, by estimating the similarity in allele frequencies in samples taken from different areas or at different times. Measuring whether alleles are reassorting between generations as expected if the population is in Hardy-Weinberg equilibrium provides information on whether the species is out-breeding. Different types of markers vary to different degrees. At one extreme, variation in gene coding regions is limited to those mutations which do not alter gene function to the point of lethality. At the other extreme, non-coding "microsatellite" regions can show extremely high numbers of variants within a population. In between, some moderately repeated polymorphic loci show intermediate numbers of alleles. Selection of genetically well-characterized markers with appropriate levels of variation for a particular problem is necessary (Hillis and Moritz 1990).

Examples of the use of DNA markers in studies of species distribution of *Armillaria* root disease, and of the mating system and population structure of *Cronartium ribicola*, are given. DNA markers provide opportunities to investigate genetic mechanisms in pathogens that have been difficult to approach by classical techniques.

MATERIAL AND METHODS

Armillaria

Within and between species variation in the first intergenic spacer (IGS-1) of the ribosomal RNA coding (rDNA) region was analysed using the PCR-based diagnostic of Harrington and Wingfield (1995), in a group of isolates which had previously been identified by mating tests. This group comprised 26 isolates of *A.*

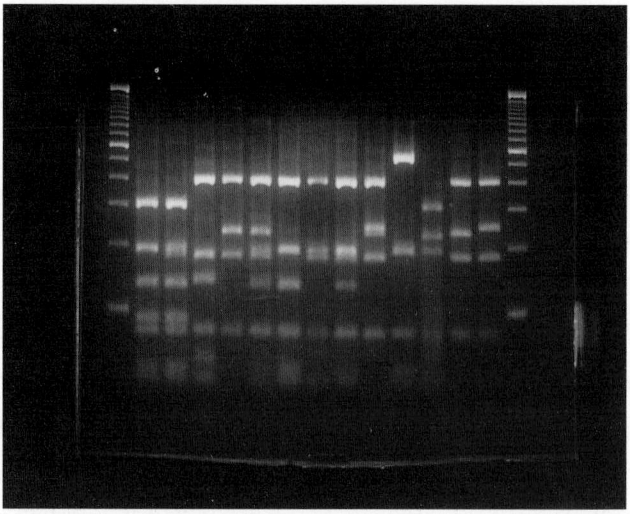

Figure 1: Within and between species variability in Alu I restriction fragments in *Armillaria* species. Left to right - size standards, 2 lanes of *A. ostoyae*, 7 *A. sinapina*, 2 *A. nabsnona*, 2 *A. gallica*, size standards.

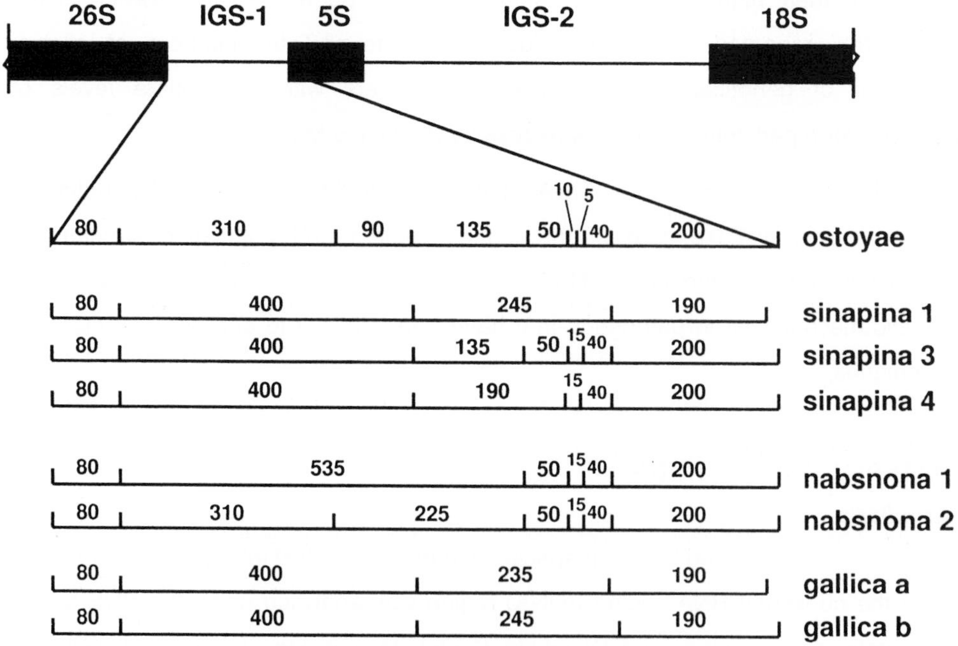

Figure 2 : Map of IGS-1 Alu I restriction sites.

ostoyae, 17 of *A. sinapina*, 15 of *A. gallica* and 10 of *A. nabsnona*. Variation in the IGS-1 was analysed in a second group of 187 isolates cultured from stumps across B.C. as part of a study of the effects of precommercial thinning on the spread of *A. ostoyae* to adjacent trees (White *et al.*, 1998).

Cronartium ribicola

Several single basidiospore cultures were obtained from individual telia originating from British Columbia, Canada, to the southern Sierra Nevada of California, USA, as well as two "outlier" origins from the eastern USA. These haploid mycelial cultures were analysed for variants at 28 isozyme loci, 90 random amplified DNA (RAPD) loci, and 94 restriction fragment length polymorphism (RFLP) loci. Putative alleles in sister basidiospore cultures from the same telium were analysed for conformance to expectation of 1:1 segregation. Reproducible markers with non-distorted segregation ratios were used for further analysis. Polymorphic loci were tested for departures from Hardy-Weinberg equilibrium expectations. Genetic distances among populations were estimated, and canonical variate analysis was used to test differences among populations (White *et al.* 1996, Gitzendanner *et al.* 1996, Kinloch *et al.* 1998).

RESULTS

***Armillaria* species**

Only one pattern of Alu I restriction fragments occurred in the IGS-1 in 26 mating-test identified isolates of *A. ostoyae*, five different patterns occurred in 17 mating-tested *A. sinapina* isolates, 10 isolates of *A. nabsnona* had two patterns, and 15 *A. gallica* isolates had two patterns. With the more intensive sampling carried out in the study of precommercial thinning effects, two more *A. sinapina* fragment patterns were found (Fig 1). All fragment patterns were consistent with a restriction site map of the IGS-1 based on the sequence data of Anderson and Stasovski (1992), (Fig. 2). *A. sinapina* isolates had the 3 patterns of restriction sites given in Fig. 2; the seven variants resulted from small (ca. 10 bp) insertions and deletions in the fragments these produced. Three isolates of *A. sinapina* which had restriction fragments identical to those of *A. gallica* in the IGS-1 could be distinguished by

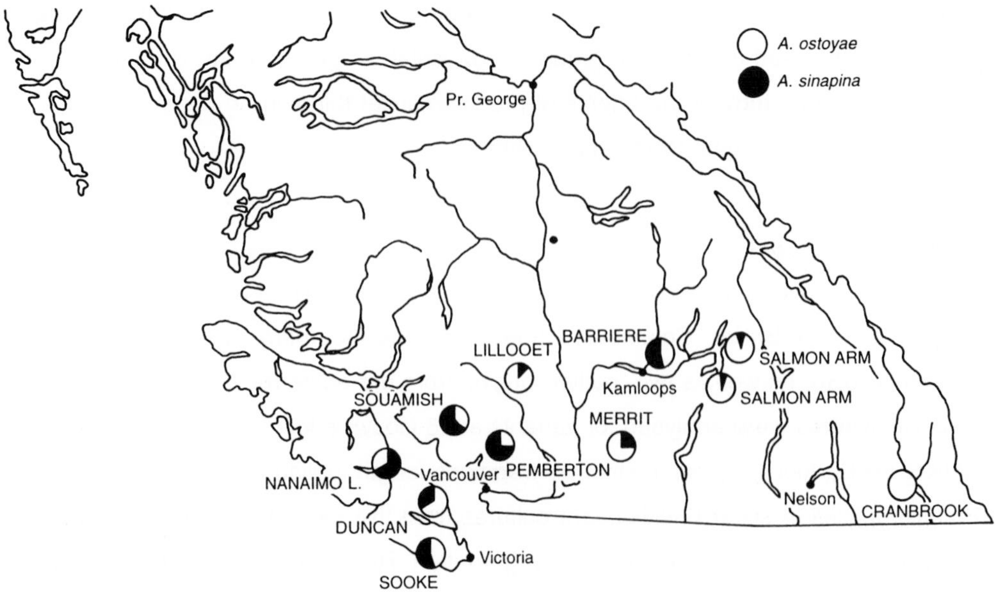

Figure 3.: *Armillaria* species distribution in samples across British Columbia.

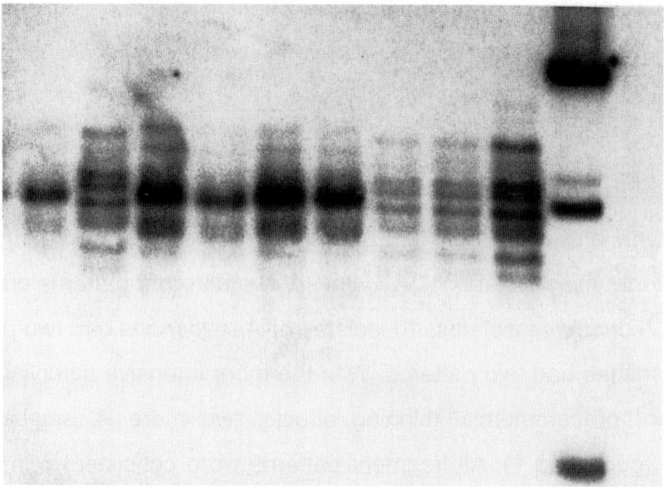

Figure 4.: Mendelian segregation of alleles at the rDNA locus. Left to right - simple (s), complex [c], s, s, s, c, c, c, lambda standard.

differences in the IGS-2. These results are presented in detail in White *et al.*, 1998. *Armillaria* species distribution in the larger survey is represented in Fig. 3.

Cronartium ribicola

Details of the results of these studies have been published in White *et al.* 1996, Gitzendanner *et* al. 1996, and Kinloch *et al.* 1998. Length heterogeneity due to sub-repeats in the IGS-1 produces a very large number of alleles at the rDNA locus in *C. ribicola*. Mendelian segregation for two of these alleles, one with a more complex (c) and another with a simpler (s) repeat pattern, is illustrated in Figure 4. This locus had an exceptionally high number of alleles; 14 other loci which met the criteria of reproducibility and adherence to expectations of 1:1 Mendelian segregation had only two alleles. Of the polymorphic loci tested for Hardy-Weinberg equilibrium only one departed from expectations. While expected heterozygosity was only 2.5%, population differentiation was substantial; the proportion of genetic diversity attributable to differences among subpopulations was 20.5%. The distribution of this variation was not associated with geographic distance. Distances in multivariate space among the eight populations examined are given in Kinloch *et al.*, 1998. The different marker types were consistent with each other for these parameters.

CONCLUSION

Armillaria species

Analysis of 68 mating-test identified isolates of *Armillaria*, comprising 4 different species, confirmed the usefulness of the PCR based diagnostic proposed by Harrington and Wingfield (1995). With more intensive sampling additional restriction site variants in the IGS-1 were found. Only three isolates had restriction fragment patterns that would have resulted in species confusion, and these could be distinguished in the IGS-2 (White *et al.*, 1998).

Large numbers of cultures can be identified with this diagnostic much more quickly than with conventional mating tests, opening new possibilities for epidemiological studies. The relative lack of variation within species, and differentiation between species, likely stems from reproductive isolation allowing fixation of differences between species. It reflects the biological species concept used in *Armillaria* taxonomy, where species are defined by interfertility determined in mating tests. On 11 sites across B.C., the frequency of stumps colonized by *A. ostoyae* appears higher in interior than coastal regions (Fig. 3).

Cronartium ribicola

Mendelian segregation of marker loci in basidiospore progeny of a single telium provides the first genetic evidence that *C. ribicola* basidiospores are meiotic products of teliospores, settling the previously unresolved issue of whether the fungus was heterothallic or homothallic. Conformance of heterozygosity estimates at polymorphic loci to expectations for Hardy-Weinberg equilibrium indicates it is highly outcrossing. The demonstration of virtually uninhibited outcrossing has profound implications for the stability of resistant selections of white pine, because of the recombinational potential in the pathogen to generate races with multiple forms of virulence (White *et al.* 1996, Gitzendanner *et al.* 1996).

The apparent paradox of high outcrossing coupled with relatively high population differentiation (with implied low gene flow), along with the lack of association between genetic and geographic distance, suggests a population that is not in equilibrium, where founder effects are important (Kinloch *et al.*, 1998). The blister rust epidemic has not yet stabilized in many areas of western North America, and the distribution and intensity of infection are not uniform. Areas of intense, light, and no infection exist in a mosaic pattern over the landscape (Kinloch and Dulitz 1990). Gene flow is restricted by the relative immobility of spermatia (pycniospores) which are vectored by insects of limited foraging range. Long range spread in the southern populations, which occurs primarily by aeciospores, is dependent on spring weather conditions, and founders are likely to arrive solitarily or in small numbers. The effect of genetic drift is most evident at the Happy Camp rust population (Kinloch and Comstock 1981). This small deme persists on a field trial of a few hundred resistant sugar pines. It is thought to have arisen by selection of a race with specific virulence to major gene resistance. Resistance in this stand exerts absolute selectivity on basidiospore inoculum and maintains founder effects on marker loci.

General

The marker loci analysed in these studies are largely neutral mutations occurring at non-coding regions of the genome. They are unlikely to have direct biological significance. These neutral mutations are trapped by the biology of the organism they occur in, so biological mechanisms are reflected in patterns of marker variation. As a result, the patterns of marker variation can be used to supplement morphological markers to assess mating systems, genetic variability and shifts in genetic variability.

The new insights into the genetics of the two tree-phytophage interactions discussed reflect major differences in the biology of the two organisms. The IGS-1 locus of *Cronartium ribicola* is highly allelic, segregation at this and other loci showed the fungus is heterothallic, and conformance to Hardy-Weinberg equilibrium expectations show it is highly outcrossing. This has important implications for the stability of resistance in white pine, because of the recombinational potential of the pathogen to produce genotypes with multiple virulence. In contrast, very few alleles were detected in the IGS-1 of *Armillaria* species, and few alleles were shared between species, indicating reproductive isolation has fixed these neutral markers. This allows the differentiation of the pathogenic species *A. ostoyae* from non-pathogenic species in epidemiological studies.

DNA markers provide new opportunities for investigating genetic mechanisms in forest pathogens that until now have been difficult to approach.

These include:

-the nature and timing of critical life cycle stages (meiotic or non-meiotic spore production, homothallic or heterothallic cycle)

-the capacity of the pathogen to evolve new virulence types through sexual recombination

-better resolution of epidemiological patterns as a result of accurate identification of species and individuals

-the roles of geographic isolation and intersterility in speciation.

REFERENCES

ANDERSON J.B., STASOVSKI E., 1992. Molecular phylogeny of northern hemisphere species of *Armillaria*. *Mycologia* 84, 505-516.

BRASIER C.M. 1988. Rapid changes in genetic structure of epidemic populations of *Ophiostoma ulmi*. *Nature* 332, 538-541.

GITZENDANNER M.A., WHITE E.E., FOORD B.M., DUPPER G.E., HODGSKISS P.D., KINLOCH JR. B.B. 1996. Genetics of *Cronartium ribicola*. III. Mating system. *Can. J. Bot*. 74, 1852-1859.

HARRINGTON T.C., WINGFIELD B.D. 1995. A PCR-based identification method for species of *Armillaria*. *Mycologia* 87, 280-288.

HILLIS D.M., MORITZ C. 1990. *Molecular Systematics*. Sinauer Associates, Sunderland, Massachusetts, USA.

KINLOCH B.B. , COMSTOCK M. 1981. Race of *Cronartium ribicola* virulent to major gene resistance in sugar pine. *Plant Disease* 65, 1912-1914.

KINLOCK B.B., DULITZ D. 1990. White pine blister rust at Mountain Home State Demonstration Forest: a case study of the epidemic and prospects for genetic control. Res. Pap. PSW-204. USDA Forest Service, Berkeley, Ca.

KINLOCH JR., B.B., WESTFALL R. D., WHITE E.E., GITZENDANNER M.A., DUPPER G. E., FOORD B.M., HODGSKISS P.B. 1998. Genetics of *Cronartium ribicola*. IV. Population structure in western North America. *Can. J. Bot*. 76, 91-98.

MILLER R.J. AND KOEPPE D.E. 1984. Southern corn leaf blight: susceptible and resistant mitochondria. *Science* 173, 67-69.

WHITE E.E., FOORD B.M., KINLOCH JR., B.B. 1996. Genetics of *Cronartium ribicola*. II. Variation in the ribosomal gene cluster. *Can. J. Bot*. 74, 461-468.

WHITE, E.E. DUBETZ C.P., CRUICKSHANK M.G., MORRISON D.J. 1998. DNA diagnostic for Armillaria species in British Columbia: within and between species variation in the IGS-1 and IGS-2 regions. *Mycologia* 90, 125-131.

Physiology and Genetics of Tree-Phytophage Interactions
Gujan (France), August 31 - September 5, 1997
Ed. INRA, Paris, 1999 (Les Colloques, n°90)

Virulence and the genetic composition of the *Cryphonectria cubensis* Bruner population in South Africa

M.J. WINGFIELD, L.M. VAN ZYL, S. VAN HEERDEN, H. MYBURG, B.D. WINGFIELD

Tree Pathology Co-operative Programme, Department of Microbiology and Biochemistry, University of the Free State, P.O. Box 339, Bloemfontein 9300, South Africa

RESUME

Cryphonectria cubensis causes a serious canker disease of *Eucalyptus*, and particularly *E. grandis* in tropical and sub-tropical areas of the world. Where these species are grown intensively, losses can be considerable. Various strategies have thus been implemented to minimise the impact of the pathogen. The most common of these has been to select clones of *E. grandis* and particularly hybrids of this and other species such as *E. urophylla*, for deployment. Screening of these clones through inoculation is also being used in various countries, to gain an early perspective of the relative susceptibility of the planting stock. Other more rapid techniques to identify disease tolerant clones, such as the selection of genetic and molecular markers are also being developed, and these hold considerable promise for the future.

While it is critically important to plant clones tolerant to infection by *C. cubensis* in high risk areas, it is also extremely costly to select such planting stock. An important consideration in this regard relates to the likely durability of disease tolerance, and thus how long clones are likely to retain this trait. The durability of disease tolerant clones will be closely linked to the diversity of the pathogen population, and particularly, its capacity to change with time. Despite this fact, almost nothing is known regarding the genetic composition of the *C. cubensis* population in any country where the pathogen is important. In recent years, we have begun to conduct studies on populations of *C. cubensis* in South Africa, various countries of South America and in Indonesia. From these investigations, we have learned that *C. cubensis* commonly occurs in the sexual state in South America and Indonesia but that it is asexual in South Africa. Consistent with this finding, we have also found that the population of the pathogen in South America and Indonesia is highly diverse, while it is much less variable in South Africa. We thus predict that disease tolerant clones in South Africa will have a higher degree of durability than those in the former two countries, where virulent strains of the fungus are likely to adapt to disease tolerant planting stock, more rapidly.

A fascinating and potentially useful strategy to reduce the impact of *Cryphonectria* canker of *Eucalyptus* would be to implement biological control of the pathogen. This could be achieved by introducing dsRNA - associated hypovirulence into the pathogen population. We have recently discovered dsRNA in isolates of *C. cubensis* from various parts of the world and have also shown that it can be associated with reduced virulence. DsRNA is typically spread through cytoplasmic fusion between isolates of similar genotype. Therefore, opportunities to capitalise on hypovirulence in the management of *Cryphonectria* canker will depend strongly on a thorough understanding of the diversity of the pathogen population. Thus, our findings indicating that the populations of *C. cubensis* in South America and Indonesia are genetically diverse, suggests that hypovirulence would be difficult to implement in those countries. Conversely, in countries such as South Africa where the pathogen appears to have been more recently introduced, and where it is not reproducing sexually, we believe that prospects for disease reduction through the spread of hypovirulence factors holds considerable promise.

INTRODUCTION

Cryphonectria canker caused by *Cryphonectria cubensis* (Bruner) Hodges is one of the most important diseases of *Eucalyptus* in tropical and sub-tropical parts of the world (Bruner, 1916, Boerboom and Maas, 1970, Davison and Coates, 1991, Davison and Tay, 1983, Florence *et al.*, 1986, Gibson, 1981, Hodges, 1980, Hodges *et al.*, 1986, Old *et al.*, 1986, Sharma *et al.*, 1985, Wingfield *et al.*, 1989). There is a growing interest in *Eucalyptus* propagation in countries outside the native range of this tree, especially for pulp production and to provide a replacement for fibre traditionally sourced from native forests. At present it is estimated that approximately eight million hectares of *Eucalyptus* plantations have been established, chiefly in the tropics and sub-tropics and the threat of diseases to this important resource is increasingly recognised (Wingfield *et al.*, 1995 a,b).

Cryphonectria cubensis was first described in by Bruner (1916) and has thus been known for a considerable time. In contrast, recognition of the fungus as an important pathogen has emerged relatively recently (Hodges, 1980, Hodges *et al.*, 1979, Alfenas *et al.*, 1982). This change in the status of the pathogen has been coincidental with the greater intensity of *Eucalyptus* propagation, but also with the onset of vegetative propagation of *Eucalyptus* clones and hybrids. Thus, the first report of the disease was from Surinam (Boerboom and Maas, 1970) and since that time, it has been reported in reasonably rapid succession from many other countries (Hodges and Reis, 1974, Hodges *et al.,* 1979; Gibson, 1981; Davison and Tay, 1983; Florence *et al.*, 1986; Old *et al.*, 1986; Swart and Wingfield, 1991; Wingfield *et al.*, 1989).

Avoidance of *Cryphonectria* canker in highly desirable *Eucalyptus* clones and clonal hybrids is an issue of high priority, for groups growing these trees. The risks associated with the inadvertent deployment of disease susceptible clones are great, and some serious losses have already been experienced. Selection and breeding strategies generally include the need to eliminate this disease and some substantial progress has already been made in this regard.

While breeding and selection of *Cryphonectria*- tolerant planting stock is being actively pursued, relatively little attention has been given to the pathogen, and its role in disease. Thus, questions as to the origin of the pathogen have as yet not been fully resolved. Furthermore, the related question regarding the genetic diversity of the *C. cubensis* population in areas where the associated disease is serious, has hardly been considered. Questions of this nature will be critically important in any programme to produce *Cryphonectria* tolerant planting stock, and thus deserve urgent attention. In this paper we briefly review progress in our understanding of the virulence and population diversity of *C. cubensis.*

ORIGIN OF *C. CUBENSIS*

Based on morphological and isozyme comparisons, it has been suggested that the clove pathogen *Endothia eugeniae* is conspecific with *C. cubensis* (Alfenas *et al.*, 1984, Hodges *et al.*, 1986, Micales and Stipes, 1987). This finding has furthermore, led to the suggestion that the pathogen might have originated in Indonesia where clove is native. This might further imply that the fungus, in areas such as South and Central America, is introduced. If this were so, it could further imply that the populations of the pathogen in these countries might be of relatively limited diversity and thus subject to a limited capacity to change.

In a recent study (Myburg *et al.*, 1998) a reasonably diverse collection of isolates of *C. cubensis* were compared based on ribosomal DNA sequence data. The results of this study confirmed that *C. cubensis* and *E. eugeniae* from clove, cannot be separated based on this part of the genome, which is known to be highly variable, and taxonomically valuable at the species level (Chambers *et al.*, 1986). Some minor differences could be found between isolates of *C. cubensis* from the Western and Eastern hemispheres. Unfortunately, only a single clove isolate was available for this study and this originated from Indonesia. It will now be most interesting to include additional clove isolates from S. America, Africa and South East Asia, and to see whether these also reside in two separate clades.

Very closely related species can share similar sequence data, even in the highly variable ITS (Chambers *et al.*, 1986) region of the rDNA. An interesting example has recently been encountered in the bark beetle associated fungi, *Ceratocystis polonica* and *Ceratocystis laricicola*. These fungi are morphologically indistinguishable and share identical ITS sequence (Visser *et al.*, 1995, Witthuhn *et al.*, 1998). They, are, carried by different but very similar bark beetles that infest spruce (*Piceae* spp.) and Larch (*Larix* spp) respectively. They can also be separated from each other based on isoenzyme comparisons (Harrington *et al.*, 1996). These fungi are, therefore, believed to be distinct but very similar, and to have undergone recent speciation.

Myburg *et al.,* 1998 has recently noted the very close similarity between *C. cubensis* and the Chestnut blight pathogen *Cryphonectria parasitica*. The implication here is that the two fungi might have had a common ancestor in the relatively recent past. This hypothesis is based not only on the morphological similarity of the two fungi, but on the fact that *C. parasitica* is able to cause cankers on *Eucalyptus* (Old and Kobayashi, 1988) and likewise, *C. cubensis* will kill artificially inoculated chestnut (*Castanea dentata*) saplings (Wingfield, unpublished). Sequence data (Myburg *et al.*, 1998) comparing these fungi has confirmed that the fungi are very closely related, although they can also be easily distinguished from each other based on analysis of rRNA sequence data.

A fascinating report by Davison and Coates (1991) has recently suggested that *C. cubensis* occurs in Australia. What is most interesting, and perhaps enigmatic about this report is the fact that the fungus was isolated from roots of *E. marginata* in western Australia. The climate of Western Australia is wholly atypical of that usually associated with *C. cubensis* and it is also unusual for a typical stem canker pathogen to be found only on the roots of trees. Despite these ecological inconsistencies, comparison of Australian and other isolates of *C. cubensis* based on sequence data have shown that the fungi are the same (Myburg *et al.*, 1998).

DIVERSITY OF *C. CUBENSIS* POPULATIONS

The genetic diversity of isolates of a pathogen, in a contained geographic area, should provide some clues as to its origin. Although only preliminary studies have thus far been completed, we have shown (Van Zyl *et al.*, 1998b) that a relatively large collection of isolates of *C. cubensis* from Brazil represents a population that has a high level of genetic diversity. Similar results have been obtained in preliminary studies of the diversity of *C. cubensis* isolates from Indonesia and from Venezuela (Van Heerden *et al.*, 1997). In contrast, a preliminary study has shown that isolates of *C. cubensis* in South Africa represent a much more uniform genetic base than those from other areas studied. This would imply that the pathogen has been introduced into South Africa relatively recently.

In South Africa, the sexual state (teleomorph) of *C. cubensis* is extremely rare (M.J. Wingfield, unpublished data). Where it has been seen, we suspect that it has arisen through homothalism and that it does not represent outbreeding. This is in contrast to the situation in various other parts of the world (Indonesia, Brazil, Venezuela) where the sexual state of the fungus has been found on virtually every infected tree examined (M.J. Wingfield, unpublished). In the latter countries, sexual reproduction is common and must, likewise, have led to a great diversity in the populations of the pathogen. This makes it difficult to determine, based on population structure, where the fungus might have originated. At the present time, we can only note that the fungus is well established and diverse in population structure in both South East Asia and South America. Based on population structure, we can not offer any resolution to the question of origin of the fungus.

A wide range of *C. cubensis* isolates from diverse geographic locations has recently been compared using RAPDS and rRNA sequence data. In these studies (Myburg, 1997) it has been shown that there are at least two distinct clades of the fungus. One of these includes South American and South African isolates and the other groups together isolates from S.E. Asia. The relevance of this observation is presently not clear to us, but it does suggest that *C. cubensis* in South Africa probably originated in South America, rather than in South East Asia.

OPPORTUNITIES TO CAPITALISE ON HYPOVIRULENCE

A reduction of virulence in isolates of fungal pathogens, also known as hypovirulence, and which is conferred by cytoplasmically transmitted dsRNA hypoviruses, is a well known phenomenon (Nuss and Koltin, 1990) Indeed the bulk of research on hypovirulence has been conducted on the chestnut blight pathogen, *Cryphonectria parasitica* (Anagnostakis and Jaynes, 1973, Choi and Nuss, 1992, Smart and Fulbright, 1996) which is very similar in both biology and taxonomy to *C. cubensis*. Opportunities to capitalise on hypovirulence to reduce the impact of *Cryphonectria* canker of eucalypts appear to be increasing rapidly.

Hypovirulence has recently been reported, for the first time, to occur in isolates of *C. cubensis* from South Africa (van der Westhuizen *et al.*, 1994) as well as Brazil (van Zyl *et al.*, 1998a). Very little is known about the dsRNA associated with this hypovirulence or how it might compare with that known in *C. parasitica*. These questions are currently the basis of a concerted research effort. The most significant problem relating to hypovirulence lies in the fact that the dsRNA hypoviruses are naturally transferred only between isolates representing similar vegetative compatibility groups also known as VCG's (Anagnostakis and Kranz, 1987). These VCG's represent distinct genets in species of fungi and thus make up the genetic diversity of a fungal population. New VCG's are generated through sexual recombination and thus, in a natural ecosystem, one would expect to find a wide diversity of VCG's present. These would then also prevent the ready spread of hypoviruses within the population. Where a pathogen has been introduced into a new environment, and where it also does not undergo ready sexual recombination, it is assumed that excellent opportunities might exist to reduce to reduce its impact through hypovirulence. We feel optimistic that this scenario reflects the South African *C. cubensis* situation.

An exciting development in the very recent past has been research leading to the transfer of hypovirulence factors from one fungal species to another through transfection and transformation (Chen *et al.*, 1996). Thus the hypovirus CHV1-713 L-dsRNA from *C. parasitica* was, for example transferred to *C. cubensis*. We are currently exploring opportunities to transfer a *C. parasitica* hypovirus to dominant VCG's of *C. cubensis* in South Africa and, potentially, to use this for biological control.

DURABILITY OF DISEASE TOLERANCE

Currently, the most effective means to reduce the impact of *Cryphonectria* canker is to select *Eucalyptus* clones that display high degrees of tolerance to the disease. This approach is being used effectively in South Africa and elsewhere in the world. It is also leading to an improved understanding of the disease tolerance trait and to breeding programmes incorporating this feature (M. and B. Wingfield, unpublished data).

The selection and testing of *Eucalyptus* clones tolerant to diseases such as *Cryphonectria* canker can be extremely time consuming. In some cases, forestry companies require up to twelve years of testing before new clones are commercially deployed. Thus, the durability of disease tolerance in these clones is a matter of crucial concern. As has been mentioned previously in this paper, the *C. cubensis* population in South Africa appears to have a relatively limited genetic base. Although the data on which we base this conclusion are of a relatively preliminary nature, all evidence available to us suggests that *C. cubensis* in South Africa has a relatively limited capacity to change. This would then suggest that newly developed disease tolerant clones will exhibit a high degree of durability to *Cryphonectria* canker.

CONCLUSION

Cryphonectria canker is one of the most important diseases of eucalypts where these trees are grown in plantations. It is likely to become more important in the future, especially with a world-wide increase in the utilisation of *Eucalyptus* for pulp production. Although it has been suggested that *C. cubensis* might have originated on clove in Indonesia, there is no firm scientific data to support this hypothesis. Populations of the fungus are diverse in both S.E. Asia and South and Central America and the pathogen has been found on native plants in both regions. Further research to resolve this question is required.

In contrast to the situation in South East Asia and South America, the genetic diversity of the *C. cubensis* population in South Africa appears to be relatively limited. In addition, sexual recombination in the fungus is common in the former areas, but virtually non existent in South Africa.

Outstanding opportunities appear to exist to utilise dsRNA-mediated hypovirulence to reduce the impact of *Cryphonectria* canker in South Africa. In South America and S.E. Asia, where the populations of *C. cubensis* are diverse, this might not be a practical option.

The durability of tolerance to *Cryphonectria* canker in *Eucalyptus* clones should be high in areas such as South Africa, where the pathogen appears to have a limited capacity to adapt. In countries where many VCG's of the pathogen exist, and where sexual outcrossing is common, a relatively rapid breakdown in disease tolerance might be expected.

REFERENCES

ALFENAS A.C., HUBBES M., COUTO L., 1982. Effect of phenolic components from *Eucalyptus* on the mycelial growth and conidial germination of *Cryphonectria cubensis*. *Can. J. Bot.*, 60, 2535-2541.

ALFENAS A.C., HODGES C.S., JENG R., 1984. Similarities in physiological characters between *Endothia eugeniae* and *Cryphonectria cubensis*, causal agents of cankers in clove and *Eucalyptus*, respectively. *Phytopathology*, 74, 841 (Abst).

ANAGNOSTAKIS S.L., JAYNES R.A., 1973. Chestnut blight control: Use of hypovirulent cultures. *Plant Dis. Rep.*, 27, 225-226.

ANAGNOSTAKIS S.L., KRANZ J., 1987. Population dynamics of *Cryphonectria parasitica* in a mixed hardwood forest in Connecticut. *Phytopathology*, 77, 751-754.

BOERBOOM J.H.A., MAAS P.W.T., 1970. Canker of *Eucalyptus grandis* and *E. saligna* in Surinam caused by *Endothia havanensis*. *Turrialba*, 20, 94-99.

BRUNER S.E., 1916. A new species of *Endothia*. *Mycologia*, 8, 239-242.

CHAMBERS C., DUTTA S.K., CROUCH R.J., 1986. *Neurospora crassa* ribosomal DNA: sequence comparison of internal transcribed spacer and comparison with *N. intermedia* and *N. sitophila*. *Gene*, 44, 159-164.

CHEN B., CHEN C.H., BOWMAN B.H., NUSS D.L., 1996. Phenotypic changes associated with wild-type and mutant hypovirus RNA transfection of plant pathogenic fungi phylogenetically related to *Cryphonectria parasitica*. *Phytopathology*, 86, 301-310.

CHOI E.H., NUSS D.L., 1992. A viral gene confers hypovirulence-associated traits to the chestnut blight fungus. *EMBO*, 11, 473-478.

DAVIDSON E.M., COATES D.J., 1991. Identification of *Cryphonectria cubensis* and *Endothia gyrosa* from Eucalypts in Western Australia using isozyme analysis. *Austral. Plant Path.*, 20, 157-160.

DAVISON E.M., TAY F.C., 1983. Twig, branch and upper trunk canker of *Eucalyptus marginata*. *Plant Dis.*, 67, 1285-1287.

FLORENCE E.J.M., J. K. SHARMA C. MOHANAN., 1986. A stem canker disease of *Eucalyptus* caused by *Cryphonectria cubensis* in Kerala. *Kerala Forest Research Institute Scientific Paper*, 66, 384-387.

GIBSON I. A.S., 1981. A canker disease of *Eucalyptus* new to Africa. FAO, *Forest Genetics Resources Information*, 10, 23-24.

HARRINGTON T.C., STEIMEL J.P., WINGFIELD M.J., KILE G., 1996. Isozyme variation in the *Ceratocystis coerulescens* complex. *Mycologia*, 88, 104-113.

HODGES C.S., REIS M.S., 1974. Identificacao do fungo causador de cancro de *Eucalyptus* spp. no Brasil. *Brasil Florestal*, 5, 19.

HODGES C.S, GEARY T.F., CORDELL C.E., 1979. The occurrence of *Diaporthe cubensis* on *Eucalyptus* in Florida, Hawaii and Puerto Rico. *Plant Dis. Rep.*, 63, 216-220.

HODGES C.S., 1980. The taxonomy *of Diaporthe cubensis*. *Mycologia*, 72, 542-548.

HODGES C.S., ALFENAS A.C., FERREIRA F.A., 1986. The conspecificity of *Cryphonectria cubensis* and *Endothia eugeniae*. *Mycologia*, 78, 343-350.

MICALES J.A., STIPES R.J., 1987. A re-examination of the fungal genera *Cryphonectria* and *Endothia*. *Phytopathology*, 77, 650-654.

MYBURG H., WINGFIELD B.D., WINGFIELD M.J., 1998. Phylogeny using DNA sequence of geographically diverse isolates of *Cryphonectria cubensis* and allied species. *Mycologia*, (submitted).

MYBURG H., *1997 Cryphonectria cubensis, a molecular taxonomic and population study*. MSc. Thesis. Univ. of the Orange Free State, Bloemfontein, South Africa. 109p.

NUSS D.L., KOLTIN Y., 1990. Significance of dsRNA genetic elements in plant pathogenic fungi. *Ann. Rev. Phytopathology*, 28, 37-58.

OLD K.M., KOBAYASHI T., 1988. Eucalypts are susceptible to the chestnut blight fungus *Cryphonectria parasitica*. *Austral. J. of Bot.* 36, 599-603.

OLD K. M., MURRAY D.I.L., KILE G.A., SIMPSON J., MALAFANT K., 1986. The pathology of fungi isolated from eucalypt cankers in South eastern Australia. *A. For. Res.* 16, 21-36.

SHARMA J.K., MOHANAN L., FLORENCE E.J.M., 1985. *Disease survey in nurseries and plantations of forest tree species grown in Kerala*. Research report 36 Kerala Forest Research Institute, India.

SMART C.D., FULBRIGHT D.W., 1996. Molecular Biology of fungal diseases. *In*: M. Gunasekaran M. and Weber D.J. (Eds.) *Molecular Biology of the Biological Control of Pests and Diseases of Plants*. CRC Press, Inc., Boca Raton, Florida.

SWART W.J., WINGFIELD M.J., 1991. Cryphonectria canker of *Eucalyptus* spp. in South Africa. Proceedings of the IUFRO International Symposium. Intensive Forestry: The Role of Eucalypts. pp. 806.

VAN DER WESTHUIZEN I.P., SMIT W.A., WINGFIELD M.J., KEMP G.H.J., 1994. First report of hypovirulence associated with dsRNA in *Cryphonectria cubensis*. *S.A. J. Sci.* 91, 7 (Abst).

VAN ZYL L.M., WINGFIELD M.J., ALFENAS A.C., CROUS P.W., 1998a. First report of hypovirulence in Brazilian isolates of *Cryphonectria cubensis*. *Pl. Pathology* (in press).

VAN ZYL L.M., WINGFIELD M.J., KEMP G.H.J., CROUS P.W., 1998b. Population diversity among isolates of *Cryphonectria cubensis*. *Forest Ecology and Management*. (submitted).

VAN HEERDEN S.W., WINGFIELD M.J., COUTHINO T., VAN ZYL L.M., WRIGHT J.A., 1997. Diversity of *Cryphonectria cubensis* isolates in Venezuela and Indonesia. Proceedings of IUFRO Conference on Silviculture and Improvement of Eucalypts. Salvador, Bahia, Brazil. b,142-146.

VISSER C., WINGFIELD M.J., WINGFIELD BD., YAMOAKA Y., 1995. Generic placement of *Ophiostoma polonicum* amongst the ophiostomatoid fungi. *Syst. & Appl. Micro.* 18, 403-409.

WINGFIELD M. J., SWART W. J., ABEAR B., 1989. First record of *Cryphonectria* canker of *Eucalyptus* in South Africa. *Phytophylactica* 21, 311-313.

WINGFIELD M.J., SWART W.J., KEMP G.H.J., 1991. *Pathology considerations in clonal propagation of Eucalyptus with special reference to the South African situation.* Proceedings of the IUFRO International Symposium. Intensive Forestry: The Role of Eucalypts. pp. 811

WINGFIELD M.J., HARRINGTON T.C., SOLHEIM H. 1995. *Do conifer bark beetles require fungi to kill trees*? Proceedings of the IUFRO International Symposium on Bark Beetle, Fungus, Tree Interactions. As, Norway.

WINGFIELD M.J., WINGFIELD B.D., COUTINHO T.A., 1995. Management of Eucalyptus diseases in subtropical areas of South Africa. Proceedings of IUFRO Conference on Silviculture and Improvement of Eucalypts. Salvador, Bahia, Brazil pp171-172.

WITTHUHN R.C., WINGFIELD B.D., WINGFIELD M.J., T.C. HARRINGTON T.C., 1998. Monophyly of the conifer species in the *Ceratocystis coerulescens* complex based on DNA sequence data. *Mycologia,* (in press).

Physiology and Genetics of Tree-Phytophage Interactions
Gujan (France), August 31 - September 5, 1997
Ed. INRA, Paris, 1999 (Les Colloques, n°90)

Are inbreeding and sex determination a key factor of *Diprion pini* L. population dynamics?

J. ROUSSELET, C. GERI, M. SIVET AND F. GOUSSARD

Institut National de la Recherche Agronomique, Département de Recherches Forestières, Station de Zoologie Forestière, Ardon 45160 Olivet, France

ABSTRACT

D. pini defoliates Scots pine stands during "eruptive" outbreaks. These sudden and spectacular pullulations are controlled by food, parasitism and diapause. On the other hand, the pre-outbreak phase is poorly known. We propose that a genetic determination in diapause, and a complementary sex determination leading to the diploid males production in association with inbreeding limits population growth when populations are low. Karyotypic observations, sibmatings and crosses between insects from various populations supported this hypothesis. The existence of diploid males in this arrhenotokous species was demonstrated and their occurrence in our lab strain and in a residual population was ascertained. Moreover, it was suggested that diapause was really dependent on genetical factors and interacted with consanguinity. Such phenomena are able to modify the population genetic structure during outbreaks. The level of diploid males production in natural populations and their possible effect on population dynamics are discussed.

INTRODUCTION

The population dynamics of forest insect pests are usually studied using demographic and environmental variables that are easily accessible and measurable. In contrast, insect endogenous factors of the utmost importance remain relatively unknown. Research on *Diprion pini* is an example of this bias in conducting studies.

This sawfly severely defoliates Scots pine, *Pinus sylvestris*, in Europe. Its outbreaks are characterized by their large amplitude and their short duration. Furthermore, they are followed by long periods with very low population levels (latency phases). Foliage availability, parasitism and diapause play a significant role during these outbreaks. At first intact foliage, low parasitism rates and low diapause rates favour a rapid increase. Then foliage deterioration, parasites and very high diapause rates result in the collapse of populations (Eichhorn, 1983; Géri, 1988; Sharov, 1993). Diapause is able to arrest the development of the eonymphs in cocoon and to distribute the adult emergences over several years. The expression of diapause depends on complex mechanisms. The effects of photoperiod and temperature explain its variation and the modification of the life cycle in relation to geographic and climatic conditions (Géri and Goussard, 1991). However it cannot explain the variation of diapause rates during the outbreaks. These variations are only partly explained by trophic factors, as food limitation and food quality, or population density (Géri *et al.*, 1988; Géri and Goussard, 1989). This phenomenon, as the reappearance of dynamic populations occurring before every new outbreak, suggests that both physiological changes and modifications of the population genetic structure are involved in diapause regulation.

We developed new hypotheses on the causes of these outbreaks based on our observations of laboratory strain. This strain had been reared for more than 50 generations in photoperiodic and thermal conditions favorable to non-diapause development. A male-biased sex ratio was developed in this population. Simultaneously the diapause rates increased to over 90 %. This was followed by a decrease in the percentage of diapausing individuals. We hypothesize that this decrease was due to selection produced by mating only non-diapausing individuals. These patterns generated the following hypotheses :

1) These patterns may be caused by the inbreeding in the lab strain.

2) Diapause is dependent on genetic factors.

3) The patterns produced by inbreeding and genetic structure in the lab may simulate those observed in the fields.

4) Diploid males may exist in this haplodiploid species, increasing the percentage of males. This diploid males production must be considered in the mechanisms hypothesized in hypotheses 1-3 above.

Diploid males result from a complementary sex determination (CSD), as was first demonstrated by Whiting (1943) in *Habrobracon hebetor*. CSD proposes that sex is determined by a series of multiple and complementary alleles at one or several loci.

Individuals that are produced from fertilized eggs are females if they have two different alleles, or males if they have the same allele. The occurrence of this latter event increases with inbreeding. Unfertilized eggs give rise to haploid individuals which are male because they are hemizygous. Diploid males have already been detected in a diprionid species (Smith & Wallace, 1971). Usually, they are sterile or father inviable offspring. It is well-known that diploid male production (DMP) affects hymenopteran population biology (Cook & Crozier, 1995). Their occurrence in *D. pini* populations was suggested by allozyme electrophoresis (Beaudoin *et al.*, 1994), and cytological evidence was needed to resolve the problem.

This paper reports the results of crossing experiments and cytological investigations carried out in order to test whether diploid males existed, and to measure the genetic dependence of diapause and effects of consanguinity. Last, the significance of these phenomena is discussed in regards to the regulation of *D. pini* attacks.

MATERIAL AND METHODS

Bulk matings

Preliminary investigations on the effects of inbreeding

Different crosses were carried out in order to compare diapause rates and sex ratio between in and outbred progenies: (1) crosses between individuals from the same colony (brothers-sisters) collected from the field, (2) crosses between males and females from colonies collected from different sites , and (3) crosses between females from a natural population and males from lab strain. Bulk matings were performed in 1990, 1992 and 1993 using insects from Fontainebleau Forest (near Paris). Offspring were reared during 2 generations in standard lab conditions described by Goussard and Géri (1989). They were kept at 16°C temperature and 15h light from egg development to the third instar. Then they were kept at 20°C - 16h30 up to egg laying on a pine in container. Diapause rates were also observed in the offspring of virgin females.

Interbreeding

Interbreeding between more distant populations (Alps, Finland, Lab Strain) was performed in 1994. Diapause rates of these population samples and their hybrids were observed under different photophases (16h30, 18h30, 20h), following egg laying, and earlier larval development under the standard lab conditions.

Single-pair matings

Investigations on the genetic control of diapause

We performed crosses between a strain native from Finland and our Lab Strain which showed different propensities for entering diapause. All the progenies were reared under 20°C, LD 16h30-7h30 up to the second instar, and thereafter at 20°C, LD 17h-7h. Diapause rates were observed as a function of sex and parents 20 days after cocooning. Preliminary results are reported in this paper.

Investigations on the sex determination

Production of diploid males by sibmating in the lab

Sibmatings were carried out in 1995, 1996 and 1997 in a Scots pine nursery or in the lab. In the first and second experiments, sister-brother matings were performed with colonies descended from mated females collected in the Fontainebleau forest. The progenies were reared in the lab on a foliage favourable to a development without mortality (Clone 15, INRA Orléans). In the third experiment, we used colonies descended from crosses between our Lab strain and a Finnish strain. When the progenies cocooned, we measured the proportion of colonies with diploid males (CDM ratio) and the proportion of diploid males to females within these colonies (DM ratio = sex ratio within the diploid offspring).

Predictions under CSD models

Under single-locus CSD model, a sister has one chance out of two to mate with one of her brothers possessing one of her alleles, and consequently to produce homozygous individuals (=diploid males). We expected 50% of the colonies to have diploid males:

Parents: ™ A_iA_j x ¢ A_k → sisters + brothers (F1): A_iA_k (™) + A_jA_k (™) + A_i (¢n) + A_j (¢n)

Two kinds of equiprobable brother-sister crosses (F2) occur :

1) The female and the male share the same sex allele, their progeny contains diploid males ; furthermore, 50% of fertilized eggs in these colonies are expected to be diploid males:

   ™ $\underline{A_i}A_k$ x ¢ $\underline{A_i}$ → $\underline{A_i}\underline{A_i}$ (¢2n) + A_kA_i (™) + A_i (¢n) + A_k (¢n)

   ™ $\underline{A_j}A_k$ x ¢ $\underline{A_j}$ → $\underline{A_j}\underline{A_j}$ (¢2n) + A_kA_j (™) + A_j (¢n) + A_k (¢n)

2) The female and the male have different sex alleles, their progeny do not contain diploid males: ™ A_iA_k x ¢ A_j → A_iA_j (™) + A_kA_j (™) + A_i (¢n) + A_k (¢n)

   ™ A_jA_k x ¢ A_i → A_iA_j (™) + A_kA_i (™) + A_j (¢n) + A_k (¢n)

Under the two-locus model, we expected 25% of broods to contain 25% diploid males (if we considered that the two loci are independent and that only the individuals homozygous at the two loci are diploid males).

Detection of diploid males by means of karyotyping

The chromosome number counts were performed using the gonads of young prepupae. We used the technique described by Guest and Hsu (1973) with slight modifications. The gonial mitoses enable the observation of many metaphase spreads. This provides a clear identification of chromosome numbers which prevents misinterpretation due to some possible artifacts. These cytological examinations are possible only during a couple of days at a precise stage of the insect development. Furthermore, it is preferable to work on individuals which have developed under conditions preventing diapause.

Diploid males characterization

Different features of the inbred progenies were noted: date of cocooning, cocoon weight, sex ratio, and sometimes diapause rates as a function of sex and ploidy level.

Looking for diploid males in lab and natural populations

Using the above criteria, we looked for diploid males either by karyotyping or weighing individuals from lab strain and natural populations. Twenty-four colonies (1101 individuals) were from Maux in Fontainebleau Forest (larvae collected in September 1995, cocoons weighed in February 1996). A sample of 49 individuals were from a small population in Vendée (larvae collected in September 1996, cocoons weighed in March 1997).

RESULTS

Incidence of inbreeding

The bulk matings performed in 1990 and 1992 showed that inbreeding rapidly led to male-biased sex ratios and high diapause rates. The inbred populations showed diapause rates significantly higher than outbred insects (Fig. 1; $p<0.001$ χ^2 test). Moreover, the males were more likely to diapause than females and the diapause rates increased as sex ratio of the colonies became more male-biased. This suggests a relation with sex determination (Géri *et al*, 1995). The colonies without females had significantly more diapausing individuals ($p<0.001$ χ^2test).

Genetic control of diapause

The bulk matings also confirmed that a selection process occurred in our lab strain leading to a non-diapause strain under 20°C/16h30 (80-90% emergences). Indeed, all the crosses between females from Fontainebleau and males from the lab strain resulted in

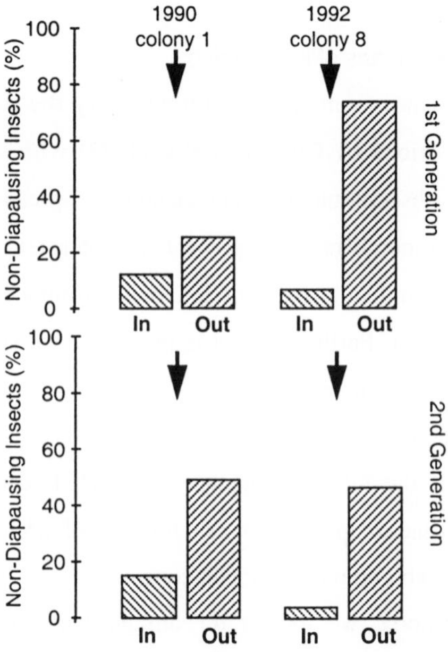

Figure 1: The percentage of individuals without diapause in the progenies of two colonies from Fontainebleau Forest following inbred crosses (brothers-sisters) and outcrosses

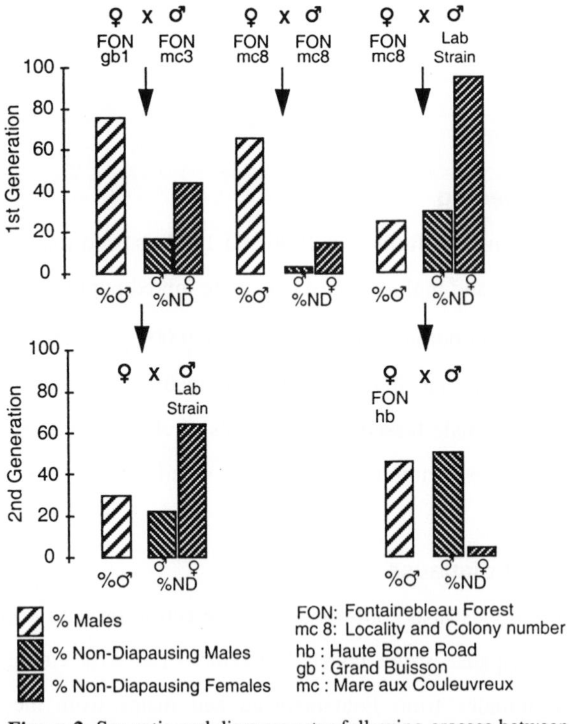

Figure 2: Sex-ratio and diapause rates following crosses between females from Fontainebleau and males from Fontainebleau or from the Lab strain

restoring a female-biased sex ratio and in a significant decrease of diapause rates in the offspring. This effect was especially evident for the females. In a haplo-diploid system, only the females receive the genes of the father. The subsequent crosses between these females and some males from Fontainebleau (from an adjoining site of collection) gave again high diapause rates and male biased sex ratio. This is illustrated by the figure 2 (see also Géri *et al*, 1995). Furthermore, all the virgin females from the Lab strain produced almost exclusively non-diapausing offspring under standard lab conditions. In contrast, virgin females from Fontainebleau produced a wide range of diapause rates (Fig. 3).

Experiments with more distant populations supported the fact that photophase sensitivity is a genetically determined trait. The critical photoperiods were : 16h30 for the lab strain and the local population, 18h30 for the Alps population, and 20h for the Finnish population. The Finnish strain maintained this photoperiod threshold over the subsequent generation. Interbreeding between females from Finland and males from the Alps led to a 18h30 photoperiod in the hybrids.

The preliminary results of single-pair matings between the Lab and Finnish strain ascertained the existence of a genetic component in diapause responses (Table 1). The crosses between a female and a male from the lab strain gave non-diapausing offspring while crosses between a female and a male from Finland did not. The haploid males showed diapause rates similar to their mother. The females resulting from the crosses between females from Finland and males from lab strain showed an intermediate diapause rate. These results showed that genetic control of critical photoperiod is polygenic. This is consistent with the persistence of few diapausing individuals in our non-diapause Lab strain.

Diploid males and sex determination

Diploid males characterization

In the first experiment, all the individuals were weighed, dissected and karyotyped. One colony contained 40% diploid males (2n=28 chromosomes). These individuals were clearly heavier than haploid males (33% on average), but the weight distributions of haploid and diploid males slightly overlap each other (Fig. 4). Diploid males have a slower development rate and their cocoon formation takes place between the times of the haploid males and females. The occurrence of diploid males was responsible for sex ratio inversion. Because of homozygosity at the sex locus (or loci), the proportion of male prepupae was 56%. It would have been 27% if all the fertilized eggs developed into females.

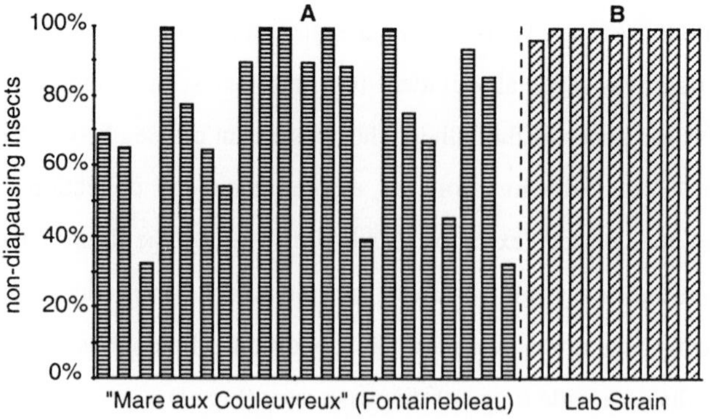

Figure 3: The percentage of non-diapausing insects in the offspring of virgin females reared under conditions favourable to a development without diapause: (A) virgin females from a natural population (Fontainebleau) (B) virgin females from the Lab strain

Table 1. Crosses between diapausing and non-diapausing strains: emergence rates 20 days after the cocooning

Crosses			(n°)	n° progenies					Non-diapausing insects	
				with males only		with males & females			males	females
female		male		n° col	n° ¢	n° col	n° ¢	n° ô	(monoparental)	(biparental)
LAB	x	LAB	(23)	3	153	3	63	80	90% (194)	78% (62)
LAB	x	FINLAND	(37)	4	111	4	190	5	94% (282)	80% (4)
FINLAND	x	LAB	(29)	5	325	10	283	251	0% (3)	48% (121)
FINLAND	x	FINLAND	(30)	4	300	7	200	150	0% (0)	0% (0)

Table 2. Diapause rates in a colony containing diploid males

	cocoon weight < 90 mg	cocoon weight [90;110mg]	cocoon weight > 110 mg
diapausing prepupae	71%	25%	21%
non-diapausing prepupae	21%	71%	79%
dead prepupae	8%	4%	0%

Table 3. The proportion of colonies containing diploid males (CDM ratio) following sibmatings and proportion of diploid males to females in these colonies (DM ratios)

	no. of colonies with diploid males	CDM ratio	DM ratios		
			mean	mini	maxi
first experiment	1 out of 4*	25%	40%		
second experiment	2 out of 8	25%	54%	53%	55%
third experiment	6 out of 13	46%	12%	5%	19%

* these colonies do not share the same "grandmother"

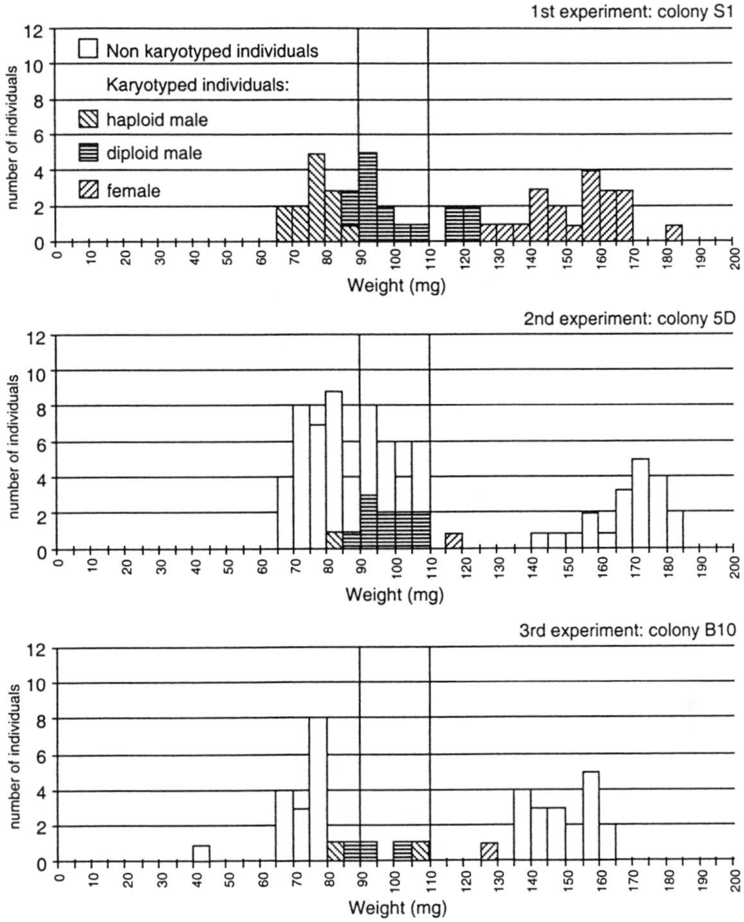

Figure 4: Cocoon weight patterns of some colonies resulted from sibmating

The second and third experiments confirmed that diploid males are heavier. The weight of haploid males cocoons was very rarely higher than 90 mg. Consequently, weight may be used as a criterion detecting diploid males within a colony when karyotyping is not practicable. In the second experiment, the individuals were graded by weight (< 90 mg and ≥ 90 mg) and only a sample was dissected and karyotyped. Diapause rates were assessed in a colony with diploid males (Table 2). Diploid individuals, male or female, showed a similar diapause rate and were mostly non-diapausing. Whereas the haploid males showed an high diapause rate.

In the third experiment, many colonies contained diploid males but they were not numerous (Table 3; Fig. 4). This was probably because they suffered an high mortality at the first instar due to the bad quality of the foliage (for egg laying in the lab, we cannot use clones but "wild" pines in container ; we do not know whether they are favourable or not to a development without mortality). Diploid males may be less viable under such drastic conditions.

Sex determination

We cannot come to definite conclusions about which of the CSD models is correct (Table 3). If we assume that diploid males have the same viability as females then the two locus model would predict a 25% diploid male to 75% female ratio (DM ratio) and the one locus model a 50:50 ratio. The same percentages would be predicted for the proportion of colonies containing diploid males (CDM ratio). The first two experiments produced the CDM ratios predicted by the two-locus model. However, a single-locus model is not ruled out, because of the low number of progenies. On the contrary, the DM ratios are clearly more consistent with this latter model. The third experiment produced a CDM ratio very close to that predicted by the one locus model. Conversely, the DM ratios were very low. We assume that the DM ratios were reduced in this experiment by preferential mortality due to the rearing conditions. On the whole the single-locus model seems more likely.

Evidence for diploid males occurrence in lab and natural populations

No colony from Fontainebleau showed a cocoon weight distribution that unambiguously suggested the presence of diploid males. However, the sample from Vendée probably contained a few diploid males. Indeed, the weight distribution was "trimodal" and some males emerged from cocoons heavier than 90 mg.

We detected, by weighing, the natural occurrence of diploid males in our lab population following a population collapse. The karyotyping of a small sample confirmed the presence of diploid males.

DISCUSSION-CONCLUSION

On the one hand, our study showed that diapause responses vary among the populations and are modifiable within a population by selection. Variations in diapause responses revealed to be partly genetically determined. On the other hand, we demonstrated that diploid males occur in *D. pini*, because of a Complementary Sex Determination. Consequently, changes in population genetic structure are able to affect sex-ratio and diapause rates, and conversely.

Diploid males were produced experimentally, in laboratory population after a population collapse and were found in the field. Evidently our laboratory results simulate field conditions. They have many implications for demographic self-limitation. We can revise the general pattern previously presented (Géri, 1988) as follows: 1) Populations quickly develop under favourable conditions (low parasitism, low predation, undamaged foliage, moderate diapause rates) 2) As soon as the conditions are unfavourable, populations start to decline and small isolated populations become inbred. 3) Inbreeding is associated with a significant diploid males production and with an increase in diapausing individuals. 4) The combination of an increasingly male sex-ratio and an increase in the frequency of diapause slows population growth. 5) Populations are released from this low level and the influx of new alleles from outside the isolated population breaks the cycle of inbreeding and the population grows.

Many points still need to be demonstrated.

In our model, sex-ratio, diapause and inbreeding can be independtly taken into account, but interactions have to be more clearly clarified. We did not show that diploid males are responsible for increasing diapause rates. The numerous males and the high male diapause rates observed after sibmating suggested a link between diapause and sex determination. This hypothesis was not confirmed by the single-pair mating experiments that showed no difference in diapause rates between diploid males and females. It is more likely that inbreeding modifies diapause rates and sex ratio simulteanously and independently.

The production of diploid males is not the only way to explain the male abundance in the lab. A variety of different causes increases the percentage of haploid males. These factors include female behavior, fertilization rates,mating behavior.

However, the detection of diploid males in a natural population supports our model and calls for further investigations. The significance of diploid males in population biology of Hymenoptera has been reported by many authors (El Agoze *et al.*, 1986 ; Ross and Fletcher, 1986, 1993 ; Stouthamer *et al.*, 1992 ; Cook, 1993a,b ; Cook and Crozier, 1995). Their incidence depends on their level of production and their occurrence is closely dependent on the number of alleles and loci involved in CSD. It also depends on their viability, breeding performance, mating system and offspring viability. In *D. pini*, CSD is probably monogenic, but its expression could be distorted by larval mortality. The biological features of diploid males are still unknown. Furthermore, we need informations about mating system, population structure, inbreeding avoidance, migrations, ... In the sawfly *Athalia rosae* with a single locus multiple alleles system, it is easy to get numerous diploid males in the lab from sister-brother mating without high developmental mortality (Naito and Suzuki, 1991). However, the authors cannot find any diploid males in the field population. In this species, several biological processes took place preventing the sibmatings and the diploid males production (Naito, 1996). Our model implies a high DMP level when a population is small enough for significant inbreeding to take place. This could be the case throughout the latency phase. If this hypothesis is confirmed, it will remain to explain from an evolutionary point of view the maintenance of such a genetic load. Nevertheless in the parasitic wasp *Diadromus pulchellus*, the authors (El Agoze *et al.*,1986 ; Periquet *et al.*,1993) observed a significant occurrence of diploid males in the field.

Finally, we do not consider only the direct incidence of diploid males. We must mainly regard them as consanguinity indicators, associated with the variations in sex-ratio and diapause rates.

REFERENCES

BEAUDOIN L., GERI C., ALLAIS J. P. &. GOUSSARD F., 1994. Influence of consanguinity on the sex-ratio and diapause of *Diprion pini* L. (Hym. Diprionidae) populations. I. Observations on a rearing population. Relation with the sex determinism and consanguinity. *J. Appl. Ent.*, 118, 267-280.

COOK J. M., 1993a. Inbred lines as reservoirs of sex alleles in parasitoid rearing programs. *Environ. Entomol.*, 22, 1213-1216.

COOK J. M., 1993b Sex determination in the Hymenoptera : a review of models and evidence. *Heredity*, 71, 421-435.

COOK J. M. and CROZIER R. H., 1995. Sex determination and population biology in the Hymenoptera. *Tree*, 10, 281-286.

CROZIER R. H., 1971. Heterozygosity and sex determination in haplodiploidy. *Am. Nat.*, 105, 399-412.

EICHHORN O., 1983. Untersuchungen zur Ökologie der Gemeinen Kiefern-Buschhornblattwespe, *Diprion pini* (L.) (Hym., Diprionidae). *J. Appl. Ent.*, 96, 291-303.

EL AGOZE M., HEDDERWICK P., PERIQUET G., 1986. Déterminisme du sexe et dynamique des populations chez l'hyménoptère *Diadromus pulchellus*. Coll. Nat. C.N.R.S. "Biologie des populations".

GOUSSARD F., GERI C., 1989. Mise au point d'un élevage permanent de *Diprion pini* L. (Hym. Diprionidae). *Agronomie*, 9, 911-918.

GERI C., GOUSSARD F., 1988. Incidence de la photophase et de la température sur la diapause de *Diprion pini* L. (Hym. Diprionidae). *J. Appl. Ent.*, 106, 150-172.

GERI C., 1988. The pine sawfly in Central France. *In*: Berryman A. (Ed.) : *Forests insects Population dynamics*. Plenum Berryman Ed. New-York. 377-405.

GERI C. , GOUSSARD F., 1991. Incidence de la photophase et de la température sur la levée de diapause de *Diprion pini* L. (Hym. Diprionidae). *J. Appl. Ent.*, 112, 220-236.

GERI C., BEAUDOIN L., ALLAIS J. P., GOUSSARD F., 1995. Influence of consanguinity on the sex-ratio and diapause of *Diprion pini* L. (Hym. Diprionidae) populations. II. Effect of inbreeding on Diapause. *J. Appl. Ent.*, 119, 35-43.

NAITO T., 1996. Why do not diploid males occur in the field population of the haplo-diploid turnip sawfly *Athalia rosa* (Hymenoptera, Tenthredinidae). *Proceedings of the XX International Congress of Entomology*, 141.

NAITO T. and SUZUKI, H., 1991. Sex determination in the sawfly *Athalia rosae ruficornis*: occurence of triploid males. *J. Heredity*, 82, 141.

PERIQUET G., HEDDERWICK M. P., EL AGOZE M. and POIRIE E M., 1993. Sex determination in the hymenopteran *Diadromus pulchellus* (Ichneumonidae): validation of the one-locus multi-allele model. *Heredity*, 70, 420-427.

ROSS K. G. and FLETCHER D. J. C., 1986. Diploid male production - a significant mortality factor in the fire ant, *Solenopsis invicta. Behav. Ecol. Sociobiol.*, 19, 283-291.

ROSS K. G. and FLETCHER D. J. C., 1993. Effect of a founder event on variation in the genetic sex-determining system of the fire ant *Solenopsis invicta. Genetics*, 135, 843-854.

SHAROV A. A., 1993. Biology and population dynamics of the common pine sawfly, *Diprion pini*, in Russia. In Sawfly life history adaptation to woody plants: Academic Pess, Wagner and Raffa Ed. San Diego, 409-429.

SMITH S. G. and WALLACE D. R., 1971. Allelic sex determination in a lower hymenopteran, *Neodiprion nigroscutum Midd. Can. J. Genet. Cytol.*, 13, 617-621.

STOUTHAMER R., LUCK R. F. et WERREN J. H., 1992. Genetics of sex determination and the improvement of biological control using parasitoids. *Environ. Entomol.*, 21, 427-435.

WHITING P. W., 1943. Multiples alleles in complementary sex determination of *Habrobracon. Genetics*, 28, 365-382.

Physiology and Genetics of Tree-Phytophage Interactions
Gujan (France), August 31 - September 5, 1997
Ed. INRA, Paris, 1999 (Les Colloques, n°90)

Genetic and ecological controls of post-diapause development in *Choristoneura*

W. JAN A. VOLNEY

Natural Resources Canada, Canadian Forest Service, Northern Forestry Centre, 5320-122 Street, Edmonton, Alberta, Canada T6H 3S5

RESUME

The conifer-feeding members of the genus *Choristoneura* in North America are among the most destructive forest pests and are capable of defoliating in excess of 100 million hectares in any one year. Although they appear to be adapted to a single host species, the budworms are often capable of exploiting several coniferous hosts. The synchrony between host bud development and spring emergence of these insects is critical to the success of larvae in colonizing the host. The genetic control of early spring development in the insect guarantees that populations retain a wide array of phenotypes. This trait is inherited with low heritability and is therefore not easily changed by selection. This strategy ensures that a segment of the insect population will persist in environments where bud break varies widely from year to year. Natural hybrids of *C. occidentalis* and *C. retiniana* suggest that reproductive isolation among the several conifer feeding *Choristoneura* species is not always effective. This permits the acquisition of additional variation in spring emergence rates in mixed populations when their host species form mixed stands either from natural or anthropogenic disturbance. The variation and adaptive capabilities encountered in these populations will frustrate attempts to select resistant host stock that depend on the asynchrony of bud development and insect emergence.

INTRODUCTION

Conifer-feeding members of the genus *Choristoneura* are among the most damaging defoliators in North America. The three species that are normally problems for forest managers are the spruce budworm, *C. fumiferana* (Clem.) feeding on spruces (*Picea* spp.) and firs (*Abies* spp.); the western spruce budworm, *C. occidentalis* Free., feeding principally on Douglas-fir (*Pseudotsuga menziesii* (Mirb.) Franco) but also on spruces and firs; and the jack pine budworm, *C. pinus* Free., feeding on jack pine (*Pinus banksiana* Lamb.). An additional species, the Modoc budworm , *C. retiniana* (Wlshm.), that feeds on white fir *Abies concolor* (Gord.. & Glend.) Lindl. ex Hildebr., seldom causes extensive damage (Furniss and Carolin 1977). A review of the taxonomic relationships among these, and other conifer feeding species may be found in Powell (1995) and their distributions are given by Harvey (1985, 1996). Collectively, these species may defoliate over 100 million hectares of forest in a single year and individual outbreaks may last for several years (Cerezke and Volney 1995). Their impacts on forest biomass production are dramatic (Maclean, 1985) and the resulting failure to fix carbon in these northern forests during these outbreaks is thought to have a significant effect on the global carbon cycle (Kurtz *et al.,* 1995). Despite their economic importance, little is know about the genetic structure of *Choristoneura* populations, particularly with respect to life history traits.

The relationship among the various named conifer-feeding *Choristoneura* entities and between the insect groups and their hosts remains enigmatic (Powell and De Benedictis, 1995) because interpreting phenetic relationships, pheromone based evidence and molecular-genetic information all suggest different evolutionary relationships. Not the least of these problems is the extreme degree of similarity among populations and variations within populations (De Benedictis, 1995). Furthermore, natural hybrids between putative species suggest that isolating mechanisms are not always effective (Volney *et al.* 1984). Stehr (1967) suggested that the key to determining species relationships among *Choristoneura* was the host associations and the mechanisms by which these insects are adapted to their hosts. In addition this understanding would assist in evaluating the genetic improvement strategies for the host populations. The purpose of this paper is to review the post-diapause development of *Choristoneura* populations with the view to understanding the ecological constraints they face in colonizing their hosts.

POST-DIAPAUSE DEVELOPMENT IN *CHORISTONEURA*

The essential features of budworm life cycles are common within the group. McGugan (1954) described the life cycle of *C. fumiferana* which can be used as a model for the group. Egg masses are laid on host foliage in mid-summer. These eggs hatch within two weeks, first instars disperse, find suitable hibernation sites and spin a hibernaculum, often on host branches. The larvae do not feed but molt to the second instar within the hibernaculum where they over-winter. By spring, diapause development is complete and, after the accumulation of sufficient heat units, larvae emerge to initiate feeding. They might mine buds at this stage if buds are sufficiently developed. More often they mine old needles until bud development permits the colonizing of the current year's developing foliage. There are usually six instars with pupation occurring on the host tree. Moths emerge in early July, mate and lay eggs. Dispersal may occur in the spring as larvae before they mine buds, again as large larvae but most importantly as adults where passive dispersal in weather fronts may carry moths several hundred kilometres in a single night (Dobesberger *et al.* 1983).

There are several variations to this pattern. The jack pine budworm seems unable to mine needles and is dependent on microsporangiate strobili for early instar survival (Nealis and Lomic, 1994). *C. bienis* Free., which occurs at high elevation in the Canadian Rocky Mountains, requires two years to complete development (Harvey, 1967). Although these are extreme variations, some members of all species probably display these traits.

The median time to complete post-diapause development in several species was found to vary very little within species from western North America and among the different rearing studies of spruce budworm (Volney, 1985). This indicates that, for these species groupings, temporal factors do not serve to isolate populations as they all complete development at the same time. The variance in total development time was found to be smaller than expected from a simple accumulation of variances in times of the different stages of post-diapause development in *C. occidentalis* and *C. retiniana* (Volney and Liebhold 1985). In analyzing this phenomenon, it was found that there was a negative correlation between successive development rates among individuals (*ibid.*). This system of controls in development almost guarantees that seasonal isolating mechanisms among sympatric western *Choristoneura* species populations would be ineffective because it reduces the variances in times of adult emergence. An analysis of post-diapuase development in *C. occidentalis* and *C. retiniana* revealed that there are no genetic differences among the species or their hybrids in the time to complete larval feeding (Volney and Liebhold 1985) as would be expected if adult emergence was to be synchronized.

It was surprising, therefore, to find that field studies of *C. fumiferana* total post-diapause development in western Canada was remarkably different from that reported for development in eastern Canada (Volney and Cerezke, 1992). A study of variation in total post-diapause development conducted in controlled temperature environments failed to show any genetic differences in this trait over 15° latitude within the range of white spruce (*Picea glauca* (Moench) Voss) in western Canada (Weber 1994). This suggests that the differences between populations might be controlled by ecological factors affecting survival at critical junctures in the life cycle of the insect.

Volney and Liebhold 1985 found marked differences among *C. occidentalis* and *C. retiniana* populations in their post-diapause pre-emergence development. The "green" morphs, diagnostic of *C. retiniana,* emerge sooner than the "brown" morphs, diagnostic of *C. occidentalis*, and their hybrids emerge at times that are intermediate to those of the parental types. Although there is considerable overlap in the emergence times, the order of emergence is the same as that of bud-break in the respective host species (Douglas-fir for *C. occidentalis* and white fir for *C. retiniana*). The variation in emergence times permit each insect population to colonize the principal host of the other species. This trait is mainly responsible for synchronizing budworm development with that of its host and is thus thought to be the ecological relationship that determines success of the various populations.

The genetic control of post-diapause pre-emergence times could only examined in the "green" morphs because it is impossible to distinguish larvae of hybrids from those of "true" *C. occidentalis*. In comparing this trait among *C. retiniana* populations, we found very low heritabilities where there was little evidence of genetic exchange with *C. occidentalis* (Volney *et al.* 1983). This is the pattern that would be expected in a life history trait that was closely associated with success of the population (Falconer, 1960). Where hybridization has occurred heritabilities are quite high, approaching 1.0, which suggests that selection can be very effective in rapidly correcting the genetic composition of inappropriately adapted populations. It is this pre-emergence development that is critical to spring survival in *Choristoneura* but the insects face a dilemma: the must synchronize their development with host phenology but, whereas their emergence depends on air temperatures, they respond to cues that are not identical to those that initiate bud development for bud break varies with soil and air temperatures. The insects apparently have solved this problem with a genetic system that conserves variation in spring emergence times. The permeable mating system among the putative insect species, adapted to particular hosts, also permits them to overcome any erosion of this variation as well.

HOST ASSOCIATIONS

Stehr (1967), in discussing the significance of hosts in determining the range of the different conifer-feeding *Choristoneura* species, suggested that the ecotone between forest regions would present problems in interpreting the relationships between species. Although Stehr (1967) recognized that *Choristoneura* species feeding on pine were ecologically isolated from those feeding on abietoid species, he offered no description for the relationship between sympatric species feeding on different abietoid species except to conclude that the evolutionary history of the group might be discerned from the geological and climatological history of North American forest communities. Speculation on the impact of this history on the

Holocene distribution of the various *Choristoneura* entities was provided by Volney (1985) and a longer evolutionary history was developed by Powell and DeBenedictis (1995). Their phylogeography depends in large part on the history of the principal host of present-day species. That Volney *et al.* (1984) would discover natural hybrids of *retiniana* and *occidenetalis* suggest that the reproductive barriers between species that cross the abitoid/pine barrier of the hypothetical cladogram (Powell and DeBenedictis, 1995) have been permeable for a long time. This would suggest that the host has had a far stronger influence on isolating populations than the mating systems that have evolved to date. I speculate here that the success of each species is primarily related to the synchrony between its host phenology and the post-diapause development.

The evidence associating *C. occidentalis* and *C. fumiferana* emergence and survival with synchrony of host shoot development was reviewed by Shepherd (1985) who indicated that insect development in the field, if properly synchronized with host bud flush, will result in elevated survival. This occurs in *C. occidentalis* when the insects emerge early to mine needles, then mine buds and so complete most of their early instar development protected in feeding tunnels adjacent to the shoots' rachis. If insects emerge late, the late instars will be forced to complete feeding exposed on fully elongated shoots. This population would incur substantially more mortality than a cohort that was properly synchronized with its host. Experimental studies by Lawrence *et al.* (1997) suggest that the phenological window for spruce budworm on white spruce may begin as much as four weeks prior to budbreak and is terminated at the end of shoot elongation. It appears that the early emergence of larvae is critical in synchronizing the population to take advantage of the swelling buds early in spring.

Several *Choristoneura* species feeding on abiatoid hosts have evolved needle mining habits. The adaptive significance of this was elegantly demonstrated by Trier and Mattson (1997) for the spruce budworm. In mining needles the second instars can sustain themselves and develop to third instars by avoiding the less nutritious structures, such as the resin ducts and cuticle, of needles. By completing an early instar in needles the insects shift their development relative to that of the host so that development is completed on the most succulent and nutritious tissues (Lawrence *et al.* 1997). By contrast *C. pinus*, which feeds on pine, is unable to mine needles. (Perhaps the spacing of resin ducts in pine needles are sufficiently close together so that larvae are unable to avoid them). Pine feeders depend, instead, on mining reproductive buds prior to mining vegetative buds to survive in the spring (Nealis and Lomic 1994.)

CONCLUSIONS

To successfully colonize its host in spring *Choristoneura* larvae face the problem of anticipating bud-break by emerging several weeks before the event. They overcome this time of adversity by either mining needles or reproductive buds. The precise cues that trigger emergence are little understood. Certainly temperature drives the process but whether there are host cues that act in concert with the thermal environment to regulate emergence is unknown. Nevertheless, the insect population seems to overcomes the uncertainty of budbreak by retaining phenotypes that spread their emergence over several weeks. Our current understanding would suggest that the host acts a phenological filter: early emerging individuals are unable to survive long enough to mine swelling vegetative buds whereas late emerging individuals must attempt to complete development on fully elongated shoots that are of lower nutritional value. It appears that the heritability of the time of emergence is low so that severe selection over several years would be necessary to change the median date of emergence. Further resisting this change is the mechanism by which the insects complete development and mate over a short time span. This ensures that late and early emerging individuals have the opportunity to contribute to the next generation. However, the adaptive association between insect species and its host can be rapidly eroded where sympatric host distributions permit the insect species to hybridize. Hybridization provides the opportunity for populations to rapidly acquire traits that permit them to colonize hosts with different phenological schedules, however.

Lawrence *et al.* (1997) reviewed the application of these results to selecting trees and provenances resistant to budworm attack. These include planting provenances in which bud-break is delayed or accelerated relative to insect emergence so that insect survival is reduced. The use of anti-feedants to induce asynchrony in the onset of feeding and suitable host phenology has also been suggested. Variation in the insect population and their ability to track host development would militate against the effectiveness of these strategies. A more promising approach may be to find and propagate host phenotypes that appear to be resistant to budworm attack. The variability in insect population densities and damage to trees within and among natural stand is substantial. The significance of this observation has not been exploited in attempting to develop resistant stock.

REFERENCES

CERZKE H.F., VOLNEY W.J.A., 1995. Forest insect pests in the Northwest Region. *In*: Armstrong J.A., Ives W.G.H. (Eds.): *Forest insect pests in Canada.*Nat. Resour. Can., Can. For. Serv., Ottawa p. 59-72.

DE BENEDICTIS J.A., 1995. Phenetic studies of spruce budworm populations(*Choristoneura* species).*In:* Powell, J.A. (Ed.) *Biosystematic studies of conifer-feeding Choristoneura (Lepidoptera: Tortricidae) in the western United States.* Univ. Calif. Publ. *Entomol.* 115:85-150.

DOBESBERGER E.J., LIM K.P., RASKE A.G., 1983. Spruce budworm (Lepidoptera:Tortricidae) moth flights from New Brunswick to Newfoundland. *Canad, Entomol.* 115:1641-1645.

FURNISS R.L., CAROLIN V.M., 1977. *Western forest insects.* Misc. Publ. 1339 U.S. Dept. Agric., Washington, D.C.

FALCONER D.S., 1960. *Introduction to quantitative genetics.* The Ronald Press Company, New York. 365 p.

HARVEY G.T., 1967. On coniferophagous species of *Choristoneura* (Lepidoptera: Tortricidae) in North America V. Second diapause as a species character. *Canad. Entomol.* 99:486-503.

HARVEY G.T., 1985. Taxonomy of the coniferophagus *Choristoneura* (Lepidoptera:Tortricidae): A review. *In:* Sanders C.J., Stark, R.W., Mullins, E.J., Murphy J. (Eds.) *Recent advances in spruce budworms research. Proceedings of the CANUSA symposium, Bangor, ME, 16-20 Sept. 1984.*Can. For. Serv., Ottawa, p. 16-48.

HARVEY G.T., 1996. Population genetics of the spruce budworm, *Choristonera fumiferana* (Clem.) Freeman (Lepidoptera: Tortricidae), in relation to geographical and population density differences. *Canad. Entomol.* 128: 219-243.

KURTZ W.A., APPS, M.J., STOCKS, B.J., VOLNEY, W.J.A., 1995. Global climate change: disturbance regimes and biospheric feedbacks of temperate and boreal forests. *In*: Woodwell G.M., Mackenzie F.T. (Eds.): *Biotic feedbacks in the global climate change system: will the warming speed the warming?* Oxford University Press, New York, p. 79-87

LAWRENCE R.K., MATTSON W.J., HAAK R.A. 1997. White spruce and the spruce budworm: defining the phenological window of susceptibility. *Canad. Entomol.* 129:291-318.

MACLEAN D.A. 1985. Effects of spruce budworm outbreaks on forest growth and yield. *In:*Sanders C.J., Stark, R.W., Mullins, E.J., Murphy J. (Eds.) *Recent advances in spruce budworms* *research. Proceedings of the CANUSA symposium, Bangor, ME, 16-20 Sept. 1984.*Can. For. Serv., Ottawa, p. 148-175.

MCGUGAN B.M. 1954. Needle-mining habits and larval instars of the spruce budworm. *Canad. Entomol.* 86: 439-454.

NEALIS V.G., LOMIC, P.V., 1994. Host-Plant influence on the population ecology of the jack pine budworm *Choristoneura pinus* (Lepidoptera:Tortricidae). *Ecol. Entomol.* 19:367-373.

POWELL J.A. 1995. Introduction: historical review, taxonomic problems, and research approaches. *In:* Powell, J.A. (Ed.) *Biosystematic studies of conifer-feeding Choristoneura (Lepidoptera: Tortricidae) in the western United States.* Univ. Calif. Publ. Entomol. 115: 1-19.

POWELL J.A., DE BENEDICTIS J.A., 1995. Evolutionary interpretation, taxonomy, and nomenclature. *In:* Powell, J.A. (Ed.) *Biosystematic studies of conifer-feeding Choristoneura (Lepidoptera: Tortricidae) in the western United States.* Univ. Calif. Publ. Entomol. 115:217-273.

STEHR G.W., 1967. On coniferophagous species of *Choristoneura* (Lepidoptera: Tortricidae) in North America I. Geographic variation in accordance with forest regions. *Canad. Entomol.* 99: 456-563.

TRIER, T.M., MATTSON W.J. 1997. Needle mining by the spruce budworm provides sustenance in the midst of privation. *Oikos* 79: 214-246.

VOLNEY W.J.A., 1985. Comparative population biologies of North American spruce budworms. *In:* Sanders C.J., Stark, R.W., Mullins, E.J., Murphy J. (Eds.) *Recent advances in spruce budworms research. Proceedings of the CANUSA symposium, Bangor, ME, 16-20 Sept. 1984.*Can. For. Serv., Ottawa, p. 71-84.

VOLNEY W.J.A., WATERS W.E., AKERS R.P., LIEBHOLD A.M., 1983. Variation in spring emergence patterns among western *Choristoneura* spp. (Lepidoptera: Tortricidae) populations in south-central Oregon. *Canad. Entomol.* 115:199-209.

VOLNEY W.J.A., LIEBHOLD A.M., WATERS W.E. 1984. Host associations, phenotypic variation and mating compatibility of *Choristoneura occidentalis* and *C. retiniana* (Lepidoptera: Tortricidae) populations in south-central Oregon. *Canad. Entomol.* 116: 813-826.

VOLNEY W.J.A., LIEBHOLD A.M., 1985. Post-diapause development of sympatric *Choristoneura occidentalis* and *C. retiniana* (Lepidoptera: Tortricidae) populations and their hybrids. *Canad. Entomol.* 117:1479-1488.

WEBER J.D., 1994. *Latitude, physiological time, and the spruce budworm.* Msc Thesis, Univ. of Alberta, 84p.

Chapter 3

Effect of Tree Resistance on the Aggressors

Physiology and Genetics of Tree-Phytophage Interactions
Gujan (France), August 31 - September 5, 1997
Ed. INRA, Paris, 1999 (Les Colloques, n°90)

The performance of the green spruce aphid (*Elatobium abietinum* Walker) on provenances of Sitka spruce (*Picea sitchensis* (Bong.) Carr.)

K.R. DAY,H.L. ARMOUR, C.J. HENRY

University of Ulster, Environmental Studies
BT52 1SA, Coleraine, N.Ireland

RESUME

There is accumulating evidence that the origins of Sitka spruce *Picea sitchensis* (provenance or genetic family) play an important role in determining the population dynamics of the green spruce aphid *Elatobium abietinum.* Genetic variability in *P.sitchensis* makes it a good candidate for tree breeding, although recent genetic gains in 'super-Sitka' have not accounted for pest resistance explicitly. This paper reviews two studies, 11 years apart, on the aphid populations of *P.sitchensis* provenances in the same experimental field demonstration. The trends in susceptibility of the provenances were consistent, with the exception of the slowest growing and most northerly provenance. There were relationships between the latitudinal origins of provenances and their aphid loads; in general it was the most vigorously growing provenances that proved to be the most resistant to aphids.

There are recorded differences between P.sitchensis provenances in the time of shoot growth cessation and budset in late summer and autumn. An hypothesis that earlier dormancy was linked with greater nutrient availability for aphids, was not supported by data on the levels of amino acids in needles in October. In fact total amino nitrogen was inversely related to the summer aphid population hosted by each provenance and most essential amino acids were at very low levels. Together with the similarity in budburst phenology among provenances, this suggested that factors other than nutrients are responsible for the differences in provenance susceptibility.

The green spruce aphid is thought to avoid some species of spruce and also new foliage by responding to volatile compounds in epicuticular wax at the needle leaf surface. A resistance mechanism based on secondary metabolites would correspond with observations, since more-vigorous trees probably sequester more effective surface deterrents.

In support of this, it was found that relative provenance susceptibility to aphids was correlated with feeding damage by a completely different insect, the large pine weevil Hylobius abietis. In a separate series of experiments, shoot material from P.sitchensis provenances was challenged with weevils of known age and cultural background, and the amount of bark removed in a feeding trial was recorded. The greatest levels of bark removal tended to be found on provenances which had hosted larger peak aphid populations. The most likely explanation for a fairly universal resistance mechanism probably derives from secondary plant metabolites rather than the nutrient levels available to both insects.

INTRODUCTION

Sitka spruce (Picea sitchensis (Bong.) Carr.) has become an indispensable component of the forest industry in maritime regions of western Europe (Henderson and Faulkner, 1987) where tree breeding programmes are already well-advanced (Lee, 1986, 1990; Roulund, 1974, 1990) and where major gains in yield are expected from superior full-sib families in future (Costa e Silva et al., 1994; Jensen et al., 1997; Nielsen and Roulund, 1996). Perhaps because it is an exotic species, Sitka spruce has so far avoided the serious pest problems associated with other spruce species in Europe (Bakke, 1991) whereas it has experienced difficulties with aggressive pests within its natural range (Alfaro, 1996). Nevertheless, two insect species, the green spruce aphid (Elatobium abietinum Walker) and the large pine weevil (Hylobius abietis L.), are ubiquitous and costly pests of plantation forestry in north western Europe (Day and Leather, 1997).

The green spruce aphid feeds on the phloem sap of Sitka spruce needles which develop a yellow spot, then banding at the point of stylet insertion. Needles may dehisce some 8-12 days later (Fisher, 1987) and the rate of premature defoliation is related to the overall aphid population level (Day and McClean, 1991). By contrast, the large pine weevil gnaws patches of bark and subcortical tissues on recently mature stems. The damage inflicted tends to be aggregated within and among stems (Tilles et al. 1986) with severe consequences for young plants. The likelihood that the two insect species respond in a similar way to a range of host plants seems as remote as their feeding biology is different, nevertheless one of the purposes of this paper is to examine the evidence for parallel trends in susceptibility among a range of Sitka spruce seed origins. Susceptibility or resistance was indicated by adult weevil feeding trials on spruce stem sections, and by population estimates of aphids in field trials of the different spruce provenances.

Resistance of Sitka spruce to attack by Elatobium could be expected to be based on characteristics such as the nutritional status of the plant, morphology or anatomy of the needle on which the aphid feeds, and secondary metabolites of the host (Jackson and Dixon, 1996). It is even possible that the redistribution of alate Elatobium is determined by tree canopy apparency (Day and Armour, 1997). If host sap nutrition differs between provenances, then it should be most easily recognised at times of the year when their bud and shoot phenology are least synchronised or when sap nutrients are at their highest overall levels. Among Sitka spruce provenances planted in the British Isles, the only known phenological differences are in the timing of cessation of shoot elongation and bud set in the late summer and autumn (Kraus and Lines, 1976; Lines and Mitchell, 1966). Needle sap nutrients peak in early May, just prior to bud break, and again, but at a lower amplitude, in early October/November around the time of bud set (Fisher and Dixon, 1986; Parry, 1974).Thus it is possible that provenances with early budset will exhibit a different needle sap nutrient profile from those with late budset, and that this presents differing opportunities for aphid performance and consequent population levels. This hypothesis would be worth considering further if there was a relationship between nutritional status in October of host plant provenances and their aphid populations. The responses of insect pests to trees of different genetic origin have rarely been considered explicitly in Sitka spruce breeding programmes, except as a component of the natural environment of trees undergoing field growth and survival trials. Profiles of Sitka spruce resistance are gradually becoming apparent (Day, 1984a;

Carter and Nichols, 1988; Jensen et al., 1997) and this investigation is an attempt to clarify the position further.

MATERIAL AND METHODS

Provenance field trial

The provenances of Sitka spruce were set out as a forest experiment at Springwell Forest, Co. Londonderry, N.Ireland. The 64 m2 plots were replicated for each of 17 provenances and in 6 randomised complete blocks. Further details of the experimental layout and sampling are given in Day (1984a). The origins of the provenances investigated are given in Table 1.

Table 1. Sitka spruce provenances on which aphid populations (Day, 1984a and Armour, 1996) or weevil damage were evaluated in Northern Ireland. A (Alaska), BC (British Columbia), W (Washington), O (Oregon), C (California).

Provenance Code	IUFRO Number	Origin locality	Latitude	Longitude
A24	3024	Duck Creek	58° 22'	134° 35'
A27	3027	Craig	55° 30'	133° 08'
BC44	3044	Inverness	54° 12'	130° 15'
BC52	3052	Tasu Creek	52° 52'	132° 05'
BC56	3056	Holberg	50° 37'	128° 07'
BC62	3062	Big Qualicum R.	49° 23'	124° 37'
W03	3003	Forks	48° 04'	124° 18'
W04	3004	Kalaloch	47° 42'	124° 25'
O12	3012	Necanicum	45° 49'	123° 46'
O18	3018	Brookings	42° 15'	124° 23'
C19	3019	Big Lagoon	41° 08'	124° 09'
STD	Standard Irish Seed Batch from Kilsheelan forest, Tipperary, EIRE (Included in graphical relationships as Queen Charlotte Islands latitude)			

Assessment of aphid populations and weevil damage

Aphids were evaluated on sample trees from 6 selected provenances in 3 of the blocks (Day, 1984a) when the trees were 8 years old. A second evaluation of aphid populations was made 19 years after planting (Armour, 1996) when 9 provenances were selected in replicate plots from two blocks. In both cases aphid counts were made on 6 sample shoots per tree, and from 3 trees within a provenance plot. The counts were standardised by the number of needles present on each sample shoot and population density expressed as aphids per 100 needles. Samples were timed to coincide with peak population density in early summer (Day and Crute, 1990) and further details of the standard sampling procedure are given in Day (1984b).

To evaluate weevil feeding damage, sections of stem were removed from branches between 1.5 and 3 m from ground level. In the laboratory further sections were taken from 2 to 3-year-old growth. These were presented to weevils in standardised trials for a period of one day at 15oC in 400 ml containers. Each replicate trial gave ten weevils the opportunity to feed on a single stem representing one provenance. There were 20 replicate trials for each of 17 provenances, although only the results for 9 provenances corresponding to the aphid counts are reported here. The weevils used were from laboratory-reared stock and were of uniform age and fed ad libitum on Sitka spruce stem material prior to the experiment. The rate of feeding was estimated from each stem as the area of bark removed by all weevils during the trial period.

Phenology, tree height and amino acid assessment

Observations on budburst phenology, similar to those employed by Lines and Mitchell (1966), were made for each of the provenances under investigation in 1983 and again in 1994. Tree heights in plots were measured throughout the experiment in 1983 and reported as mean tree height for a provenance. Amino acid levels in the sap of trees in the field experiment were estimated in October 1984, when the trees were 9 years old. By October buds of the most northerly provenances had set and there was little or no shoot elongation continuing in the most southerly provenances. If differences in amino nitrogen levels emerged, they were expected to be attributable to continued mobilisation of nutrients in needle sap of southerly provenances and lower levels following bud set for the northernmost provenances. A similar method to Parry (1974) was adopted for assessing nutrients. Needle samples

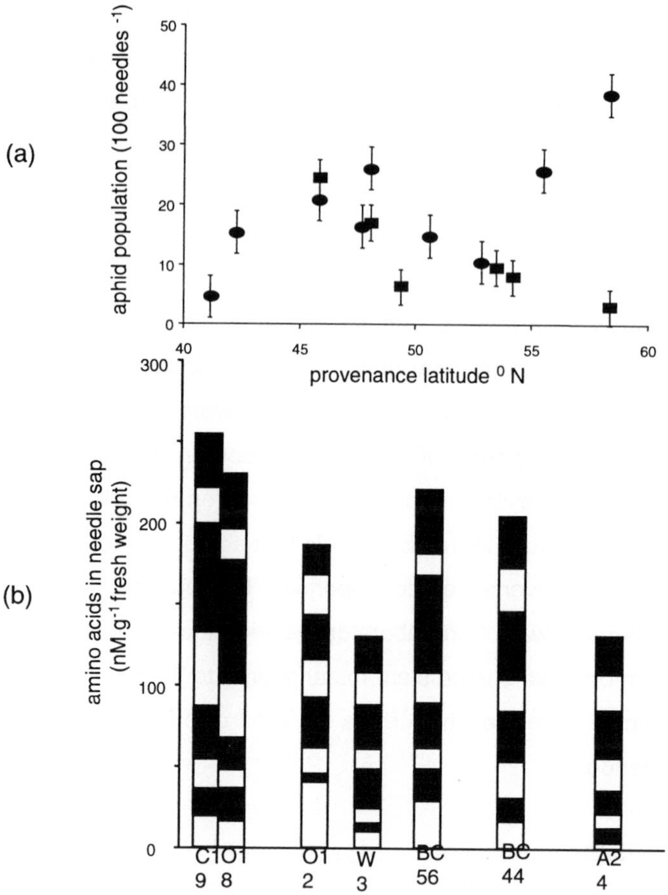

Fig.1 Relationships between aphids, needle sap amino acids and the original latitude of provenances; (a) aphid peak population densities in the same provenance trial at 8 years ■(Day, 1984) and 19 years ●(Armour, 1996) after planting (bars signify 95% confidence limits); (b) total and individual soluble amino acid levels in needles sampled in October (in order from the top of each bar - alanine, glycine, glutamic acid, glutamine, serine, threonine aspartic acid and asparagine). Provenance positions coincide with (a) above.

were clipped from one year old foliage from four branches on each tree around midday and frozen in liquid nitrogen for transportation. Needles were prepared in 2 g units and ground to a fine paste with 20 ml ethanol and the filtrate dried and rehydrated with distilled water. Chlorophyll was removed by partitioning with petroleum ether. Sub-samples of 2ml were sealed and hydrolysed at 100oC with an equal amount of 2N H Cl and a dried residue taken up in 5ml pH 2.2 buffer. Runs were made on an L.K.B. 4101 Amino acid analyser.

RESULTS

Comparative aphid population densities

Although a substantial proportion of the variation in aphid numbers could be attributed to the location (block) within the experiment, more than 50% of the variation resulted from differences between provenances (Day, 1984a). This was a promising result for the potential of tree breeding for resistance, since the provenance which appeared to be the most resistant to aphids hosted only 12% of the population found on the least resistant provenance (1983 and 1994). Unexpectedly there was a relationship between aphid population and the original latitude of the seed origin, i.e. for tree age 8 years the southern provenances supported the highest aphid numbers. In the second study at 19 years a greater range of provenances were evaluated (Armour, 1996) and differences between provenances were equally marked although there appeared to be some differences from the earlier results (Fig. 1a). Most of the data (the middle latitudinal range) are consistent between the two studies. The only major disparity is focused on the most northerly provenance (Alaska 24) for which the aphid population in the recent survey was the highest overall.

The levels of amino acids in needle sap were low in all provenances investigated (cf. Fisher and Dixon, 1986; Parry, 1974) and of those identified, all but one (threonine) were non-essential amino acids (Fisher, 1987). The trend by original provenance latitude corresponded to expectations, in that there was a slight tendency for the more northern provenances, whose shoots would have ceased

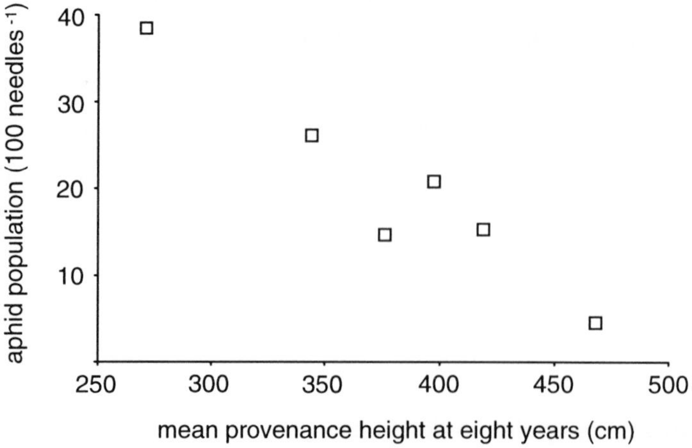

Fig. 2 Relationship between mean aphid peak population density on six provenances and their mean height after eight years.

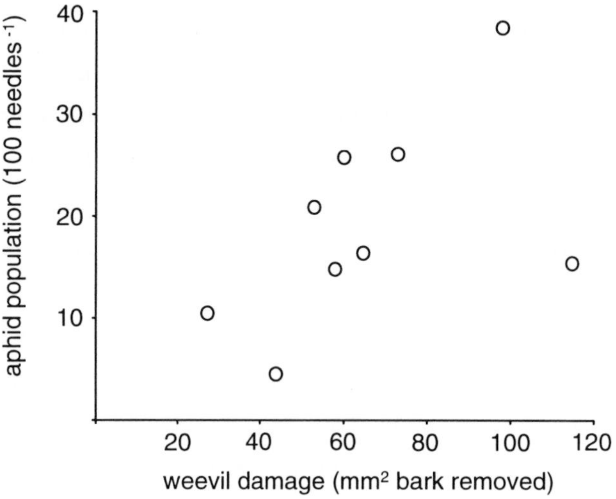

Fig.3 Similarity between aphid population density estimated on nine provenances and the damage to the same provenance stems presented to weevils in feeding trials.

growth early in the season, to have lower amino acid levels (Fig. 1b).However, the aphid population estimates were almost inversely related to these amino nitrogen levels, suggesting that nutrient availability at the end of the growing season played little part in determining differences in aphid performance and hence host resistance. It was unlikely, also, that major nutrient differences between provenances were involved before bud break since there were no differences between the provenances in bud break phenology in the experiment in 1983 or 1994 (and Kraus and Lines, 1976).

There was an inverse relationship between aphid population density on a provenance and its growth performance signified by height after 9 years (Fig. 2). More strongly growing Sitka spruce provenances, it seems, support fewer aphids.

There was a positive correlation between the population density of aphids hosted by a provenance and the amount of bark consumed by the large pine weevil in laboratory culture (Fig. 3). Although the provenance results for weevil feeding in this "no choice" trial were not statistically significant, a parallel experiment where weevils were given all 17 provenance stems from which to chose, proved highly significant (square root transformed damage levels, $F = 3.629$, df 17,414, $p<0.01$) (Henry and Day, in prep.).

CONCLUSION

Aphid populations on a range of Sitka spruce provenances were substantially different. Translated into the life of a forest and if consistent, such differences could mean the suppression of aphid populations to a level where needle loss was negligible (Day and McClean, 1991) and below a threshold where any economic damage could be perceived. This result is promising for efforts to incorporate aphid resistance into tree breeding programmes.

The connection of aphid abundance with original latitude of provenance suggests that provenance-related phenology could be functionally involved, and since the only known phenological differences between Sitka spruce provenances in the British Isles correspond with shoot growth cessation (Kraus and Lines, 1986), the levels of sap nutrients available to aphids in October were measured. These proved to be not high enough to have a significant differential influence on aphid performance although they were related to provenance origin. The broad similarity in the date of budbreak and the existence of more aphids on stronger growing provenances also suggest nutrients are unlikely to be the prime cause of resistance/susceptibility.

There were some similarities, but also differences, in the field results obtained prior to and after canopy closure in the provenance trial. Similarities in aphid susceptibility were evident in a provenance range from Oregon to British Columbia, but a major difference in results for the most northerly Alaskan provenance was also noted. This might suggest an element of temporal instability in resistance at the provenance level. Furthermore, the response of aphids to these provenances may not be locally consistent either since Danish results provide no evidence for trends based on the latitude of provenance origins (Harding et al., 1997). Despite this, there was a surprisingly good correlation between aphid abundance and pine weevil damage; these are two species which feed on the same plant but in a completely different manner, so a correspondence in resistance mechanism to both would seem unusual. Nevertheless, more convincing evidence for similar insect responses is emerging from work on the white pine weevil (Pissodes strobi) and the green spruce aphid feeding on white spruce in British Columbia (Alfaro, in prep.).

There is little evidence from this investigation that differences in sap nutrient levels are responsible for different aphid population levels on the spruce provenances. Plant morphological differences could play a role, but more likely is a mechanism based on plant secondary metabolites; these seem already to be implicated in the choice of spruce species by the aphid (Nichols, 1984, 1987). Recent evidence strongly suggests that volatile substances in the epicuticular wax of needles determine the unsuitability of new Sitka spruce foliage to Elatobium (Jackson and Dixon, 1996). Such allomones could act at high concentrations, but as kairomones at lower concentrations (Jackson and Dixon, 1996) and monoterpenes are known to decrease in concentration as the needle ages (Hruitfiord et al., 1974) and could operate in this manner. Monoterpenes, however, are not thought to be implicated in resistance of Scots pine to Hylobius (Selander and Kalo, 1979). The most striking known chemosystematic differences between Sitka spruce provenances are among polyphenols such as stilbene (Forrest, 1975) although the responses of either Elatobium or Hylobius to these substances is unknown. Nevertheless, both insect species respond to secondary plant metabolites at some distance from their sources (Jackson and Dixon, 1996; Nordlander et al., 1986) suggesting considerable potential for Sitka spruce volatiles in determining resistance to quite different pests.

ACKNOWLEDGEMENTS

Support for this study was gratefully received from the European Commission through AIR3-CT94-1883 and FAIR3-CT96-1792 and from the National Council for Forest Research (COFORD) for project 2-4-95.

REFERENCES

ALFARO R., 1996. Role of genetic resistance in managing ecosystems susceptible to white pine weevil. *For. Chron.* 72, 374-380.

ARMOUR H.L., 1996. *Response of green spruce aphid populations to variation in host plant genotype. Unpublished D.Phil. thesis*, University of Ulster, 248 pp.

BAKKE A., 1991. *Socioeconomic aspects of an integrated pest management program in Norway.* Proceedings of a Symposium, "Integrated Pest Management of Forest Defoliators", A.G. Raske and B.E. Wickman (eds.). *For. Ecol. Manage.* 39, 299-303.

CARTER C.I., NICHOLS J.F.A., 1988. *The green spruce aphid and Sitka spruce provenances in Britain.* Forestry Commission Occasional Paper No. 19. HMSO, London.

COSTA E, Silva J., NIELSEN U.B., ROULUND H., 1994. Sitka spruce clonal performance with special reference to wood density. *Silvae Genetica* 43, 82-90.

DAY K.R., 1984a. Systematic differences in the population density of green spruce aphid, *Elatobium abietinum* in a provenance trial of Sitka spruce, *Picea sitchensis. Annals of Applied Biology* 105, 405-412.

DAY K.R., 1984b. The growth and decline of a population of the spruce aphid *Elatobium abietinum* during a three year study, and the changing pattern of fecundity, recruitment and alary polymorphism in a Northern Ireland forest. *Oecologia* 64, 118-124.

DAY K.R., ARMOUR H., 1997. Spruce aphid population dynamics in relation to canopy character: scope for cultural regulation. *In*: J.C. Grégoire, A. M.. Liebhold, F.M. Stephen, K.R.Day, and S.M. Salom (eds) *Proceedings: Integrating cultural tactics into the management of bark beetle and reforestation pests.* USDA For. Serv. Gen. Tech. Rep. NE-236, 1-16.

DAY K.R., CRUTE S., 1990. The abundance of spruce aphid under the influence of an oceanic climate. In: A.D.-Watt, S.R. Leather, M.D. Hunter and N.A.C. Kidd, eds. *Population dynamics of forest insects.* Intercept, Andover, 25-33.

DAY K.R., LEATHER S.R., 1997. *Threats to forestry by insect pests in Europe* (Chapter 11). *In* A.D. Watt, N.E. Stork and M.D. Hunter (eds.) *Forests and Insects* Chapman & Hall. *Symposia of the Royal Entomological Society of London*, 18,177-205

DAY K.R., MCCLEAN S., 1991. Influence of the green spruce aphid on defoliation and radial stem growth of Sitka spruce. *Annals of Applied Biology*, 11, 415-423.

FISHER M., 1987. The effect of previously infested spruce needles on the growth of the green spruce aphid, *Elatobium abietinum*, and the effect of the aphid on the amino acid balance of the host plant. *Ann. appl. Biol.* 111, 33-41.

FISHER M., DIXON A.F.G., 1986. Role of photoperiod in the timing of dispersal in the green spruce aphid *Elatobium abietinum. J. Anim. Ecol.* 55, 657-667.

FORREST G.I. 1975. Polyphenol variation in Sitka spruce. *Can. J. For. Res.* 5, 26-37.

HARDING S., DAY K.R., ARMOUR H., 1997. Selecting for resistance in genetically defined Sitka spruce, Ch.7 *In* Day, K.R., Halldorsson, G., Harding, S.H.,Straw, N. *The green spruce aphid in western Europe: ecology, status and prospects for management.* Forestry Commission (UK) Technical Bulletin, in press.

HENDERSON D.M., FAULKNER R., 1987. Sitka spruce. *Proc. R.Soc.Edin.*, B 93 (1/2), 1-234.

HRUITFORD B.F., HOPLEY S.M., GARA R.I., 1974. Monoterpenes in Sitka spruce: within tree and seasonal variation. *Phytochemistry* 13, 2167-2170.

JACKSON D.L., DIXON A.F.G., 1996. Factors determining the distribution of the green spruce aphid, *Elatobium abietinum*, on young and mature needles of spruce. *Ecological Entomology* 21, 358-364.

JENSEN J.S., HARDING S., ROULUND H., 1997. Resistance to the green spruce aphid (*Elatobium abietinum* Walker) in progenies of Sitka spruce (*Picea sitchensis* (Bong.) Carr.). *Forest Ecolology and Management* (in press).

KRAUS J.F., LINES R., 1976. Patterns of shoot growth, growth cessation and budset in a nursery test of Sitka spruce provenances. *Scottish Forestry* 30, 1-9.

LEE S.J., 1986. Tree breeding in Britain. 3. Advance generation breeding and future prospects. *Forestry and British Timber* 15, 24-25.

LEE S.J., 1990. Potential gains from genetically improved Sitka spruce. *Forestry Commission Research Information Note* No. 190. HMSO, London.

LINES R., MITCHELL A.F., 1966. Differences in phenology of Sitka spruce provenances. *Forestry Commission Report on Forest Research 1965*, 173-184. HMSO, London.

NICHOLS J.F.A. 1984. *The performance of the green spruce aphid (*Elatobium abietinum *Walker) on various spruce species and the effect of foliar amino acids and secondary compounds.* Unpublished M. Phil. thesis, University of Reading.

NICHOLS J.F.A. 1987. Damage and performance of the green spruce aphid, *Elatobium abietinum* on twenty spruce species. *Entomologia Experimentalis et Applicata* 45, 211-217.

NIELSEN U.B., ROULUND H., 1996. Genetic variation in characters of importance for stand establishment in Sitka spruce (*Picea sitchensis* (Bong.) Carr.). *Silvae Genetica* 45, 197-204.

NORLANDER G., EIDMANN H.H., JACOBSON U., NORDENHEM H., SJODIN K., 1986. Orientation of the pine weevil *Hylobius abietis* to underground sources of host volatiles. *Ent. exp. appl.* 41, 91-100.

PARRY W.H., 1974. The effects of nitrogen levels in Sitka spruce needles on *Elatobium abietinum* (Walker) populations in north-eastern Scotland. *Oecologia*, 15, 305-320.

ROULUND H., 1974. Forædling af Sitkagran. *Skoven* 3, 56-58.

ROULUND H., 1990. Outline for a revision of the Sitka spruce breeding plan in Denmark. *Forest Tree Improvement* 23, 132-143.

SELANDER J., KALO P., 1979. Evaluation of resistance of Scots pine seedlings to *Hylobius abietis* L. (Coleoptera, Cuculionidae) in relation to their monoterpene composition. *Silva Fennica* 13, 115-130.

TILLES D.A., NORLANDER G., NORDENHEM H., EIDMANN H.H., WASSGREN A., BERGSTROM G., 1986. Increased release of volatiles from feeding scars: a major cause of field aggregation in the pine weevil *Hylobius abietis* (Coleoptera: Curculionidae). *Environmental Entomology* 15, 1050-1054.

Physiology and Genetics of Tree-Phytophage Interactions
Gujan (France), August 31 - September 5, 1997
Ed. INRA, Paris, 1999 (Les Colloques, n°90)

Effects of foliage quality of different *Pinus sylvestris* L. clones on *Diprion pini* L. biology (Hymenoptera, Diprionidae)

F. PASQUIER-BARRE, M.-A. AUGER-ROZENBERG

INRA, Station de Zoologie Forestière, 45160 Olivet, France

SUMMARY

The sawfly *Diprion pini* causes significant damage in Europe on *Pinus sylvestris*. The biological cycle of this pine sawfly demonstrated three different interactions between foliage and life stage: 1/ the females which choose a plant to deposit their eggs; 2/ the eggs which are inside a needle damaged by the females with their ovipositor and 3/ the larvae which eat the foliage. To evaluate the effect of foliage on the 3 life stages, oviposition tests with or without host-choice, feeding bioassays and egg survival tests were simultaneously performed.

D. pini females were able to deposit their eggs on all the tested clones but demonstrated significant host-choice preference among Scots pine clones. Egg survival differed significantly between the clones. Eggs oviposited on some clones resulted in poor egg hatching. These experiments enabled us to determine *P. sylvestris* clones favorable and unfavorable to sawfly egg survival. Larval feeding bioassays revealed the importance of foliage quality to survival and development of *D. pini* larvae and permitted grouping clones into two categories according to their effects on larval survival.

Nevertheless, no correlation was found between *D. pini* oviposition preference, egg survival and larval performance. Some clones were always suitable for the sawfly, others were always unsuitable and most were suitable for some life stages and unsuitable for the others. Consequently the differential response of adults and offspring could be used in *P. sylvestris* breeding programs to prevent high levels of insect populations.

INTRODUCTION

For many insects, egg and larval development is limited to the plant where the female lays its eggs. Consequently the oviposition site choice of these insects is an important factor in population dynamics. Several studies assumed that females choose their host-plants according to a parameter which reflects the value for its offspring (Thompson and Pellmyr, 1991; Tisdale and Wagner, 1991).

Several recent studies showed that female insects don't lay eggs at random. There was classification of host by females (Craig *et al.,* 1989). But the host suitability for females and for larval performances were often different. In this way, the knowledge of tree effects on all the life stages are necessary in order to develop resistance to insect in tree selection programs.

The pine sawfly *Diprion pini* causes significant damage to Scots pine (*Pinus sylvestris*) during outbreaks which are rare, unpredictable and devastating (Géri, 1988). Auger *et al.* (1990; 1992) showed the importance of foliage quality on survival and development of *Diprion pini* larvae. The first and second instars are the most sensitive of any instars to foliage quality. These instars move little and scarcely change of tree. Consequently, the oviposition preference of females of this species are very important for the success of offspring. In contrast to other defoliators, the eggs of the pine sawfly are inserted by females in the needles and exchanges take place between eggs and needles during development of the embryo (Eliescu, 1932). Variation in tree foliage quality or variation following these injuries may modify the hatching rate.

In this paper, we report results of investigations that evaluated the biological and behavioral aspects of the relationship between *Diprion pini* and different Scots pine clones. The objectives of this research were:

1/ to determine suitability for oviposition and preference of adults among clones.

2/ to determine the impact of Scots pine clones on eggs.

3/ to confirm the foliage suitability of different clones for the larvae.

4/ to compare the egg survival rates, the larval performances and the oviposition choice on the different tested clones.

MATERIALS AND METHODS

The eight *Pinus sylvestris* clones selected in this study were grown in National Institute of Agronomic Research (INRA) nursery (Orléans, France). Vegetative copies, ramets, were grafted in 1987 and 1989. Three clones had been collected in Taborz (Poland) and five in Hagueneau (France). Based on larval performance, four clones were presumed suitable (clones 130, 133 and 872 from France and 586 from Poland) and four clones unsuitable for *D. pini* (clones 136, 147 from France and clones 588 and 649 from Poland) (Auger *et al.,* 1990, 1992).

Third instar *D. pini* collected in Fontainebleau Forest (France) in May 1996 were reared under lab conditions (Goussard and Géri, 1989). The cocoons were stored in outside conditions under a shelter. Adults emerging in April 1997 were used immediately for oviposition tests in choice and non-choice experiments. Some of these adults were mated. Egg experiments occurred in May 1997 and larval experiments in June 1997 with the offspring of the earlier experiment.

Egg tests were performed in the field at the INRA nursery. Two-host oviposition choice tests were performed in the laboratory (20°C, 16h30 of daylight). Non-host oviposition choice tests were conducted simultaneously in the field and in the laboratory.

Field experiments

No choice oviposition tests

In no choice oviposition tests, females can lay eggs on only one kind of foliage. One female and one male were netted one per ramet and 10 ramets were used per clone. We observed the oviposition frequency (the number of females that laid eggs per clone). By needle dissection, we counted the number of eggs laid by each female (N) and by female dissection, we counted the number of eggs remaining in the female abdomen after death (n). We calculated (N/N+n): the ratio of eggs oviposited per female as oviposition performance.

Egg survival tests

Two experiments were conducted. First, five females per clone were placed in individual nets in the field. Then the damaged needles were removed. The slits cut by each female were measured and the needles were dissected to count the eggs inside. Second, for each clone, 10 females were placed in individual nets and the length of slits were observed per female without removing the needles from the trees. Twelve days after the hatching of the first larvae, we counted the number of first instars alive and the number dead to determine the egg survival rate for each clone. Initial number of eggs was estimated using length of slits and regression equation between the number of eggs and the length of slits established from the previous experiment. The estimate of hatching number was confirmed by dissection of some needles of this second experiment.

Experiments under controlled conditions

Larval feeding tests

One twig per clone was placed in a transparent plastic box (10 * 25 * 25 cm). Fifty second instars were placed in each box. The eight selected clones were tested with three replications per clone. The foliage was renewed every three days. Number of larvae still alive after 12 days, weight of cocoons and potential female fecundity by dissection were observed and female percentage were calculated.

No choice oviposition tests under lab conditions

No choice oviposition tests were performed by placing two freshly-cut twigs of one clone in a box (60 * 60 * 30 cm). One female and one male were selected randomly and placed in each box. There was only one female per box to avoid competition or stimulation between females. The oviposition performance (N/N+n) was determined for each female. A minimum of 15 tests was conducted for each clone.

Oviposition choice tests

Two twigs of two different clones were placed as previously described in a box with one female and one male. Twenty tests were conducted for each of the 28 pairs of clones randomized in blocks. After two days, we observed the clone on which the female deposited its eggs and how many times each clone had been chosen. The preference of a clone was quantified by the number of times it was selected among all the combinations in percent (oviposition preference rate).

Statistical analysis

Statistical analysis were processed using Statistica software. Nonparametric X2 tests were performed to compare oviposition frequencies in field and lab according to the clones and to compare oviposition preferences on the different clones. ANOVA was performed on oviposition performance with two factors (experiment and clone), on larval survival rates and egg survival rates with one factor (clone). Clones were classified according to Newman-Keuls tests for feeding bioassays and egg survival test. Classification of clones according to oviposition preference rates were performed with X^2 tests for oviposition choice tests between two clones for all the combinations. Regression analysis were performed to estimate the number of eggs and to determine the relationship between egg survival rates, larval performance and oviposition preference rates.

RESULTS

No choice oviposition tests in lab and in field

The oviposition frequencies in no choice oviposition tests were not significantly different among clones ($X^2 = 4.7$; df = 15; $p > 0.98$ in field tests and $X^2 = 2.97$; df = 15; $p > 0.99$ in lab tests). But the oviposition frequencies were higher in field (85 %) than in lab conditions (73 %; $X^2 = 23.3$; df = 15; $p < 0.05$). Oviposition performances (N/N+n) were not different between clones ($F_{7;216} = 0.42$; $p > 0.89$) nor between experiment conditions ($F_{1;216} = 1.88$; $p > 0.17$). No interaction between clones and conditions has been noticed ($F_{7;216} = 0.39$; $p > 0.91$). Results showed that all the clones tested were suitable for females to lay eggs in field or in lab conditions.

Oviposition choice tests

For the oviposition choice tests, X^2 test shows that females do not choose oviposition site randomly ($X^2 = 22.1$; df = 7; $p < 0.01$). The mean values for each clone are presented and ranked in Table 1. Comparisons two by two showed a classification of clones according to female choice from clone 133 to clone 586 (Table 1).

Egg survival tests

The slit length (L cm) made by a female was significantly linked to the number of eggs oviposited ($r^2 = 0.99$; $p < 0.01$; n = 40). This relation was independent of clone and of the number of needles damaged. The number of eggs oviposited (E) may be estimated by " $E = -0.9 + 6.5 * L$ ".

Table 1. Oviposition preference rates and progeny performances of *Diprion pini* on 8 *Pinus sylvestris* clones. H means that the clone was collected in Hagueneau and T in Taborz. According to previous study, the suitable clones were noticed S and unsuitable U. Results of classifications are indexed (Newmann-Keuls or X^2 tests, $p < 0.05$).

Clone number	Origin and classification		Oviposition preference (%)	Larval survival (%)	Egg survival (%)
130	H	S	13.7_{d}	73.3_{b}	70.2_{e}
133	H	S	1.4_{a}	77.3_{b}	52.1_{bcd}
136	H	U	10.4_{bc}	13.3_{a}	67.3_{e}
147	H	U	8.0_{b}	4.0_{a}	8.3_{a}
586	T	S	23.0_{f}	72.6_{b}	45.0_{bc}
588	T	U	13.0_{cd}	5.3_{a}	57.8_{cde}
649	T	U	16.2_{e}	2.6_{a}	42.3_{b}
872	H	S	14.3_{e}	76.0_{b}	61.9_{de}

Table 2. Classification of 8 *Pinus sylvestris* clones according to *D. pini* oviposition preference and progeny performance compared to mean values. Clone were represented by their INRA clone number.

Larval survival							
< 15 %				> 70 %			
Egg survival (%)				Egg survival (%)			
< 50.6		> 50.6		< 50.6		> 50.6	
Oviposition preference		Oviposition preference		Oviposition preference		Oviposition preference	
< 12.5	> 12.5	< 12.5	> 12.5	< 12.5	> 12.5	< 12.5	> 12.5
147	649	136	588	/	586	133	130; 872

There was a significant difference among clones in egg survival rates ($F_{7;72} = 25.1$; $p < 0.0001$) (Tab. 1). But there was no significant relationship between egg survival rates and oviposition preferences ($p > 0.79$).

Larval feeding tests

Larval survival rates were significantly different based on the foliage eaten ($F_{7;16} = 253$; $p < 0.0001$), revealing two categories of clones for larvae in agreement with the anticipated categories (Tab. 1). Cocoon weight, percentage of females among all the cocoons and female fecundity were also decreased by unsuitable foliage compared to suitable foliage.

However larval survival rates were not significantly linked to egg survival rates ($p > 0.31$) or to oviposition preferences ($p > 0.88$). In addition, product "egg hatched number x larval survival rate" considered as an estimation of the offspring survival rate, was not correlated to the oviposition preference ($p > 0.17$).

Mean egg survival rates among clones was 50.6 % and mean oviposition preference was 12.5 %. Table 2 summarizing clone characterizations by comparison to these mean values shows the diversity of their aptitude to ensure sawfly development.

DISCUSSION

Results of biological tests clearly indicated that there were three different response patterns of *D. pini* life stages in relation to Scots pine clones. Oviposition choice tests revealed that females discriminate between the Scots pine clones. Choice of an oviposition site is not based on the value of host for its offspring. Tables 1 and 2 clearly show that there was no correlation between the three life stage in terms of preference. In other words, clones that are preferred by adults may not be the best for larval performance. However when they are forced, females can lay eggs on any clone. For instance if a female finds only clone 133 in a stand or in periods of overpopulation, it can lay eggs and develop on this clone. Consequently care must used in selection trees that will be used as trap tree for example. A clone that may be resistant based on adult choice may be susceptible based on larval performance.

Important factors could explain the diversity in insect-plant interactions we observed. These factors include competition or predation. *D. pini* larvae accumulate compounds from foliage and form oviposition repellent droplets against conspecific females (Hilker and Weitzel, 1991). In addition, Björkman *et al.* (1997) found a strong relationship between predation by ants and oviposition preference of the sawfly *Neodiprion sertifer*. But our experiments were conducted in the absence of predation or competition and these factors did not affect our results.

Others factors can be directly linked to the host-plant, such as morphology (Rausher, 1978), hardness (Constant *et al.,* 1996), density and presence of certain secondary compounds (Feeny *et al.*, 1997). *Neodiprion sertifer* females seem to prefer to lay eggs on foliage with high resin acid concentrations (Björkman *et al.*, 1997). Monoterpenes of *D. pini* larval droplet seem to be repellent against females. All these factors can be linked or may act simultaneously on the host-choice of females. For example, in a very high insect population, competition between insects and poor density of host-plant might act on the choice made by females. Foliage characterization will be the subject of further investigations.

The foliage eaten had a significant effect on larval development. *D. pini* larvae survived well on four of the eight clones, as expected according to the results of Auger *et al.* (1990; 1992). Our results support these studies and shows the stability of clone value for larvae. Moreover, there were significant differences of egg survival rates on *P. sylvestris* clones. But the effects of foliage on the eggs and larvae were significantly different. Sometimes when we evaluated egg survival rates, there were dead first instars but we counted them in eggs that hatched. In fact, *D. pini* first instars are the most sensitive to foliage quality as for *Neodiprion fulviceps* (Wagner and Zhang, 1993). A tree favorable for egg development could be unfavorable for larvae and we once found the opposite situation.

Wagner and Frantz (1990) showed that, in response to a water stress treatment of *Pinus ponderosa*, egg survival of the sawfly *Neodiprion fulviceps* was the most significant affected parameter of the biology of the insect. Our study revealed that eggs may be the critical stage of the development of *D. pini.* Variations of the foliage quality according to an abiotic stress might act on the *D. pini* - *P. sylvestris* interaction. Many authors have reported insect outbreaks associated with periods of drought stress (Mattson and Haack, 1987). The results presented here correspond to the performance of *D. pini* on *P. sylvestris* in a non-drought period. Future researches will examine the clone suitability for *D. pini* in drought period.

ACKNOWLEDGMENTS

We are grateful to Dr Claude Géri and Dr Jean Pouzat for their constructive comments and to Annie Yart, Francis Goussard and Blandine Bauer for helpful contributions.

REFERENCES

AUGER M.A., GÉRI, C., JAY-ALLEMAND C. AND BASTIEN C., 1990. Comestibilité de différents clones de pin sylvestre pour *Diprion pini* L. (Hym., Diprionidae) I. Incidence de la consommation des aiguilles de différents clones de pin sylvestre sur le développement de *Diprion pini* L. *J. Appl. Ent.*, 110, 489-500.

AUGER M.A., GÉRI C. AND HAVERLANT J., 1992. Incidence de la consommation de certains clones de Pin sylvestre pour *Diprion pini* L. (Hym., Diprionidae). *Mém. Soc. R. Belge Ent,* 35, 491-497.

BJÖRKMAN C., LARSSON S. AND BOMMARCO R., 1997. Oviposition preferences in pine sawflies: a trade-off between larval growth and defence against natural enemies. *Oïkos*, 79, 45-52.

CONSTANT B., GRENIER S., FEBWAY G. AND BONNOT G., 1996. Host plant hardness in oviposition of *Macrolophus caliginosus* (Hemiptera : Miridae). *Entomological Society of America,* 89, 1446-1452.

CRAIG T.P., ITAMI J.K. AND PRICE P.W., 1989. A strong relationship between oviposition preference and larval performance in a shoot-galling sawfly. *Ecology,* 70, 1691-1699.

ELIESCU,G. 1932. Contribution à la connaissance de la morphologie, de l'anatomie et de la biologie de *Lophyrus pini* L. *Z. ang. Ent.,* 19, 22-67.

FEENY P., ROSENBERRY L. AND CARTER M,. 1997. Chemical aspects of oviposition behavior in butterflies. In: Ahmad S. (Ed.) *Herbivorous insects : Host-seeking behavior and mechanisms*, pp. 27-76. New York: Academic press.

GÉRI C., 1988. The pine sawfly in central France. In: Berryman A.A. (Ed.) *Dynamics of forest insect populations. Patterns, Causes, Implications.* pp. 377-405. New York and London: Plenum Press.

GOUSSARD F. AND GÉRI C., 1989. Mise au point d'un élevage permanent de *Diprion pini* L. (Hym., Diprionidae) en laboratoire. *Agronomie,* 9, 911-918.

HILKER M. AND WEITZEL C., 1991. Oviposition deterrence by chemicals of conspecific larvae in *Diprion pini* (Hymenoptera : Diprionidae) and *Phyllodecta vulgatissima* (Coleoptera : Chrysomelidae). *Entomol. Gener.*, 15, 293-301.

MATTSON W.J. AND HAACK R.A., 1987. The role of drought stress in provoking outbreaks of phytophagous insects. In: Barbosa P. and Schultz J. (Eds.) *Insect outbreaks.* New York: Academic press.

RAUSHER M.D., 1978. Search image for leaf shape in a butterfly. *Science,* 200, 1071-1073.

THOMPSON J.N. AND PELLMYR O., 1991. Evolution of oviposition behavior and host preference in Lepidoptera. *Annu. Rev. Entomol.,* 36, 65-89.

TISDALE R.A. AND WAGNER M.R., 1991. Host stress influences oviposition preference and performance of a pine sawfly. *Ecological Entomology,* 16, 371-376.

WAGNER M.R. AND FRANTZ D.P., 1990. Influence of induced water stress in ponderosa pine on pine sawflies. *Oecologia,* 83, 452-457.

WAGNER M.R. AND ZHANG Z.Y., 1993. Host plant traits associated with resistance of ponderosa pine to the sawfly, *Neodiprion fulviceps. Can. J. For. Res.,* 23, 839-845.

Physiology and Genetics of Tree-Phytophage Interactions
Gujan (France), August 31 - September 5, 1997
Ed. INRA, Paris, 1999 (Les Colloques, n°90)

Role of Resin Acids in Ponderosa Pine *Pinus ponderosa* Laws Resistance to *Neodiprion fulviceps* Cresson (Hymenoptera: Diprionidae)

M.R. WAGNER[1], L. REN[1], T. G. HUNTSBERGER[2], M. MIHAY[3], R.D. FOUST[3]

[1] *School of Forestry, Northern Arizona University Flagstaff, AZ 86011 USA*

[2] *Bilby Research Center, Northern Arizona University Flagstaff, AZ 86011 USA*

[3] *Department of Chemistry, Northern Arizona University Flagstaff, AZ 86011 USA*

RESUME

Diterpene resin acid concentrations in ponderosa pine (*Pinus ponderosa*) were determined for trees phenotypically resistant and susceptible to the pine sawfly, *Neodiprion fulviceps* (Cresson). Nine diterpene resin acids were identified in 1 year-old needles including pimaric, sandaracopimaric, levopimaric, palustric, isopimaric, abietic, dehydroabietic, neoabietic and isocupressic acids. Levopimaric and palustric acids were significantly higher in trees that were phenotypically susceptible to pine sawflies based on paired-t test analysis. Larval survival tended to increase with increases in levopimaric and palustric acid but this relationship was not significant. Resin acids do not appear to serve as defensive compounds in ponderosa pine to pine sawflies, but may play other roles that improve sawfly survival.

INTRODUCTION

Variation in the susceptibility of forest trees is a widely observed phenomenon. Environmental and genetic factors both contribute to phenotypic differences in susceptibility. Previously we examined host plant traits that were associated with ponderosa pine resistance to pine sawflies (Wagner and Zhang, 1993). Our previous work indicated that anatomical and nutritional factors were most likely responsible for observed patterns. Terpenes were not useful in distinguishing resistant from susceptible trees. However, previous work examined lower molecular weight compounds including monoterpenes, oxymonoterpenes, and sesquiterpenes but did not include the higher molecular weight diterpene resin acids.

The role of diterpene resin acids in tree resistance to pine sawflies has recently been reviewed (Geri et. al, 1993). Resin acids cause toxicity in several animal taxa and have been previously shown to serve as antifeedants in young foliage of *Pinus banksiana* to *Neodiprion swainei* and *N. rugifrons* (All et al., 1975). For *Neodiprion sertifer* on *Pinus sylvestris*, high resin acid has a negative effect on young larvae but may have positive effects on older larvae (Larsson et al., 1986). However, Buratti et al. (1990) found no effect of increased resin acid on the sawfly *Diprion pini*. While no general pattern has emerged, there is some evidence that resin acids could play a role in resistance among pines to pine sawflies.

Because our previous examination of defensive chemistry in ponderosa pine did not include an examination of diterpene resin acids, we decided to test these compounds in the same trees used in the previous study by Wagner and Zhang (1993). In this paper we report that no resin acid was higher in sawfly resistant trees than in susceptible trees and that two resin acids (levopimaric and palustric) are higher in susceptible trees.

MATERIALS AND METHODS

General methods included the selection of ten matched tree pairs (one resistant and one susceptible to *Neodiprion fulviceps*). Trees were located during sawfly outbreaks in 1986. Within a pair, the resistant tree had no visible defoliation while the susceptible tree was heavily defoliated by *N. fulviceps*. A series of insect bioassays were conducted including: field natural bioassay, field caged bioassay and laboratory bioassay. All bioassays conclusively showed that all measures of insect survival (egg, larval, total) were higher on susceptible than resistant trees (Wagner and Zhang, 1993). For additional experimental details see Wagner and Zhang (1993).

For the results reported in this paper we resampled all trees used in our original experiments (Wagner and Zhang, 1993). Foliage was collected in May 1997 from the ten resistant and susceptible trees during the usual period of *N. fulviceps* feeding. During 1997 no sawflies were present at this site. For purposes of correlation analysis between resin acids and sawfly performance we used data from the laboratory bioassay conducted in 1988.

Sample Preparation

Approximately 2 g ponderosa pine foliage was extracted in 20 mL anhydrous diethyl ether. Samples were spiked with 600 mg heptadecanoic acid as an internal standard. Extracts were separated into neutral and acidic fractions using micro DEAE-Sehpadex columns prepared by the method of Magee and Zinkel (1986). Neutral fractions were eluted with a solvent mixture of 79:20:1 (ether, methanol, water). The acidic fraction was eluted with the above solvent acidified by bubbling CO_2 through the mixture for more than 20 minutes.

The acidic eluate was evaporated under nitrogen and the resin material re-dissolved in diethel ether. Methyl ester derivatives of the resin acids were formed by the micromethylation method of Schwartz and Bright (1974). N-methyl-N-nitroso-p-toluene-sulfonamide in 2-(2-ethoxyethoxy) ethanol and diethyl ether was used as the methylating reagent. Additional sample preparation details are repeated in Magee and Zinkel (1986) and Schwartz and Bright (1974).

Analytical Method

Resin acid methyl ester derivatives were analyzed by capillary column gas-liquid chromatography on a Hewlett-Packard model 5890 series II gas chromatograph equipped with an on-column injector and a flame ionization detector. Chromatographic separation occurred on a HP-1 Hewlett-Packard 30 meter, 0.25

mm i.d. fused silica capillary column with a 0.25 um-thick film of methyl silicone liquid stationary phase. Helium was used as the carrier gas and nitrogen was used as a makeup gas. The gas chromatograph was programmed to hold at an initial temperature of 170 degrees C for 16 minutes and ramped at 2 degrees C per minute to a final temperature of 250 degrees C. Total run time was 60 minutes. GC analysis was based on Hans and Zinkel (1990) and Zinkel and Hans (1986) with minor modifications (e.g. longer column length and slower temperature ramping).

Peak areas were quantified with a Hewlett-Packard 3396A integrator and resin acid concentrations were calculated by comparison with the peak area of a known quantity of internal standard added to each sample. Resin acid compounds were identified by order of elution and retention time after comparison with an analyzed resin sample provided by Duane F. Zinkel known to contain all of the common resin acids. Additionally, pimaric, sandaracopimaric and levopimaric acids in sample extracts were confirmed by comparison with retention time of eluted single compound standards. Abietic acid in samples was confirmed by GC/MS.

Statistical analysis

Paired t-test was used to compare resin acids between resistant and susceptible trees. Homogeneity of variance tests indicated homogeneous variance in all variables. Regression analysis was used to determine the relationship between resin acids that were significantly different based on the t-tests and larval and total survival. Alpha to reject the null hypothesis was set at $\propto = 0.05$.

RESULTS

The analytical methods used resulted in 9 diterpene resin acids that could be identified (pimaric, sandaracopimaric, levopimaric, palustric, isopimaric, abietic, dehydroabietic, neoabietic, isocupressic acids) and two unidentified resin acids. Neoabietic acid was the most abundant resin acid followed by isocupressic acid (Fig. 1). Levopimaric and palustric acid were both significantly ($n = 10$, $p = 0.012$ and $p =$

0.04 respectively) higher in sawfly susceptible trees than in sawfly resistant trees (Fig. 1).

Regression analysis failed to show a significant correlation between larval survival or total survival for either levopimaric or palustric acid (Fig. 2 & 3). However, for all of the regression analyses the trend was for sawfly survival to increase when concentrations of resin acid increased.

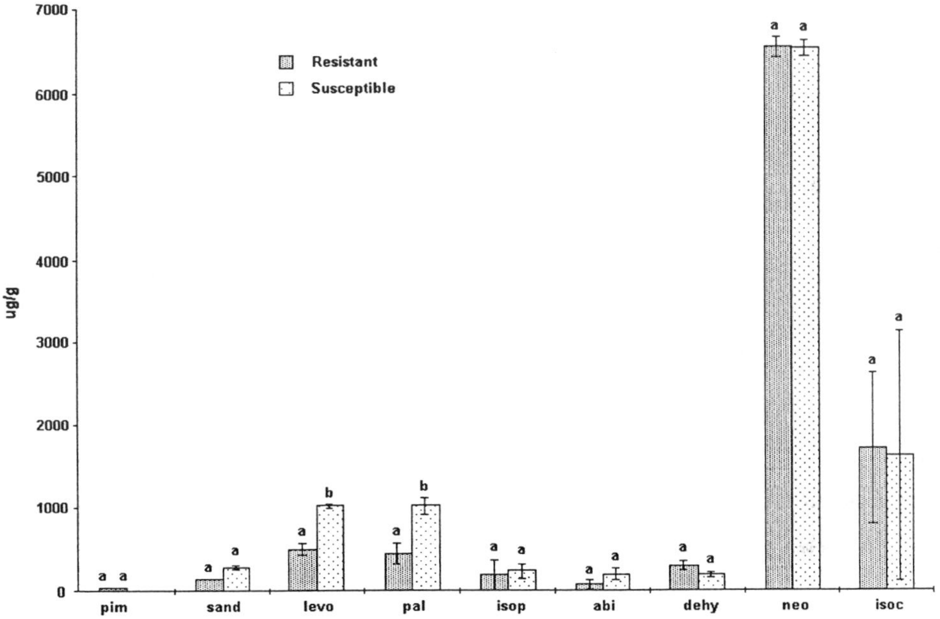

Figure 1. Resin acid concentration in ponderosa pine needles from sawfly resistant and susceptible trees. Different letters above the bars indicate significant differences based on paired t-test. Resin acid codes include: pimaric (pim), sandaracopimaric (sand), levopimaric (levo), palustric (pal), isopimaric (isop), abietic (abi), dehydroabietic (dehy), neoabietic (neo), isocupressic (isoc).

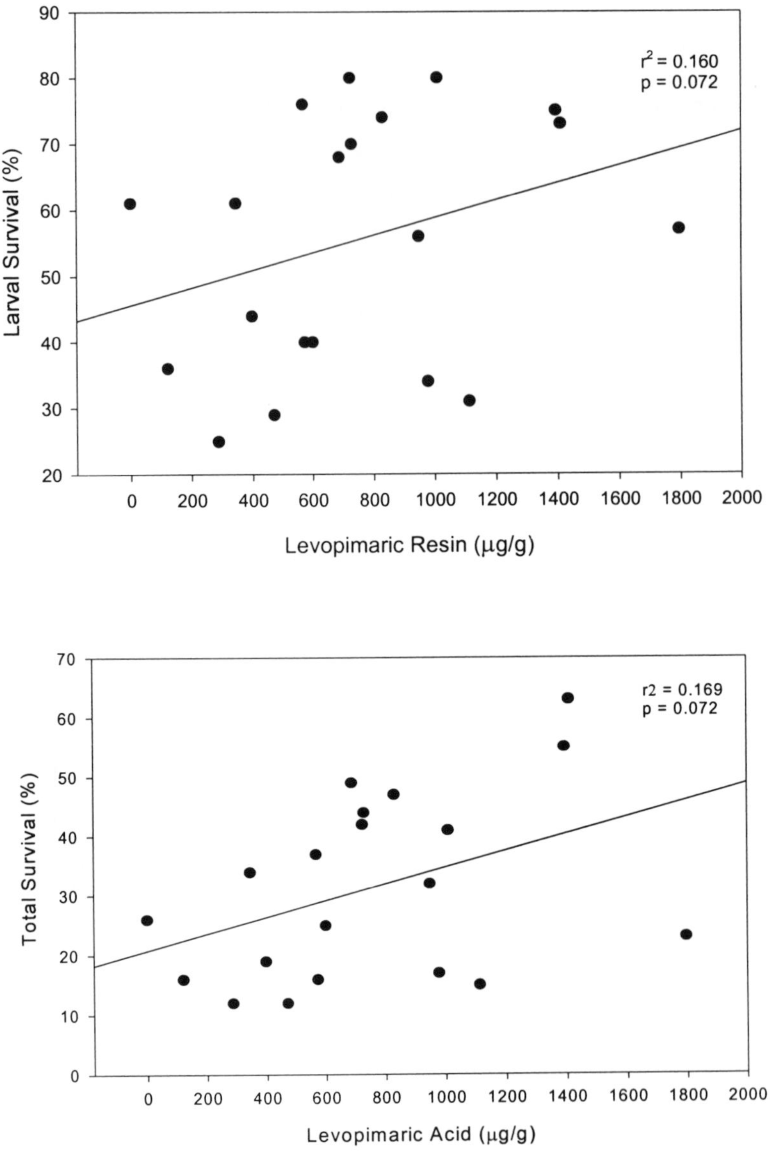

Figure 2. *Neodiprion fulviceps* larval (top) and total survival (bottom) as related to concentrations of levopimaric acid in ponderosa pine foliage.

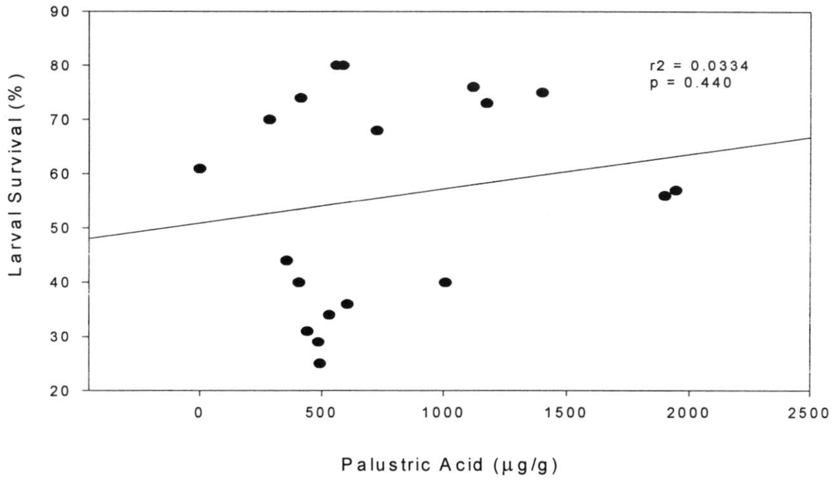

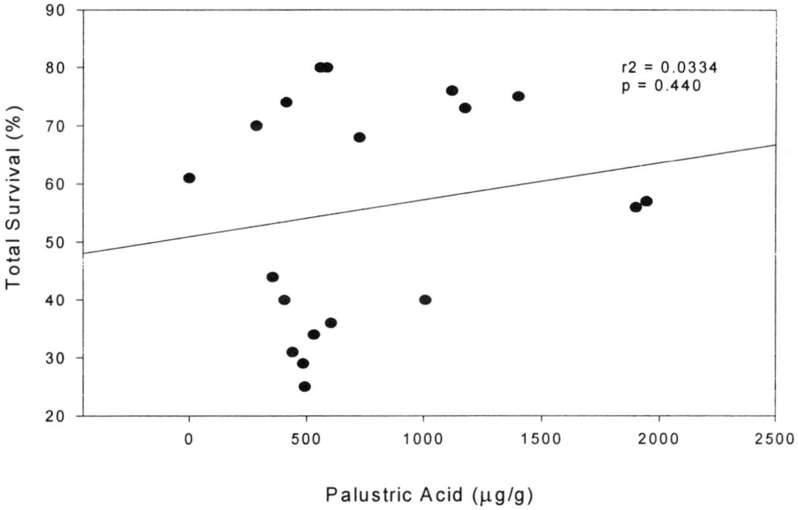

Figure 3. Neodiprion fulviceps larval (top) and total survival (bottom) as related to concentrations of palustric acid in ponderosa pine foliage.

CONCLUSIONS

It appears that diterpene resin acids in ponderosa pine are not functioning as defensive chemicals against *Neodiprion fulviceps*. If these compounds were playing an antifeedant function as reported for *Pinus banksiana* (All et al., 1975; Schuh and Benjamin, 1984a, b) then we would expect to see lower survival on those trees with higher resin acids. This was not the case. For seven of the resin acids (pimaric, sandaracopimaric, isopimaric, abietic, dehydroabietic, neoabietic, isocupressic) there was no significant difference between susceptible and resistant trees. In total, these resin acids comprise the vast majority of total resin acids in ponderosa pine foliage. In general, sawflies obviously tolerate high concentrations of these compounds without difficulty.

The higher concentration of levopimaric and palustric acid in susceptible trees tends to support the role of these compounds as phagostimulates or possibly as larval defensive compounds (Larsson et al., 1986; Buratti, 1988). However, commercial samples of these two compounds were determined to be effective larval antifeedents for *Neodiprion dubiosus*, *N. rugifrons*, and *N. lecontei* (Schuh and Benjamin, 1984a, b). Most likely, the effect of diterpene resin acids is dependent on the pine/pine sawfly system and concentration of these compounds. It is also quite possible the sawflies regulate the levels of certain resin acids in their diverticular pouches that store sequestered resin. Eisner et al. (1974) reported that both levopimaric and palustric acids were higher in diverticular pouches of *Neodiprion sertifer* than in the foliage of their host, *Pinus sylvestris*. Apparently the sawflies obtain these compounds by chewing on branches where those compounds occur in higher concentration than in needles. We have observed this branch-chewing behavior for several species of sawflies that feed on ponderosa pine. These observations lead us to believe that much more needs to be known about the role of resin acids in the interaction between pine sawflies and pines.

REFERENCES

ALL, J.N., BENJAMIN, D. M., MATSUMURA, F. 1975. Influence of semipurified constituents of juvenile jack pine, *Pinus banksiana*, foliage and other pine-derived chemicals on feeding of *Neodiprion swainei* and *N. rugifrons* larvae. *Ann. Entomol. Soc. Am.*, 68, 1095-1101.

BURATTI, L. 1988. *Etude des acides diterpéniques des aiguilles du pin sylvestre,* Pinus silvestris *L. Incidence sur le comportement alimentaire des larves de* Diprion pini *L. (Hymenoptera: Diprionidae).* Thèse de l'Université d'Orléans. Orleans.

BURATTI, L, ALLAIS, J.P., BARBIER, M. 1990. A resin acid from *Pinus sylvestris* needle. *Phytochemistry* , 29, 2708-2709.

EISNER, T., JOHNESSEE, J., CARREL, J. 1974. Defensive use by an insect of a plant resin. *Science*, 184, 996-999.

GÉRI, C., ALLAIS, J-P., AUGER, M-A., 1993. Effects of plant chemistry and phenology on sawfly behavior and development. *In*: Wagner, M.R., Raffa, K.F. (Eds.): *Sawfly Life History Adaptations to Woody Plants.* San Diego, Academic Press, p. 173-199.

HAN, J.S., ZINKEL, D.F. 1990. Gas chromotography of resin acids with a methyl silicone fused-silica !capillary column. *Naval Stores Review*, 100(1), 11-15.

LARSSON, S., BJORKMAN, C., GREF, R. 1986. Responses of *Neodiprion sertifer* (Hym., Diprionidae) larvae to variation needle resin acid concentration in Scots pine. *Oecologia*, (70), 77-84.

MAGEE, T. V., ZINKEL, D.F. 1986. A rapid method for diterpene resin acid analysis of pine needle oleoresin. *Canadian. Journal of Forestry Research* 16, p. 1107.

SCHUH, B. A., BENJAMIN, D. M. 1984a. The chemical feeding ecology of *Neodiprion dubiosus* Schedl, *N. rugifrons* Midd., and *N. lecontei* (Fitch) on jack pine (*Pinus banksiana* Lamb.). *Journal of Chemical Ecology* 10 (7), 71-79.

SCHUH, B. A., BENJAMIN, D. M. 1984b. Evaluation of commercial resin acids as feeding deterrents against *Neodiprion dubiosus*, *N. lecontei*, and *N. rugifrons* (Hymenoptera: Diprionidae). *Journal of Ecological Entomology*, 77, 802-805.

SCHWARTZ, D. P., BRIGHT, R.S. 1974. A column procedure for the esterification of organic acids with diazomethane at the microgram level. *Analytical Biochemistry*, 61, p. 217.

WAGNER, M.R., Z-Y. ZHANG. 1993. Host plant traits associated with resistance of ponderosa pine to the sawfly, *Neodiprion fulviceps*. *Canadian Journal of Forestry Research*, 23, 839-845.

ZINKEL, D.F., HAN, J.S. 1986. GLC determination of the resin acid composition in resins and oleoresins: state of the art. *Naval Stores Review*, 96(2), 14-19.

Physiology and Genetics of Tree-Phytophage Interactions
Gujan (France), August 31 - September 5, 1997
Ed. INRA, Paris, 1999 (Les Colloques, n°90)

Influence of food quality of two oak species on the development and growth of gypsy moth larvae

A. SCHOPF[1], G. HOCH[1], A. KLAUS[1], J. NOVOTNY[2], M ZUBRIK[2], C. SCHAFELLNER[1]

[1] *Universität für Bodenkultur Wien, Institute of Forest Entomology, Forest Pathology, and Forest Protection, A-1190 Vienna, Austria*

[2] *Forest Research Institute Zvolen, Research Station B. Štiavnica SK-969 23 Banska Štiavnica, Slovakia*

RESUME

The oak species, *Quercus petraea* and *Q. cerris*, are two of the main host plants of gypsy moth larvae in areas of frequent outbreaks in middle and eastern Europe. Although gypsy moth larvae are well known as highly polyphagous herbivores, we found high variability, but also significant differences in growth and development caused by feeding on these two oak species.

Comparing two gypsy moth populations (one from Austria and one from Slovakia), which had been fed with fresh oak leaves in the lab, both gypsy moth populations developed faster and gained more weight on *Q. cerris* than on *Q. petraea* during their early instars. This changed during the fourth instar, thus female pupae from *Q. cerris*-larvae were significantly larger and the adults laid significantly more eggs than those from *Q. petraea.*

Field studies also showed a clearly faster development with less mortality of the caged gypsy moth larvae feeding on *Q. cerris* compared to those on *Q. petraea*. Furthermore, pupae of both sexes from larvae which fed on *Q. cerris* had significantly higher weights than those from *Q. petraea.*

To reduce the variability in food quality and to study the causes of the more favorable development at conditions for gypsy moth on *Q. cerris,* we fed gypsy moth larvae with a leaf diet which was prepared from lyophilized leaf powder of one single host tree of each species. Those larvae which were fed on *Q. petraea*-diet showed two different patterns of development: 40% of the male and 50% of the female larvae developed synchronously with *Q. cerris*-larvae, but had reduced growth rates and minor pupal weights (70% with males, 80% with females). The rest of the tested larvae went through a supernumerary instar and yielded a similar pupal weight as larvae on *Q. cerris*-diet, however, at the cost of a prolonged developmental period.

Biochemical analyses of the leaf-powder revealed a markedly higher variation of nutrients and allelochemicals in *Q. petraea* during the period of leaf maturation compared to *Q. cerris*. However, to answer the question, which compounds are responsible for the minor suitability of *Q. petraea* for the development of gypsy moth larvae, further studies are required.

INTRODUCTION

The gypsy moth is a common pest of oak forests in Austria and its eastern and south-eastern neighbors Slovakia and Hungary. In Austria outbreaks of gypsy moth mainly occur in mixed oak forests, where *Quercus petraea* and *Q. cerris* are the dominant tree species. Hatching of the larvae coincides well with budbreak of *Q. petraea* during late April, while leaves of *Q. cerris* begin to develop about 2 weeks later. *Q. petraea* leaves might serve as the primary food source for the young larvae which probably switch to the *Q. cerris* diet. In Slovakia, however, oak forests are dominated by *Q. cerris* and outbreaks are more frequent and have higher intensities than in Austria.

The aim of this study was to examine the influence of the food quality of the two oak species on larval performance and fecundity of gypsy moth. In a first step we wanted to investigate whether the Austrian and/or the Slovakian gypsy moth population differ in their demands on food quality. Thus, we tested the development and growth of both populations on fresh foliage of both oak species under laboratory and field conditions, and – to minimize the effect of food variability – we reared larvae on leaf powder diet made from two tree individuals of each species. Biochemical analyses of the oak diets should provide first information about nutrient components which might influence larval development.

MATERIAL AND METHODS

Insect material

Gypsy moth larvae which were tested for developmental differences due to their origin, came from egg clusters which were collected from the field in Austria and Slovakia in autumn 1995. Those which were tested for differences in their development on both oak powder diets in the laboratory were obtained from the USDA - APHIS Methods Development Center in Otis, MA (U.S.A.).

For laboratory investigations 50 larvae each from both Austrian and Slovakian origin were reared under standardized conditions, at 20° C, 65% r.h. and a 16-hr photoperiod on fresh leaves from five 40 to 60-year old *Q. petraea* and *Q. cerris* trees. First and second instar larvae were kept in groups of 50, later instars singly on Petri dishes. Fresh leaves were provided daily.

Larvae were weighed during the premolt into the next instar. Duration of time of each larval stage was determined by the time of molting. Head capsules and exuviae were collected and weighed. Pupal mass was determined at day three after pupation. At the time that larvae were assigned for the feeding experiment, randomly selected aliquots of 10 larvae were also taken from both oak species to calculate an initial wet-to-dry weight ratio for the insects. Head capsule and exuvia weights were subtracted from the calculated dry weight of the premolting stage to determine the initial dry weight of the instar. For eclosion the adult moths were kept separately in mating boxes. After mating and oviposition egg masses were weighed and counted.

To study the development of gypsy moth larvae under field conditions, a total pool of 250 newly hatched larvae were placed for rearing on each host species.

Larvae were caged in cotton bags on twigs of 20 tree individuals from both oak species. Each bag held 5 first instar larvae with an adequate food supply for several days. The bags were transferred to another twig when food was running short. Larval development and mortality were controlled every two to three days, starting on May 3rd.

The use of a leaf powder diet should help us to find components which might explain the different suitability of the oak species for gypsy moth larvae. To eliminate the variability in the biochemical composition of leaves between trees of the same species we sampled only one tree individual of *Q. petraea* and one *Q. cerris* tree. The trees were similar in age, exposition, and tree vigor. Leaf sampling for the diet corresponded with the feeding period of the larvae on *Q. petraea* in the field in spring 1996: twigs were randomly cut from throughout the crown on May 8th (1st and 2nd instar), May 24th (3rd instar), June 10th (4th instar), and June 21st (5th and following instars), while *Q. cerris* leaves – due to the retarded budburst - were first harvested on May 14th (1st and 2nd instar). Dates of the other collections were identical for both trees.

Based on the method reported from Sheppard and Friedman (1992), we replaced the total nutrient content of the high wheat germ diet, which is commonly used in gypsy moth mass rearing (Bell *et al.*, 1981), by oak leaf material. After cutting, the leaves were immediately ground in liquid nitrogen, lyophilized and milled. Leaves from each collecting date were combined into single samples. 15 g agar was mixed with 825 ml of boiling distilled water. After cooling to 50°C 165,5 g oak leaf powder was added together with 2 g sorbic acid and 1 g methylparaben for preservation.

Since no test moths were available from local populations in spring 1996, we used gypsy moth egg masses from our lab culture originating from APHIS (U.S.A.) for the experiments with the leaf-powder diet. During the experimental period test larvae were kept at 20°C and LD conditions (16h light:8h dark). For each oak species larvae from 6 egg masses (approximately 1800 larvae) were reared in groups on the leaf powder diet from the beginning of their first instar up to the premolt into the 3rd instar. Then 50 synchronously molting larvae were separated individually in Petri dishes. The leaf diet was replaced every second day.

Biochemical analyses of the oak leaves

Aliquots of the frozen powder were pulverized in a sample mill (MM2, Retsch) and extracted with hot distilled water (4%, w/v). Organic acids were determined in the water extracts by ion chromatography with suppressed conductivity detection (Winter et al. 1997). Separation of organic acid anions was achieved by linear gradient of NaOH (0.5 mM to 37.5 mM within 14 min) on an anion-exchange column (Ionpac AS11; 250 mm long, 4 mm I.D.; Dionex). Low molecular weight carbohydrates and cyclitols were estimated as their trimethylsilyl derivatives by GLC. Derivatization was performed with BSTFA and TMCS (10 + 1) in pyridine for 45 min at 75° (Richter 1992). Amino acids were analyzed by HPLC using the post-column derivatization method with ninhydrine (Kedenburg 1971). For determination of starch content, 25 mg of the finely ground powder was extracted with 1 ml 80 % ethanol at room temperature, centrifuged and the pellet reextracted twice with 1 ml of 96 % ethanol at 60°C. Dried pellets were then incubated with heat-stable α-amylase (from *Bacillus licheniformis*) at 85°C for 30 min. Aliquots of the supernatant were incubated with amyloglucosidase (from *Aspergillus niger*) in 20 mM sodium acetate (pH 4.6) at 55°C. The reaction was terminated after 30 min by addition of 0.5 ml chloroform. Glucose was quantified by HPLC on an anion-exchange column (Carbopac PA 100; 250 mm long, 4 mm I.D.) as described by Winter et al. (1997). Total protein content was estimated according to Peterson (1977) using bovine serum albumin as a standard.

We used a single extract preparation from each leaf sample for the three tannin assays. Leaf material (60 mg) was extracted twice for 8 min with 4 ml of boiling 50% (v/v) aqueous methanol in a centrifuge tube (capped with a marble) placed in a heat block at 95°C. After centrifugation the volume of the combined supernatants was adjusted to 10 ml, and aliquots of the stock solution were used in the following procedures. To measure the total phenolic content we used the Folin-Denis assay after the method of Swain and Hillis (1959; modified by Martin and Martin 1982). Results were calculated in tannin acid equivalents (TAE). We measured condensed tannin concentrations by the method of Govindarajan and

Mathew (1965), which is based on the hydrolytic conversion of proanthocyanidins to anthocyanidins. Condensed tannin data are presented as quebracho equivalents. Protein-binding capacity of the tannin extracts was determined according to Martin and Martin (1982), and results are expressed as mg BSA (bovine serum albumin) precipitated per g of dry leaf tissue.

Statistical analysis

Mean values were compared by ANOVA and Scheffé test or with equal numbers of replicates by Student-Newman-Keuls (SNK) procedure. Significant differences were tested at $P<0.05$. Biochemical analyses were performed at least in two replicates and the mean value of both are displayed.

RESULTS

Larval performance on fresh leaves

The duration and mode of development of the Austrian moth population reared under laboratory conditions on both oak species are displayed in Fig. 1. Most of the males and females developed through 5 instars; 19% (5 of 27) of the tested females on *Q. cerris* and 9% (3 of 33) of the females on *Q. petraea* needed six instars before reaching the pupal stage.

The main groups (without a supernumerary instar) did not significantly differ in their total development on both oak species, but females reared on *Q. cerris* had markedly higher mean pupal masses than those fed with *Q. petraea* leaves (Fig. 1) and 1st and 3rd instars as well as the pupal stage of the Austrian population and 1st instar of Slovakian larvae were significantly longer on *Q. cerris* (Fig. 2).

Young larvae from both origins gained more weight (up to the 3rd instar) when fed with *Q. petraea*-leaves, - indicated by different initial dry weights of 3rd instars on both host trees (Fig. 3). The situation changed during the 3rd instar (resulting in similar initial dry weights in the 4th instar). At the beginning of the 5th instar females reared on *Q. cerris* already had higher initial weights (Fig. 3).

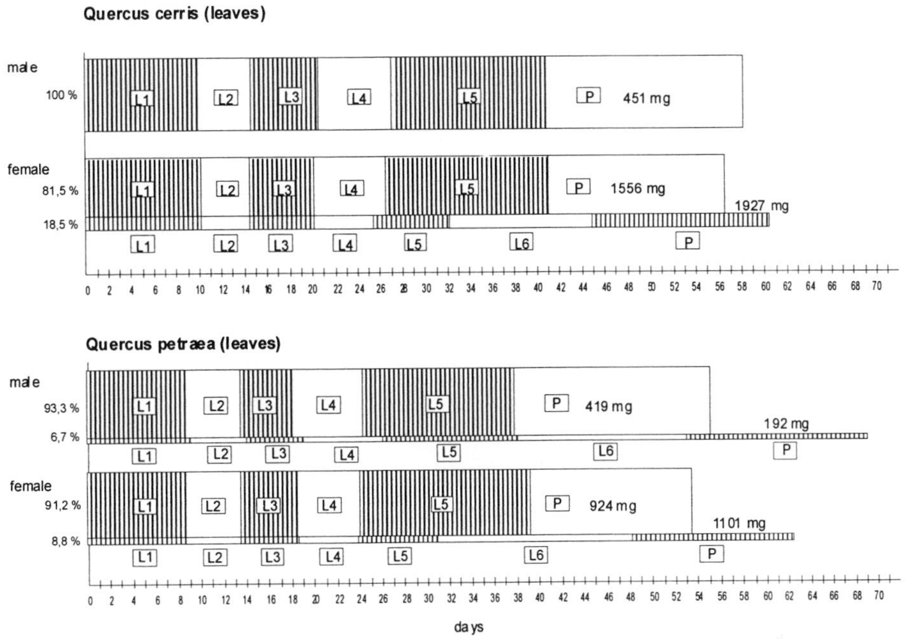

Figure 1. Mode of the development of gypsy moth larvae (L3 – pupa (=P)) fed with fresh oak leaves of *Q. petraea* or *Q. cerris*. The width of the bars reflects the relative number of larvae of the various developmental groups for each sex; the number inside the gray bars shows the mean pupal fresh weight, measured at the 3rd day after pupation; at the x-axes, the days after hatching are given.

Table 1. Mean female pupal dry weight (mg dwt) and mean number of eggs/cluster laid by gypsy moth females from two populations (A=Austria, SK=Slovakia) developing on fresh leaves of *Quercus cerris* or *Q. petraea*.

	origin		female pupa (dwt)		eggs/cluster	
		n	x	S.D.	x	S.D.
Q. cerris	A	27	498,8	111,0	730	108.6
	SK	33	527,5	147,6	704	158.0
Q. petraea	A	30	199,3	85,1	395	120.6
	SK	28	208,5	100,6	394	137.6

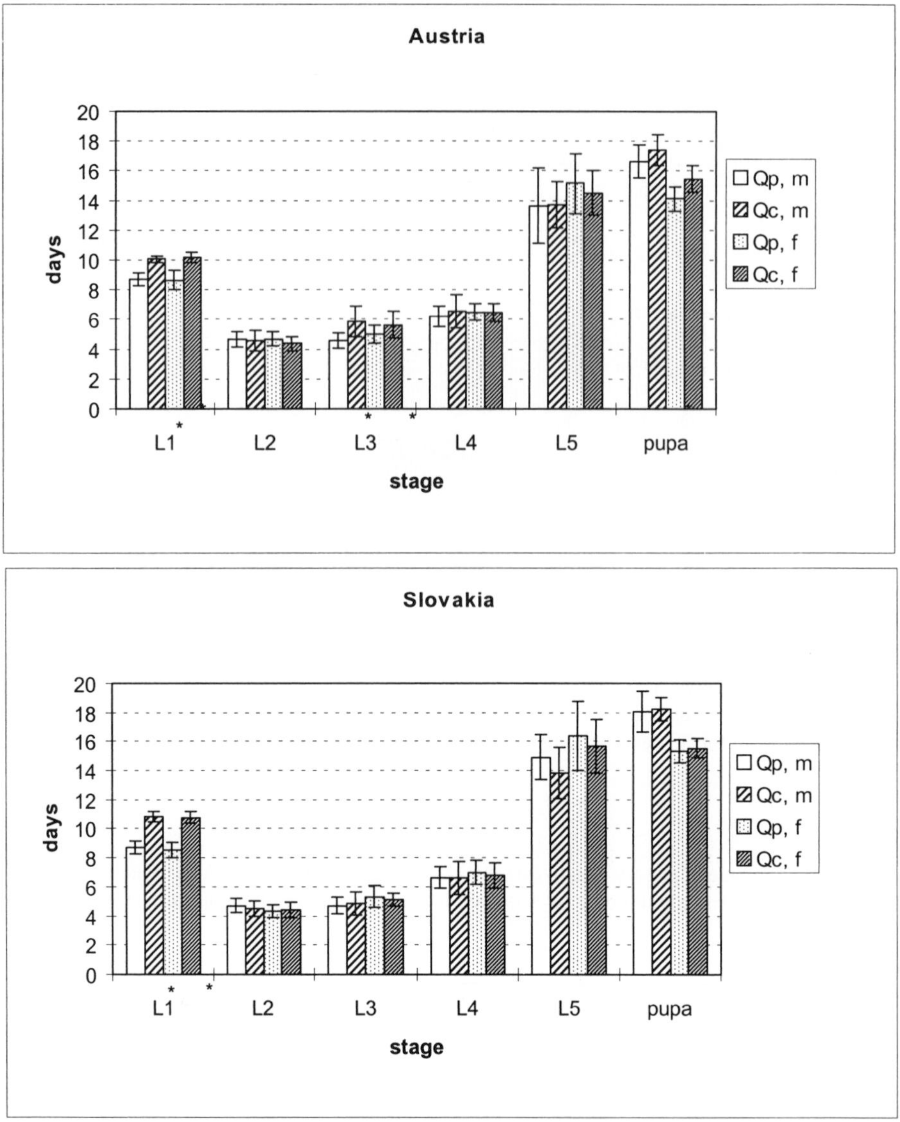

Figure 2. Mean duration of development (± S.D.) of Austrian and Slovakian gypsy moth of both sexes (m=male, f=female) from the 1st instar (L1) to the pupal stage (pupa) fed with oak leaves of *Quercus petraea (Qp)* or *Q. cerris (Qc)* in days at 20°C and LD-conditions; * = significant differences between the values of the corresponding bars ($P<0.05$).

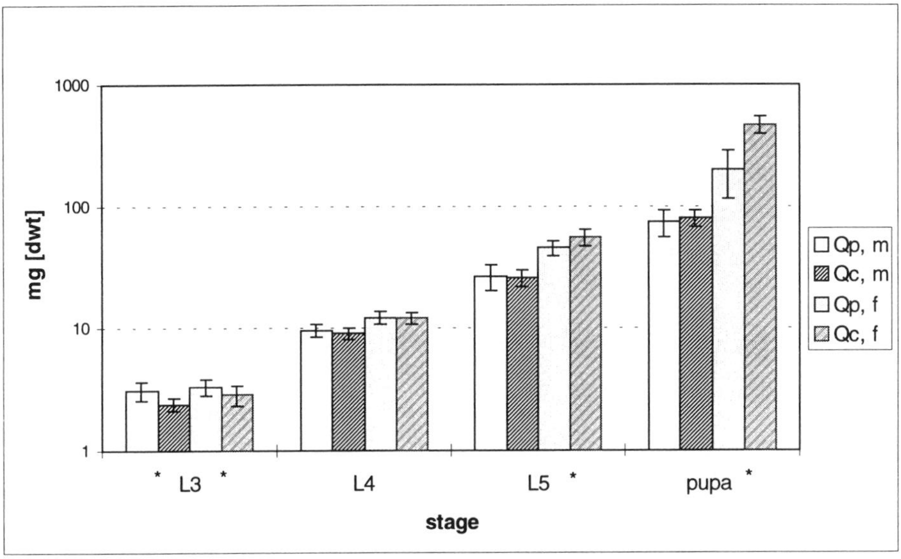

Figure 3. Mean initial dry weight (mg dwt, ± S.D.) of gypsy moth larvae (3rd to 5th instar (L3 – L5)) and pupae (3rd day after moulting) of both sexes (m=male, f=female) which developed on oak leaves of *Quercus petraea (Qp)* or *Q. cerris (Qc)* without a supernumerary 6th instar; * = significant differences between the values of the corresponding bars (P<0.05).

Table 2. Median day (x_m) and interval between the first and last occurrence of the various instars of gypsy moth after caging on branches of the two oak species (min., max. in days after exposure in L1; n=250 per host species) in the field; mort. = sum of mortality at the median day of each instar (in %).

	Quercus cerris				*Quercus petraea*			
instar	x_m	min	max	mort.	x_m	min	max	mort.
L1	4	0	7	0	5	0	10	17.2
L2	9	3	14	3.6	13	3	24	29.6
L3	18	5	31	11.6	27	5	49	44.2
L4	27	17	38	12.6	37	17	56	48.0
L5	38	19	56	16.8	51	33	68	57.6
L6	45	26	63	17.2	59	45	72	59.6

Table 3. Mean pupal fresh weight (mg) of gypsy moths which were caged as larvae on branches of the two oak species.

	Quercus cerris			*Quercus petraea*		
pupa	x	S.D.	n	x	S.D.	n
male	369	74	45	273	56	16
female	861	327	14	591	95	14

The higher pupal masses of moths reared on *Q. cerris* corresponded well with the mean number of eggs laid by the eclosed females, which was nearly twice as much as from females developed on *Q. petraea*-leaves (Tab. 1).

Development of caged larvae in the field

Under field conditions the caged gypsy moth larvae developed markedly faster on *Q. cerris*-trees than on *Q. petraea*, especially from the 3rd instar onwards (Tab. 2). Larval mortality was significantly higher ($P<0.05$) on *Q. petraea* trees, which was in contrast to our experiments with larvae fed on fresh leaves in the lab. One reason might be a higher impact of predators, like pentatomids on *Q. petraea* than on *Q. cerris.* Despite a shorter development the caged larvae performed markedly higher ($P<0.05$) pupal masses on *Q. cerris* than on *Q. petraea*-trees (Tab. 3).

Larval performance on leaf powder diet

Since leaf quality often varies enormously among tree individuals of the same species and even between branches of the same tree, we tested larval performance on leaf powder diet from a single tree individual of each oak species. The leaves were collected at four time points during gypsy moth feeding period from the beginning of May until the 3rd week of June. Gypsy moth larvae were fed with diet made from leaves of the respective collecting date that corresponded to the age of the larvae in the field.

All tested male larvae on *Q. cerris*-diet (n=19) developed through 5 instars and pupated about 35 days after molting into the 3rd instar (Fig. 4). Their mean pupal mass (534 mg) was similar to the value of *Q. cerris*-leaf feeders (451 mg, n=23). Female larvae on *Q. cerris*-diet (n=24) mainly developed through 6 instars and took about 10 days longer than males to reach the pupal stage. Their mean pupal weight was 1600 mg, which was equal to the pupal mass of the main female group reared on fresh *Q. cerris*-leaves (1550 mg). Leaf feeding larvae, however, developed through only 5 instars, while diet feeding larvae needed 6 instars. Only 2 out of the 30 tested females needed 5 instars, and 1 larva even needed 7 instars to pupate.

On *Q. petraea*-diet only 40% of males developed through 5 instars, while 60% of male larvae needed 6 instars (in total 5 days longer than 5-instar males). While

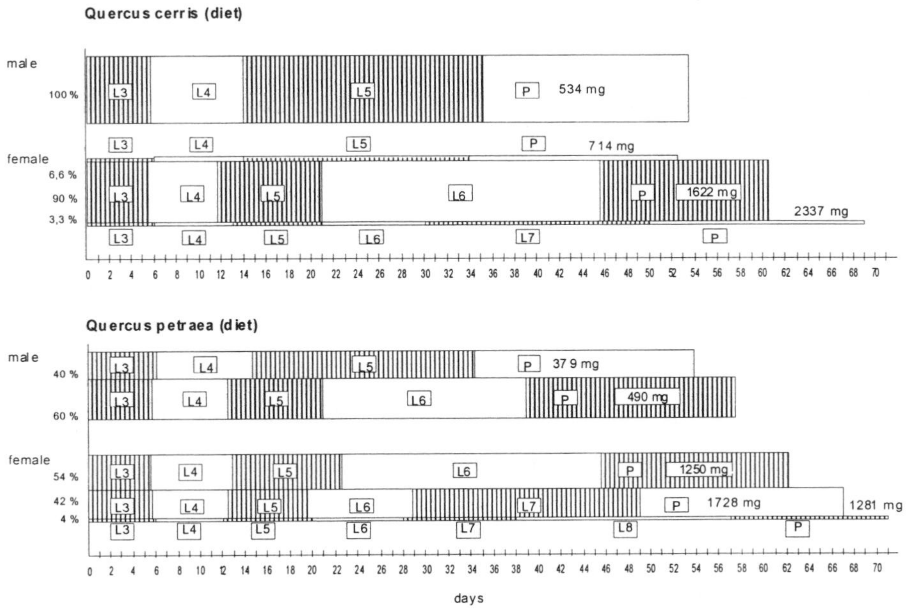

Figure 4. Mode of the development of gypsy moth larvae (L3 – pupa (=P)) fed with leaf powder diet of *Q. petraea* or *Q. cerris*. The width of the bars reflects the relative number of larvae of the various developmental groups for each sex; the number inside or beside the bars shows the mean pupal fresh weight, measured at the 3rd day after pupation; at the x-axes, the days after hatching are given.

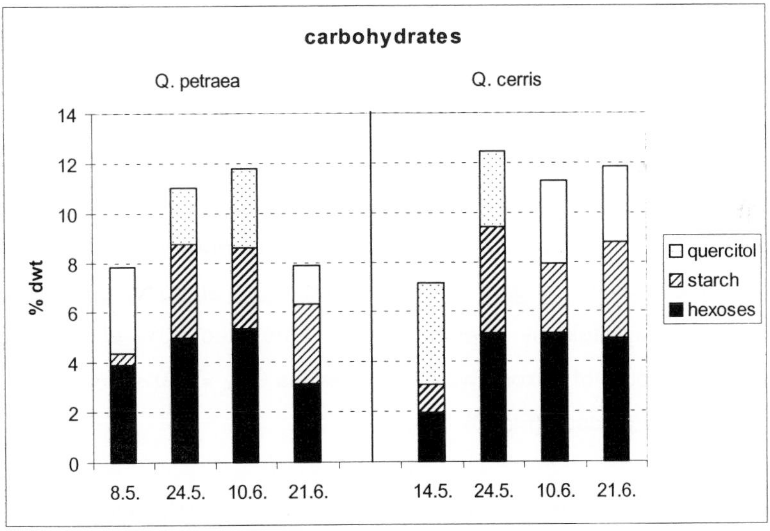

Figure 5: Content of soluble carbohydrates (hexoses, starch, quercitol) in leaves of *Quercus petraea* and *Q. cerris* (% dry weight) at several time points during spring 1996.

development of the 5-instar males on *Q. petraea*-diet lasted for the same period as all the tested male larvae on *Q. cerris*-diet, their mean pupal mass amounted to only 70% of that of *Q. cerris*-larvae. On *Q. petraea*-diet, 6-instar males gained a similar pupal mass like the pupae on *Q. cerris*-diet.

With females on *Q. petraea*-diet we observed a similar developmental pattern: 54% developed through 6 instars, 42% through a supernumerary 7th instar, and 1 out of the 24 tested larvae even needed 8 instars to pupate. Again, 6-instar females developed synchronously with female larvae on *Q. cerris*-diet, but gained only 77% of the pupal mass of the latter ones. Females with a supernumerary 7th instar, however, did not differ from *Q. cerris* 6-instar-females.

Although the condition for gypsy moth development seemed to be more favorable on *Q. cerris*-diet, we observed a higher mortality rate (40%) during metamorphosis and eclosion than on *Q. petraea*-diet (10%). These results indicate nutritional imbalances in the leaf powder diet of *Q. cerris*. On neither one of the diets we found any mortality during the larval stadia from the 3rd instar onwards.

Biochemical analyses

To gain insight into the nutritional relationships between the oak species and gypsy moth's performance we analyzed the main dietary components of the leaf powder used.

Carbohydrates

The content of carbohydrates was distinguished between soluble sugars, starch and cyclitols. Soluble sugars were dominated by sucrose, glucose, and fructose, the pool of cyclitols by quercitol, which amounted 70% of all cyclitols detected. The total amount of hexose was calculated as C_{hex} = Glu + Fru + Suc and the amount of starch as glucose (Fig. 5).

Differences in sugars between both oak species were mainly found in samples of the first and the last leaf collecting dates. While the very young *Q. petraea*-leaves already contained twice as much sucrose and fructose as the *Q. cerris*-leaves, we found the nearly opposite situation in the leaves of the last collecting date.

The concentration of starch, that gypsy moth larvae are obviously able to digest (unpubl. data), did not differ very much between the oak species and amounted 3 to 4% of the leaf dry matter during the last three collecting dates. In the young developing leaves, however, starch content was generally very low. These young leaves, however, contained high levels of cyclitols (quercitol, viburnitol, leucanthemitol, syllo- and myo-inositol) which are known to play an important role as metabolically compatible storage compounds during leaf expansion and periods of stress (Popp et al., 1997). Their concentration decreased markedly from the penultimate to the last collecting date in *Q. petraea*, but remained high in *Q. cerris*-leaves.

Amino acids and protein content

The concentration of free amino acids was highest in emerging leaves and levels were again higher in *Q. petraea*-leaves (Fig. 6). During leaf development, however, the soluble amino acids, specially the dominant ones, arginine and asparagine, dropped significantly in *Q. petraea* foliage from the first to the second collecting date at late May. This decline was less pronounced in *Q. cerris* leaves.

Protein content was also highest in the youngest leaves of both *Q. petraea* and *Q. cerris.* While in *Q. petraea*-leaves leaf proteins decreased until mid-June and increased again at the end of June, the fluctuations were much lower in *Q. cerris*-leaves (Fig. 6).

Organic acids

In the leaf extracts of *Q. petraea* and *Q. cerris* quinic and shikimic acid were the dominating organic acids (Fig. 7). Comparing the oak species, we found that quinic acid was markedly higher in the emerging leaves of *Q. cerris,* while, on the other hand, young *Q. petraea*-leaves showed a markedly higher level of shikimic acid. Both acids decreased with time in *Q. cerris*, like it did for shikimic acid in *Q. petraea*-leaves. The quinic acid concentration, however, was higher in *Q. petraea*-leaves than in *Q. cerris* at the second (late May) and the last collecting date (end of June).

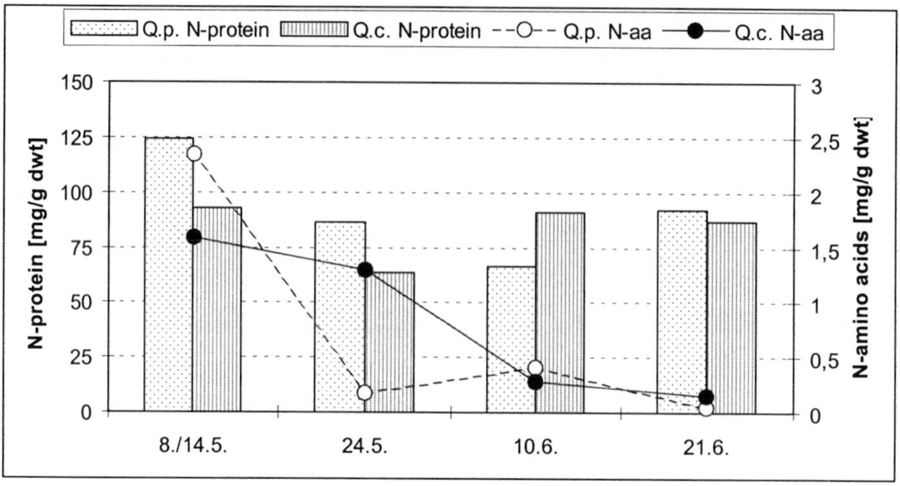

Figure 6. N-concentrations of total protein content (bars) and in soluble amino acids (N-aa) (lines) in mg/g dry weight (dwt) of leaves of *Quercus petraea* (Q.p.) and *Q. cerris* (Q.c.) at several time points during spring 1996.

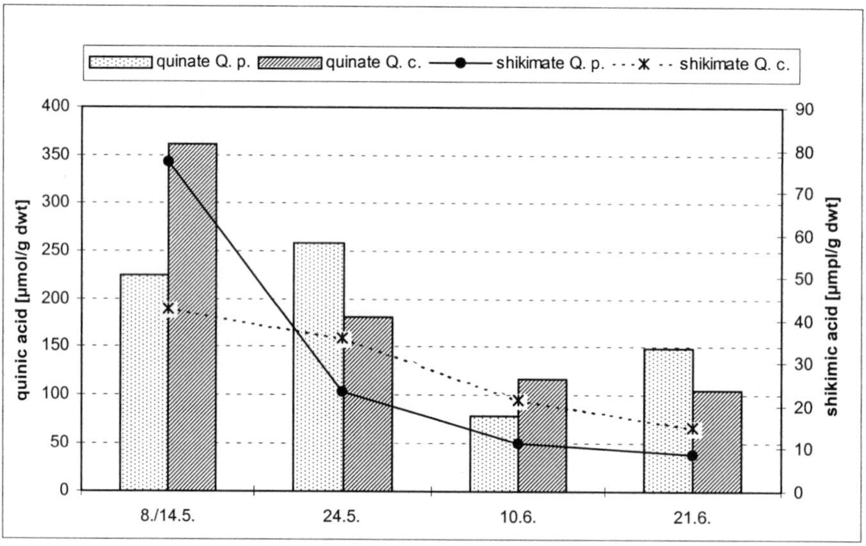

Figure 7: Concentration of shikimic acid (lines) and quinic acid (bars) in µmol/g dry weight (dwt) in leaves of *Quercus petraea* and *Q. cerris* at several time points during spring 1996.

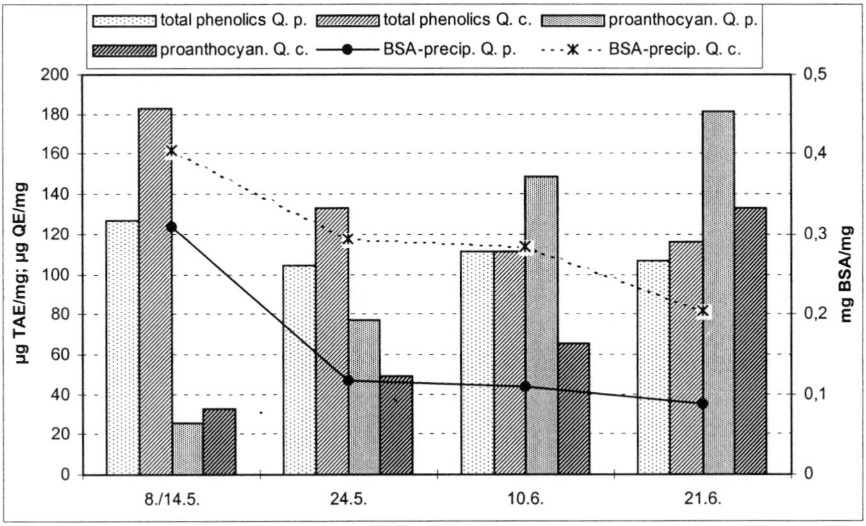

Figure 8: Content of phenolic compounds: total phenolics in tannic acid equivalents (mg TAE/g dry weight), condensed tannins in Quebracho-equivalents (mg QE/g dry weight), and protein precipitation capacity (mg BSA pptd. mg/g dry weight) in leaves of *Quercus petraea* and *Q. cerris* at several time points during spring 1996.

Phenolics

Total phenolic content and the protein-binding capacity were higher in *Q. cerris*, especially in young leaves and decreased at the later dates (Fig. 8).

The condensed tannin concentration, however, increased with time from low levels in young leaves to highest levels at the end of June and was clearly higher in *Q. petraea* than in *Q. cerris*-leaves.

CONCLUSIONS

Our study confirms that - during the first three instars - gypsy moth larvae perform better on young foliage of *Q. petraea* than on *Q. cerris*. Last instar larvae, however, gain more weight when fed with *Q. cerris*. This better performance is supported by the very close synchrony between the time of gypsy moth egg hatching and the flushing of *Q. petraea* leaves. Budburst of *Q. cerris* generally occurs about two weeks later.

Regarding the results of the biochemical analyses of the host trees food quality of *Q. petraea*-leaves seems to decline faster with time than in leaves of *Q. cerris.* This is indicated by lower amino acid, protein, and carbohydrate levels as larval development proceeds. The lower nutritional quality of mature *Q. petraea*-leaves might also be influenced by a striking increase in allelochemicals (condensed tannins) during last instar feeding. Thus, larvae fed on *Q. cerris* developed into pupae with higher masses and to females with higher fecundity than on *Q. petraea*-leaves.

Different suitability of host plants in the course of gypsy moth's development was already reported by Stoyenoff *et al.* (1994a, b) under field conditions. The different mode of development (supplementary instars in males and females) which we observed with larvae fed on the less optimal leaf powder diet made from *Q. petraea*-leaves suggests the existence of various thresholds of minimum weights in a population that allows last instars to metamorphose. This effect might be beneficial for a polyphagous species like gypsy moth to spread the risks in a population even under suboptimal nutritional conditions: on the one hand by a short larval development to avoid an excessive exposure to natural enemies at the costs of a low number of offspring, and on the other hand by a prolonged development through a supernumerary instar to invest in a high fecundity at the risk of being attacked by predators or parasitoids.

REFERENCES

BELL R.A., OWENS C.D., SHAPIRO M., TARDIF J.R., 1981. Development of mass-rearing technology. *In* Doane C.C., McManus M.L. (Ed.): *The Gypsy Moth: Research Toward Integrated Pest Management.* Washington, DC, US Dept. Agric. Tech. Bull. 1584, 599-633.

GOVINDARAJAN V.S., MATHEW A.G., 1965. Anthocyanidins from leucanthocyanidins. *Phytochemistry*, 4, 985-988.

HILLIS W.E., SWAIN T., 1959. The phenolic constituents of *Prunus domestica.* II. The analysis of tissues of the Victoria plum tree. *J. Sci. Food Agric.*, 10, 135-144.

KEDENBURG C.P. 1971. A lithium buffer system for accelerated single-column amino acid analysis in physiological fluids. *Analytical Biochemistry,* 40, 35-42.

MARTIN J.S., MARTIN M.M., 1982. Tannin assays in ecological studies: Lack of correlation between phenolics, proanthocyanidins and protein-precipitating constituents in mature foliage of six oak species. *Oecologia*, 54, 205-211.

POPP M., LIED W., BIERBAUM U., GROSS M., GROSSE-SCHULTE T., HAMS S., OLDENETTEL J., SCHÜLER S., WIESE J. 1997. Cyclitols - stable osmotica in trees. In. *Trees - Contributions to Modern Tree Physiology* (eds. Rennenberg H., Eschrich W., Ziegler, H.), Backhuys Publishers, Leiden, The Netherlands, pp. 257-270.

PETERSON G.L., 1977. A simplification of the Protein Assay Method of Lowry et al. which is more generally applicable. *Analyt. Biochem.*, 83, 346-356.

RICHTER A. 1992.Viscumitol, a dimethyl-ether of muco-inositol from Viscum album. *Phytochemistry*, 11, 3925-3927.

SHEPPARD C.A., FRIEDMAN S., 1992. Effect of dietary nitrogen on gypsy moth larval nutritional indices, development and lipid content. *Entomol.exp.appl.*, 64, 269-280.

STOYENOFF J.L., WITTER J.A., MONTGOMERY M.E., CHILCOTE C.A., 1994a. Effects of host switching on gypsy moth (*Lymantria dispar* (L.)) under field conditions. *Oecologia*, 94, 143-157.

STOYENOFF J.L., WITTER J.A., MONTGOMERY M.E., 1994b. Nutritional indices in the gypsy moth (*Lymantria dispar* (L.)) under field conditions and host switching situations. *Oecologia*, 94, 158-170.

SWAIN T., HILLIS W.E., 1959. The phenolic constituents of *Prunus domestica*. I. The quantitative analysis of phenolic constituents. *J. Sci. Food Agric.*, 10, 63-68.

WINTER K., RICHTER A., ENGELBRECHT B., POSADA J., VIRGO A., POPP M., 1997. Effect of elevated CO_2 on growth and crassulacean-acid-metabolism activity of *Kalanchoe pinnata* under tropical conditions. *Planta,* 201, 389-396.

Physiology and Genetics of Tree-Phytophage Interactions
Gujan (France), August 31 - September 5, 1997
Ed. INRA, Paris, 1999 (Les Colloques, n°90)

Monoterpene content and monoterpene emission of Norway spruce (*Picea abies* (L.) Karst.) bark in relation to primary attraction of bark beetles (Col., Scolytidae)

P.BAIER, R. BADER, S. ROSNER

Institute of Forest Entomology, Forest Pathology and Forest Protection, Universität für Bodenkultur Wien, Hasenauerstrasse 38, A-1190 Vienna, Austria

RESUME

The quantitative and qualitative composition of volatile monoterpenes emitted by uninjured spruce stem bark, and the corresponding internal monoterpene composition of the bark were determined for 15 felled trees in the field. Total emission rates ranged between 0.66 and 60.18 µg/dm² bark surface/h. Total monoterpene content, bark temperature, and field storage time were the most important factors affecting the amount of volatiles released. The most abundant compounds released were α-pinene, β-pinene, and limonene. The composition of emitted volatiles did not at all reflect the internal composition of monoterpenes. Colonisation of the trap trees by different bark beetle species was closely related to the composition of released monoterpene enantiomers.

INTRODUCTION

There is considerable controversy about, whether bark beetles select susceptible host trees by olfactory recognition of volatile compounds emitted by the host tree or not. Monoterpenes are volatile hydrocarbons found in large amounts in conifers and basically act as a solvent in the tree's resin. At high concentrations, they are toxic to insects and fungi and thus protect the tree against attacks. The ability of a tree to defend itself against boring bark beetles with resin flowing from ducts of the secondary phloem, and with a hypersensitive wound reaction, is dependent on the quantity of terpenes (Christiansen *et al.*, 1987). Bark beetle attack can induce an increased release of terpenes and terpene-related compounds. Bark beetles also convert monoterpenes stereospecifically and even produce pheromones from them (Lindström *et al.*, 1989). Therefore, volatile terpenes are considered to be important for the chemical communication system of the bark beetles and emitted terpenes may act as important signals for primary orientation to, and olfactory recognition of, susceptible hosts (Führer *et al.*, 1993). In this context the enantiomeric composition is of great importance (Persson *et al.*, 1996).

MATERIAL AND METHODS

Experimental arrangement, tree material and bark sample preparation

Fifteen spruce trees were felled at different times in two different study areas to be used as trap trees (Tab. 1). The bark was sampled for analysis of monoterpene content at three different tree heights (0.3 of tree height, crown base and mid-crown) immediately after felling and at the end of the study period after all emission measurements had been made. Bark samples were removed with a knife and immediately frozen in liquid nitrogen in the field, transported to the laboratory in dry ice and stored at - 40°C.

Bark sample extraction and GC-analysis

Before extraction, the samples were pulverised in a rubbing vessel containing liquid nitrogen. Monoterpenes of the pulverised bark (250 mg) were extracted using a closed loop stripping apparatus (CLSA) (Lorbeer *et al.*, 1984). N-nonane (internal standard) was added to the sample just before extraction. CLSA-system parameters: water bath temperature, 40°C; condenser temperature, 75°C; trap temperature, 45°C; extraction time, 90 min.; and filter, 1.5 mg activated charcoal. The charcoal filters were eluted with n-hexane (40µl). Analysis of the monoterpenes was done using gas chromatography. GC-method: on-column-injection; sample volume: 1-1.5 µl; retention gap: apolar; methyldesactivated, length: 2.5 m; ID: 0.32 mm; column type: CP-Chirasil-Dex CB (Chrompack) (length: 25 m, ID: 0.25 mm, film thickness: 0.25 µm, stationary phase: β-Cyclodextrin); operational temperature program: 50°C ⇒ 4°C/min. ⇒ 70°C / 2.5 min. const. / 10°C/min. ⇒ 110°C / 15 min. const.; FID-detector temperature: 220°C; carrier gas: nitrogen 5.0.

Table 1. Time-table of field experiments, number of examined trees, number of emission measurements and field storage time of the trap trees for the different study areas.

Study area; Altitude (m)	felling date	stand exposition	number of trees	tree age (years)	number of emission measurements	field storage time (in days)
Ofenbach;	29.5.1996	north	3	75 – 78	4	12
630 m	11.6.1996	north	3	71 – 75	7	42
	22.7.1996	north-west	3	73 – 74	6	31
Glein; 1200 m	25.6.1996	south	6	52 - 62	5	59

Sampling of volatile monoterpenes

The monoterpene emission rates from uninjured bark at the crown base and at 0.3 tree height were measured 4 - 7 times between felling and initial bark beetle attack (Tab. 1). Measurements were made when warm weather favoured flight activity and beetle attacks. The apparatus for sampling volatile monoterpenes consisted of a plastic chamber (16 x 4.5 x 3.2 cm) with an open rectangular face shaped to the contour of the bark surface and with 3 bore-holes (ϕ: 1.5 cm; 2 air-inlets and 1 outlet) on the upper side of the chamber. The sampling chamber was held against the bark surface with two fastening belts encircling the bole. The chamber was sealed to the bark surface using a solvent-free glue. Two glass sampling cartridges, containing activated charcoal, were used to clean the ambient air before it entered the chamber. The charcoal filters were fitted into the air inlets with silicone stoppers. Samples of volatiles were taken with an vacuum pump. One glass sampling cartridge with activated charcoal was connected with a hose to the vacuum pump and with a silicone stopper to the outlet of the sampling chamber. The glass sampling cartridge (type B/G, Dräger AG) consisted of a control layer (300 mg charcoal) and an adsorption layer (750 mg charcoal). Sampled gas volume was 10 l and sampling time 19 min.. After sampling, the charcoal filters were sealed with polyethylene-stoppers and stored at 4°C. The control- and adsorption layer of the sampling cartridge were separately eluted with n-hexane. The eluted substances of the adsorption layer (sample volume: 0.5 ml) were analysed with GC.

Bark temperature and bark anatomy

Bark surface and phloem temperature were measured and recorded continuously using thermocouples and a data-logger. Anatomical characteristics of the bark, namely the resin duct system of the secondary phloem and periderm formation, were analysed using methods applied by Pollak (1993).

Analysis of initial bark beetle attack

Bark beetle colonisation of the trap trees was observed continuously. Attack densities (by species) were recorded along the bole close to where monoterpene content and emission was measured (Bader, 1997).

Statistics

All data were analysed using SPSS 7.5.1 for Windows™. Linear associations were examined using simple correlation and multiple regression analysis. Multiple mean comparisons were made by analysis of variance followed by multiple range tests.

RESULTS

Monoterpene content and monoterpene composition of the bark

The monoterpene content of the phloem increased significantly with tree height ($p \leq 0.001$) (Tab. 2). The enantiomeric composition of the monoterpenes also varied with tree height. Some compounds, like myrcene, Δ-3-carene, (-)-β-phellandrene, (-)-β-pinene, and (-)-limonene increased with tree height; all other compounds (especially (-)- and (+)-α-pinene) deceased with increasing tree height. The most abundant monoterpene compounds of the bark tissues were (-)-β-pinene, α-pinene, with varying proportions of (-)- and (+)-α-pinene, (+)- and (-)-limonene, (-)-β-phellandrene, and myrcene (Tab. 2). Tricylene, (-)- and (+)-camphene, and Δ-3-carene were found only in small amounts (≤ 2%). Bark samples taken at the end of the study period had significantly smaller amounts of monoterpenes in the mid-crown ($p \leq 0.05$) than found in the initial samples. There was no difference in monoterpene content from the crown base and 0.3 of tree height between samples.

Monoterpene emission

The internal composition of monoterpenes did not at all reflect the composition of emitted monoterpenes (Tab. 2). The most abundant compounds released were (-)- and (+)-α-pinene, (-)-β-pinene, and (-)-/(+)-limonene. Other main compounds, like myrcene and (-)-β-phellandrene, could only be found in low amounts in the emission gas (Tab. 2). The main reasons for the compositional differences between emitted and internal monoterpenes are the physical properties of the monoterpenes themselves, such as vapour pressure and boiling point. However, (+)-α-pinene and (+)-limonene were emitted in higher amounts than would be expected based on the internal monoterpene composition and its physical properties.

Table 2. Monoterpene content (µg/g fresh weight and relative percent) in the bark at varying tree heights and percent emissions (mean ± SD).

	0.3 of H µg/g f.w.	crown base µg/g f.w.	mid-crown µg/g f.w.	grand mean µg/g f.w.	
myrcene	94.7 ± 84.1	190.5 ± 152.3	319.7 ± 204.6	**201.6** ± 177.9	
(-)-α-pinene	247.1 ± 173.5	368.6 ± 218.2	669.8 ± 464.0	**428.5** ± 354.3	
(+)-α-pinene	164.5 ± 115.2	187.8 ± 80.4	286.0 ± 240.5	**212.8** ± 165.9	
(-)-camphene	5.5 ± 3.4	9.2 ± 6.3	14.4 ± 10.4	**9.7** ± 8.0	
(+)-camphene	2.2 ± 2.6	1.7 ± 2.3	5.3 ± 7.2	**3.1** ± 4.8	
Δ-3-carene	9.8 ± 7.5	16.7 ± 17.4	44.3 ± 46.8	**23.6** ± 32.2	
(-)-β-pinene	462.6 ± 286.2	810.0 ± 419.8	1373.3 ± 642.4	**882.0** ± 597.9	
(-)-limonene	203.2 ± 281.5	312.9 ± 524.0	714.4 ± 963.9	**410.2** ± 676.4	
(+)-limonene	37.8 ± 31.9	55.6 ± 30.2	84.3 ± 61.2	**59.2** ± 46.7	
(-)-β-phell.	165.6 ± 123.5	343.7 ± 284.4	549.5 ± 367.2	**352.9** ± 314.1	**emitted**
tricyclene	11.4 ± 17.5	20.3 ± 19.8	27.6 ± 36.4	**19.8** ± 26.2	**monoterpenes**
sum	**1424.9** ± **893.3**	**2346.0** ± **1310.4**	**4129.4** ± **2289.0**	**2633.4** ± **1938.1**	**(grand mean)**
	%	%	%	%	%
Myrcene	6.00 ± 2.61	7.47 ± 2.88	7.69 ± 2.49	**7.06** ± 2.71	**0.81** ± 2.20
(-)-α-pinene	17.69 ± 4.75	16.11 ± 4.61	16.08 ± 4.71	**16.63** ± 4.64	**22.71** ± 5.21
(+)-α-pinene	13.73 ± 7.20	9.93 ± 6.17	7.57 ± 4.55	**10.41** ± 6.46	**25.62** ± 6.49
(-)-camphene	0.45 ± 0.29	0.48 ± 0.43	0.40 ± 0.29	**0.44** ± 0.34	**0.03** ± 0.16
(+)-camphene	0.17 ± 0.16	0.10 ± 0.13	0.14 ± 0.17	**0.14** ± 0.15	**0.00** -
Δ-3-carene	0.77 ± 0.42	0.66 ± 0.46	1.13 ± 1.08	**0.85** ± 0.73	**0.01** ± 0.05
(-)-β-pinene	33.30 ± 7.21	34.70 ± 8.59	34.92 ± 7.37	**34.31** ± 7.61	**23.50** ± 6.58
(-)-limonene	11.42 ± 11.47	12.41 ± 12.20	14.64 ± 13.36	**12.82** ± 12.16	**12.27** ± 5.63
(+)-limonene	2.59 ± 0.67	2.55 ± 0.85	2.03 ± 0.81	**2.39** ± 0.80	**14.18** ± 7.05
(-)-β-phell.	11.61 ± 4.89	13.51 ± 6.31	13.87 ± 6.03	**13.00** ± 5.73	**0.40** ± 1.37
Tricyclene	0.75 ± 0.67	0.84 ± 0.69	0.59 ± 0.56	**0.72** ± 0.64	**0.42** ± 2.05

Observed monoterpene emission rates, calculated as µg/dm² bark surface/hour, showed a very high variation within- and among-trees and between time of investigation, ranging from a maximum of 60.18 µg/dm2/h to a minimum of 0.66 µg/dm²/h. In most cases, the emission rates were higher at the crown base than at 0.3 of tree height (Fig.1). Higher emission rates at the crown base could be traced back to a larger monoterpene content in the upper part of the stem (Tab. 2) and to different periderm properties of the bark. Bark with a superficial periderm had higher emission rates (mean: 3.63 ± 8.35 µg/dm²/h) than bark with sequent periderms (mean: 2.55 ± 2.03 µg/dm²/h).

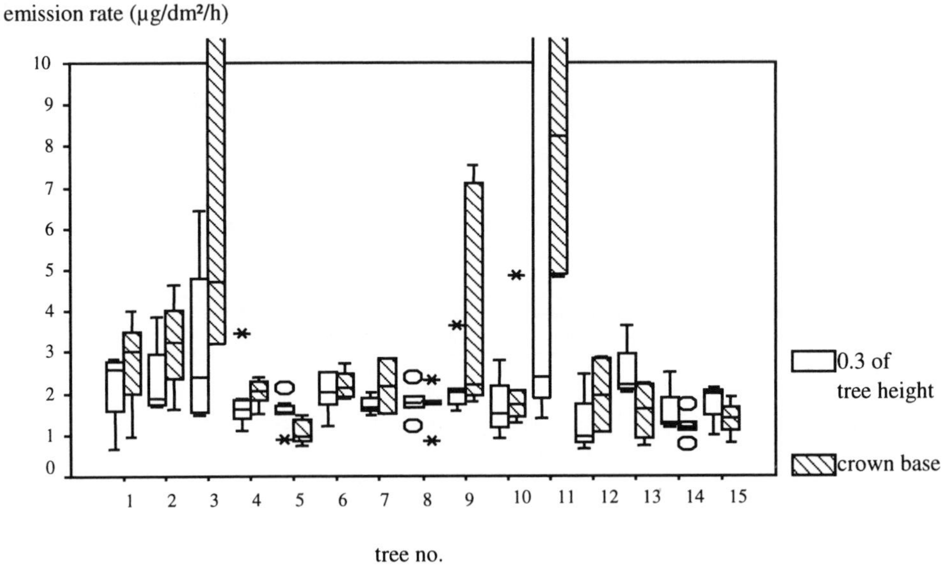

Figure 1. Monoterpene emission rate of individual trees at 0.3 of tree height and crown base (box - and whiskers-plot: median, lower and upper fourth, largest and smallest values that are not outliers, outliers (o: cases with values between 1.5 and 3 box-lengths from lower/upper fourth; *: cases with values more than 3 box-lengths from lower/upper fourth)); tree no. 1 - 3: felling date [f.d.] 29.5.1996; tree no. 4 - 6: f.d. 11.6.1996; tree no. 7 - 9: f.d. 22.7.1996; tree no. 10 - 15: f.d. 25.6.1996.

The monoterpene content of bark was significantly correlated with the number of primary resin canals of the cortex ($r = 0.742$, $p = 0.003$). Both number of resin canals of the cortex and the bark surface temperature were significant in the multiple regression model explaining monoterpene emission rates of trees at Ofenbach (Tab. 3).

Table 3. Results of multiple regression model explaining monoterpene emission rate (dependent variable) in terms of bark surface temperature and the number of resin canals of the cortex (independent variables).

Dependent	independent variables	coefficients B	t-value	sig.
Emission rate	constant	-5.082	-2.959	0.005
	temperature of bark surface	0.309	3.856	<0.001
R = 0.571	number of resin canals	0.137	3.240	0.002

Bark surface temperature appeared to be the most important factor explaining monoterpene emission rate (Tab. 3). The emission rate increased significantly with increasing temperature, but at temperatures above 30°C, we observed an erratic increase of released volatiles (Tab. 4).

Table 4. Monoterpene emission rate (mean ± SD) at different bark surface temperature levels (Oneway-Anova: $F = 33.97$; $p \leq 0.001$; values followed by different letters are significantly different (multiple range test, p • 0.05)).

temperature level	emission rate ($\mu g/dm^2/h$)
< 20°C	1.730 ± 0.787^a
20 – 24.9°C	2.451 ± 1.951^a
25 – 29.9°C	3.974 ± 3.926^a
> 30°C	26.230 ± 27.600^b

Host colonisation by bark beetles

The trap trees were attacked by three different bark beetle species. Five trees were attacked by Ips typographus (L.) and Pityogenes chalcographus (L.), six were infested by P. chalcographus alone, and four trees were attacked by Polygraphus poligraphus (L.) (dominant) and P. chalcographus (Tab. 5).

Bark beetle colonisation of the trap trees depended both on changes in monoterpene emission rates and in composition. Initial attack by bark beetles occurred only in the upper part of the stem, where monoterpene emission was usually the highest. Trees that showed high emission rates immediately after felling were attacked by I. typographus and P. chalcographus at high attack densities.

Trees with low emission rates were attacked exclusively by either P. chalcographus or P. poligraphus. The composition of emitted monoterpenes was significantly different between trees infested by different bark beetle species (Fig. 2).

Table 5. Mean initial attack densities (mean ± SD) of the investigated trap trees.

number of trees	initial attack densities (number of entrance holes / dm² bark surface)		
	I. typographus	*P. chalcographus*	*P. poligraphus*
5	0.157 ± 0.181	0.643 ± 0.560	0
6	0	0.347 ± 0.223	0
4	0	0.025 ± 0.050	0.119 ± 0.189

DISCUSSION

Except for the rare situation when high populations of bark beetles, like Ips typographus and Pityogenes chalcographus, may kill vigorous spruce trees, a certain degree of weakness of the host is necessary for successful infestation (Rudinsky, 1962). Drought stress is considered to be the main reason for this type of tree weakness (Christiansen et al., 1987). The release of monoterpenes may be affected by water stress (Mattson and Haack, 1987) and an increased release of these volatiles may play an important role in olfactory recognition of susceptible host trees by bark beetles. However, this hypothesis postulates not only monoterpene emission through intact, uninjured bark tissues, but also, reversible, dynamic changes in the permeability of the bark to volatile monoterpenes (Führer et al., 1993).

Monoterpene emission rates of felled spruce trees were highly variable and related to the total monoterpene content, which is correlated with the number of resin canals of the cortex, the bark surface temperature, storage time in the field (Baier and Bader, 1997) and anatomical properties of the bark tissues. The composition of the released monoterpenes did not at all reflect the internal monoterpene composition of the bark. This discrepancy can be explained by different physical properties of the different compounds (Hanover, 1972, Schindler and Kotzias, 1989), differences in monoterpene composition between superficial phloem tissues and the whole bark (Baier and Bader, 1997), varying anatomical properties of the bark surface and by seasonal changes in the permeability of the lenticels (Parameswaran et al., 1976).

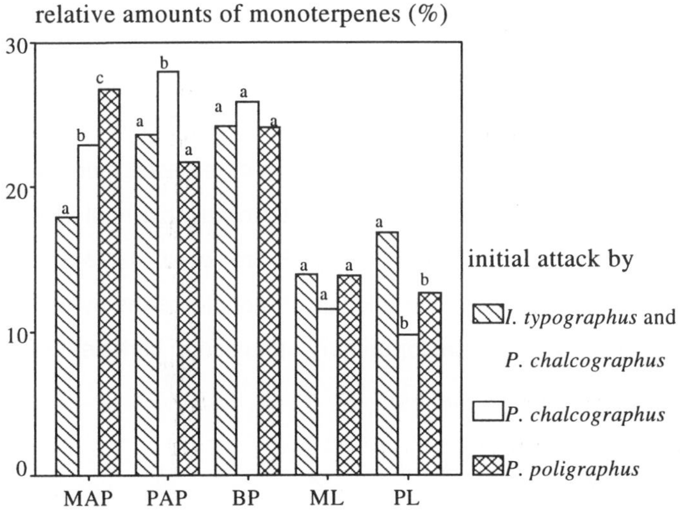

Figure 2. Mean relative amounts of released monoterpenes of the trap trees attacked by different bark beetle species; (MAP: (-)-α-pinene; PAP: (+)-α-pinene; BP: (-)-β-pinene; ML: (-)-limonene; PL: (+)-limonene; different letters within substances indicate significant differences between different bark beetle attack (multiple range test; p • 0.05)).

Different periderm formation is related to properties of the resin duct system and to different defence mechanisms of the tree against bark beetle attack (Baier, 1996). The within-tree variation of the monoterpene content (Bader, 1997) and emission rate is also related to different periderm formation. Bark tissues with a superficial periderm in the upper part of the stem, where initial attacks by Ips typographus and Pityogenes chalcographus usually occur (Führer et al., 1993), have both a higher monoterpene content and emission rate of monoterpenes.

The emission rate significantly increased with increasing temperature, but, at temperatures above 30°C, we observed an erratic increase of released volatiles. This phenomenon may be very important for understanding host selection by bark beetles. The bark surface temperature of tree trunks exposed to the sun (e.g. at the edge of a stand) can easily reach more than 30°C, inducing a very high release of volatiles. Under dry weather conditions, exposed trees may be susceptible to bark beetle attack because of water stress, and can be recognised by bark beetles due to a higher release of monoterpenes.

Bark beetle colonisation of trap trees depended on the monoterpene emission rate, the dynamics of emission (Baier and Bader, 1997) and the relative amounts of released chiral monoterpenes. The large among- and within-tree variation of the monoterpene content, the enantiomeric composition of released monoterpenes, and monoterpene emission rate may guide the insects to suitable hosts and to certain areas of the tree for aggregation and breeding (Führer et al., 1993, Persson et al., 1996). Therefore, we conclude that the release of monoterpenes by the host has to be considered as an important signal for primary attraction of bark beetles.

ACKNOWLEDGEMENTS

Financial support from the Austrian Science Fund is gratefully acknowledged.

REFERENCES

BAIER P., 1996. Defense reactions of Norway spruce (*Picea abies* Karst.) to controlled attacks of *Ips typographus* (L.) (Col., Scolytidae) in relation to tree parameters. *J.Appl.Ent.* 120, 587-593.

BAIER P., BADER R., 1997. Gehalt und Emission von Monoterpenen der Fichtenrinde und deren Bedeutung für die Primärattraktion von Borkenkäfern (Col.,Scolytidae). *Mitt. Dtsch. Ges. Allg. Angw. Ent.* 11, 639-643.

BADER R., 1997. *Die Zusammensetzung enantiomerer Monoterpenkohlenwasserstoffe in der Rinde unterschiedlich gestreßter Fichten und ihre Rolle bei der Primärattraktion rindenbrütender Borkenkäferarten.* Diploma thesis, University of Vienna, p. 86.

CHRISTIANSEN E., WARING R.H., BERRYMAN A.A.., 1987. Resistance of Conifers to Bark Beetle Attack: Searching for General Relationships. *For.Ecol.Manage.* 22, 89-106.

FÛHRER E., HAUSMANN B.., WIENER L., 1993. Brutraumdifferenzierung zwischen *Ips typographus* L. und *Pityogenes chalcographus* L. (Col., Scolytidae) an Fichtenstämmen in ihrer Beziehung zu Monoterpenmustern. *Mitt. Dtsch. Ges. Allg. Angw. Ent.* 8, 491-495.

HANOVER J.W., 1972. Factors affecting the release of volatile compounds by forest trees. In: *Wirkungen von Luftverunreinigungen auf Waldbäume.* Mittl. FBVA Wien, Österr. Agrarverlag Wien, 97/II, 625-644.

LINDSTRÖM L., NORIN T.., BIRGESSON G., SchLyter F., 1989. Variation of enantiomeric composition of α-pinene in Norway spruce, *Picea abies*, and its influence on production of verbenol isomeres by *Ips typographus* in the field. *J.Chem.Ecol.*, 15/2, 541-548.

LORBEER E., MAYR M., HAUSSMANN B., KRATZL K., 1984. Zur Identifizierung flüchtiger Substanzen aus biologischem Material mit Hilfe der CLSA (closed loop stripping apparatus). *Monatsh. Chem.* 15, 1107-1112.

MATTSON J.W., HAACK R.A ., 1987. The Role of Drought in Outbreaks of Plant-eating Insects. *BioSience* 2, 110-118.

RUDINSKY J.A., 1962. The ecology of the Scolytidae. *A. Rev. Ent.* 7, 327-348.

PARAMESWARAN I., KRUSE J., LIESE W., 1976. Aufbau und Feinstruktur von Periderm und Lenticellen der Fichtenrinde, *Z. Pflanzenphysiol.* 77, 212-221.

PERSSON M., SJÖDIN K., BORG-KARLSON A., NORIN T., EKBERG I., 1996. Relative amounts and enantiomeric compositions of monoterpene hydrocarbons in xylem and needles of *Picea abies*. *Phytochemistry* 42, 5, 1289-1297.

POLLAK P., 1993. *Untersuchungen zum Harzkanalsystem und der Rinde der Fichte (*Picea abies *Karst.).* Diploma thesis, Universität für Bodenkultur Wien, p.103.

SCHINDLER T., KOTZIAS D., 1989. Comparison Monoterpene Volatilization and Leaf-oil Composition of Conifers. *Naturwissenschaften* 76, 475-476.

Physiology and Genetics of Tree-Phytophage Interactions
Gujan (France), August 31 - September 5, 1997
Ed. INRA, Paris, 1999 (Les Colloques, n°90)

Tolerance of blue-stain fungi to plant defensive chemicals

N.V. PASHENOVA[1], V.P. VETROVA[2], G.G. POLYAKOVA[3]

[1] *Institute of Forest, Russian Academy of Sciences, Laboratory of Microbiology 660036 , Krasnoyarsk , RUSSIA*

[2] *Institute of Forest, Russian Academy of Sciences, Laboratory of Forest Zoology 660036 , Krasnoyarsk , RUSSIA*

[3] *Institute of Forest, Russian Academy of Sciences, Laboratory of Plant Physiology 660036 , Krasnoyarsk , RUSSIA*

RESUME

Effect of tannin and non-volatile components of lesion resin on the growth of blue-stain fungi - *Ceratocystis laricicola* , *C. polonica, Ophiostoma minus, Leptographium sp. and Ophiostoma sp.* - the primary invaders of conifers in Siberia (Russia) , has been studied. The fungi under study exhibited tolerance to plant's defensive substances in bioassays. The cultures of *Leptographium sp., C. polonica, and Ophiostoma sp.* proved to be the most tolerant to tannin. In the range between 0.05 and 0.15% tannin concentration their growth tended to stabilize. Less tolerant to tannin were *C. laricicola* and *O. minus.* With an increase in tannin concentration their biomass gradually decreased. The fungi more tolerant to tannin regulated the medium pH about 5.0 and higher, while the species which were less tolerant preferred lower pH values. Lesion resins of conifers differed in their inhibitory effect on fungal growth. Fir resin had the greatest inhibitory effect of all the conifer resins tested, causing reduction to 50-60% in fungal growth. When fungi were grown on the resin of any other conifer, the reduction in the linear growth rate did not exceed 20 to 30%. The assumption that fungi are more tolerant to the resin of a host plant than to that of a non-host plant has not been confirmed.

INTRODUCTION

Pathogenic blue-stain fungi associated with bark beetles induce defence responses when inoculated into healthy trees (Paine *et al.*,1997). Induced response of conifers against "fungi-insects" associations involves a series of chemical changes in host tissue, including changes in phenolic and terpenoid chemistry and accumulation of more toxic compounds (Shrimpton, Whitney, 1968; Shrimpton, 1973; Wong, Berryman,1977; Raffa, Berryman,1983; Gottstain, Gross, 1992; Brignolas *et al.,*1995; Paine *et al.*, 1997). Condensed tannins possess antimicrobial properties (Stafford, 1988) and accumulate in wound lesion of some species of conifers (Hemingway *et al.*,1977; Wong, Berryman, 1977; Polyakova *et al.*, 1995; Vetrova *et al.*, 1995), therefore these phenolics are considered to be involved in plant defence reactions. Other chemical groups such as terpenes also accumulate in conifer defence responses (Raffa, Berryman, 1982; Raffa et al., 1985; Cook, Hain, 1987) and can inhibit fungal growth (Cobb *et al.*, 1968; Raffa *et al.*, 1985; Bridges, 1987; Delorme, Lieutier, 1990; Solheim, 1991). The concentration of induced resins in the lesions is an important factor in resistance of conifers (Raffa, Berryman, 1982; Cook, Hain, 1987; Christiansen, 1985). To be successful, pathogenic fungi must adapt to plant defensive chemicals.

In this experiment, we studied the effects of condensed tannins and induced resins on growth of blue-stain fungi - primary invaders of the conifers in Central Siberia . The objects of the investigation were *Ceratocystis laricicola* Redfern & Minter associated with *Ips cembrae* Heer., *C.polonica* (Siem.) C.Moreau associated with *I.typographus* L., *Ophiostoma minus* (Hedge.)H.&P.Syd associated with *Tomicus piniperda* L. , *Ophiostoma sp.* and *Leptographium sp* associated with the fir sawyer beetle *Monochamus urussovi* (Fisch.). The fungi *C. laricicola*, *C.polonica* and *O.minus* are known to be highly pathogenic for conifers in Europe and North America (Christiansen, Solheim, 1990; Paine *et al.*,1997). Pathogenicity of the fungi associated with *M.urussovi* was proved experimentally by mass inoculation of fir trees (unpublished data of the authors). The purpose of the present study was to assess the ability of the fungi to tolerate plant defensive chemicals.

MATERIAL AND METHODS

In the work we used cultures of five fungal species isolated during 1993-96: *C.laricicola* (from the Siberian larch, *Larix sibirica* Ldb.), *C.polonica* (from the Siberian spruce, *Picea obovata* ldb.), *Ophiostoma minus* (from the Scotch pine, *Pinus sylvestris* L.), *Leptographium sp.* and *Ophiostoma sp.* (from the Siberian fir, *Abies sibirica* Ldb.).

Tolerance to tannin

The fungi were cultivated on liquid beer wort (4B). Tannin was dissolved in sterile water and added to autoclaved media so that resulting concentrations were 0.005, 0.01, 0.05, 0.10, and 0.15%. The tannin free medium was used as the control. The media were poured into Petri dishes 90 mm in diameter, 20 ml/dish. Each of the five species under study was represented by two isolates. Fungal mycelia grown on beer-wort agar for 7 days were used to inoculate the media. The dishes with non-inoculated media were used to control spontaneous changes in the media. All the dishes were incubated for 10 days at 22 C. Then fungal biomass was collected by filtering, and the dry weight was measured. The pH of the media were measured before and after incubation. Three replicates per isolate were used.

Tolerance to conifer resins

Effects on fungal growth of resin enclosed in lesions following fungal inoculation were studied. Induced resins of four conifers: *Larix sibirica, Picea obovata, Pinus sylvestris, Abies sibirica* were assayed. The resin-soaked phloem was removed 3 weeks after fungal inoculation and resin was collected as described by E.Christiansen (1985) and H.Solheim (1991). The resin was solved in pentane and applied to paper filters placed in Petri dishes (d = 50 mm), about 100 mg of resin per filter. The dishes were left open for 24 hours for pentane to evaporate. Sterile paper filters, soaked with pentane and dried, were used as the controls. The filters in the dishes were coated with a thin agar layer. For the inoculum we used agar-mycelium discs 6 mm in diameter, cut from fungal colonies prepared as described above. Fungal inoculum was placed in the centre of the agar-coated paper discs and incubated for 3 days at 24 C., after which the radial growth of isolates was measured. There were 3 replicates of each variant.

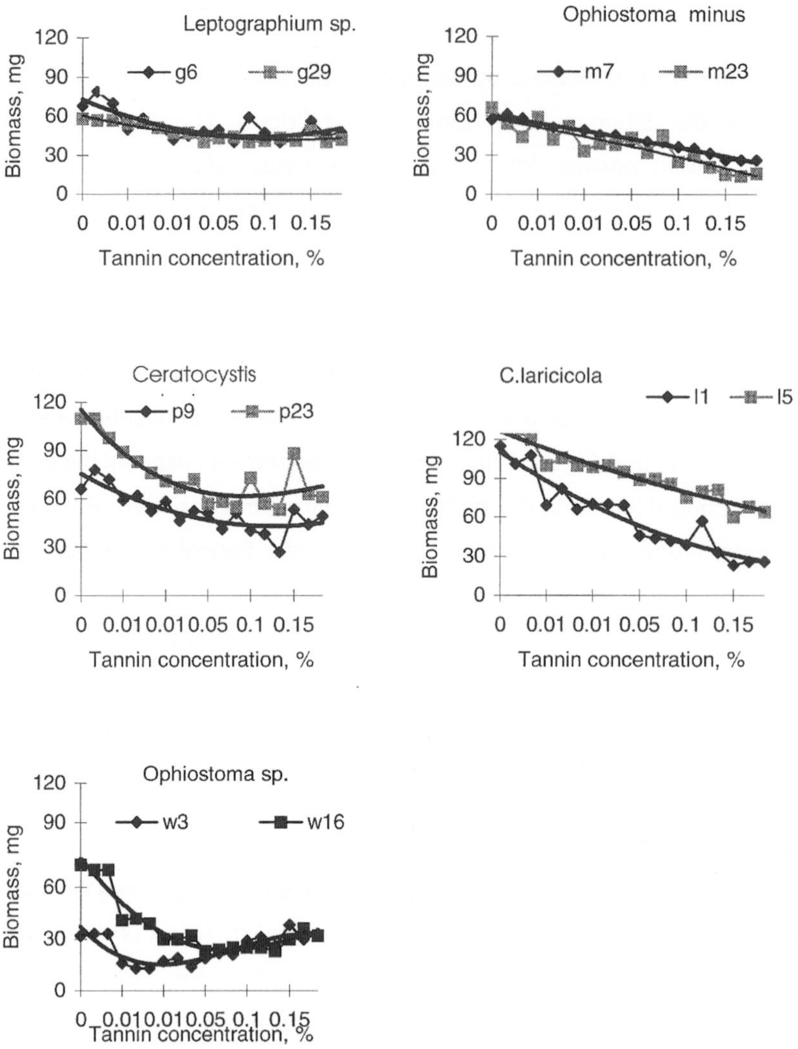

Figure 1. Effect of tannin on biomass of the blue-stain fungi. Data are measurements of biomass (mg) after 10 days growth of the fungi on liquid media (3 replicates for each treatment) and interpolation of empirical data by polynom function.

Two-way ANOVA was used to test for the effect of plant defensive chemicals on growth of the fungi. Biomass and radial growth rate of the fungi were measured for each treatment and estimated as percentage of fungal biomass or growth rate, observed on media without additions of tannin and resin. Arcsine square root transformation of percentage biomass and percentage growth rate was used before ANOVA. Means were compared using multiple t-test at the 0,05 confidence level. Means were back transformed for presentation.

RESULTS AND DISCUSSION

Tolerance to tannin

In our experiments tannin inhibited growth of all the blue-stain fungi investigated. Confidence of the effect of this factor on the variation of fungal growth parameters was proved statistically, Table 1. At tannin concentrations of 0.005 and 0.010% the biomass of all the isolates decreased, Fig.1. In this range of concentrations the influence of tannin did not result in any significant intraspecific differences. Only for the *Ophiostoma sp.* isolates growth inhibition was stronger than for the others, Fig.1. At higher tannin concentrations, 0.05 - 0.15%, differences among the species were more distinct. In this range of inhibitor concentrations the growth of *C.laricicola* and *O.minus* isolates kept slowing down while the growth of other isolates became stable, Fig.1. Isolates of *Leptographium sp.*, *Ophiostoma sp.*, and *C. laricicola* exhibited considerable intraspecific variability in tolerance to tannin. This variability was the most pronounced in the *Ophiostoma sp.* isolates, Fig.1, Table 1.

The results of the experiment showed that the isolates of *Leptographium sp.*, *C.polonica*, and *Ophiostoma sp.* were the most tolerant to tannin, those of *C. laricicola* and *O. minus* the least tolerant.

Table 1. F statistics from ANOVA of effects of tannin concentration in media and interspecific variability of blue-stain fungi on change of fungal biomass

Source	SS	df	MS	F	% Total variability
			Ceratocystis polonica		
Tannin concentration (TC)	5,98	5	1,19	28,15***	83,4
Fungal isolates (FI)	0,003	1	0,003	0,08	0,5
Interaction TCxFI	0,17	5	0,80	0,56	2,4
Error	1,02	24	0,04		14,2
Total	7,17	35			100
			Ophiostoma minus		
Tannin concentration (TC)	9,94	5	1,99	36,17***	84,4
Fungal isolates (FI)	0,13	1	0,13	2,34	1,0
Interaction TCxFI	0,39	5	0,08	1,40	3,3
Error	1,32	24	0,05		11,2
Total	11,77	35			100
			Ophiostoma sp.		
Tannin concentration (TC)	10,35	5	2,07	89,85***	61,0
Fungal isolates (FI)	2,47	1	2,47	107,23***	14,6
Interaction TCxFI	3,58	5	0,72	31,03***	21,1
Error	0,55	24	0,02		3,2
Total	16,95	35			100
			Leptographium sp.		
Tannin concentration (TC)	5,11	5	1,02	37,85***	75,9
Fungal isolates (FI)	0,80	1	0,80	29,68***	11,9
Interaction TCxFI	0,18	5	0,04	1,31	2,6
Error	0,65	24	0,03		9,6
Total	6,73	35			100
			Ceratocystis laricicola		
Tannin concentration (TC)	10,28	5	2,06	97,93***	82,5
Fungal isolates (FI)	1,32	1	1,32	62,91***	10,6
Interaction TCxFI	0,36	5	0,07	3,44*	2,9
Error	0,50	24	0,02		4,0
Total	12,47	35			100

*,P<0,05; **, P<0,01; ***P<0,001

The fungal growth was accompanied by the changes in pH of the media. Intraspecific variability as to pH values was characteristic of *Leptographium sp.*, *O.minus*, and *Ophiostoma sp.*, while the isolates of *C. laricicola* and *C. polonica* showed insignificant differences in pH values. These data are plotted in Fig. 2. As the little differences appeared between two isolates, the results for each *Ceratocystis* species are combined in one graph, Fig. 2. In the control (growth on the tannin-free medium) fungi reduced pH from 5.9 (the pH value prior to fungal cultivation) to 3.9 - 4.2 (*O.minus*), 4.7 (*C.laricicola*), 5.2 (*C. polonica*), 5.3 - 6.3 (*Leptographium sp.* and *Ophiostoma sp.* isolates), Fig. 2. For fungi growing on the media containing tannin variations of pH values followed different patterns, Fig.2. Generally speaking, the fungi regulated pH of the media in the ranges of the values close to those recorded in the control, Fig.2. The analysis of variance confirms that variations of the pH values of the media are primarily determined by the fungal species, Table 2. The fungi *C.polonica, Leptographium sp.* and *Ophiostoma sp.* , more tolerant to tannin, regulated the medium pH about 5.0 and higher, while *C.laricicola* and *O.minus* which were less tolerant preferred lower pH values.

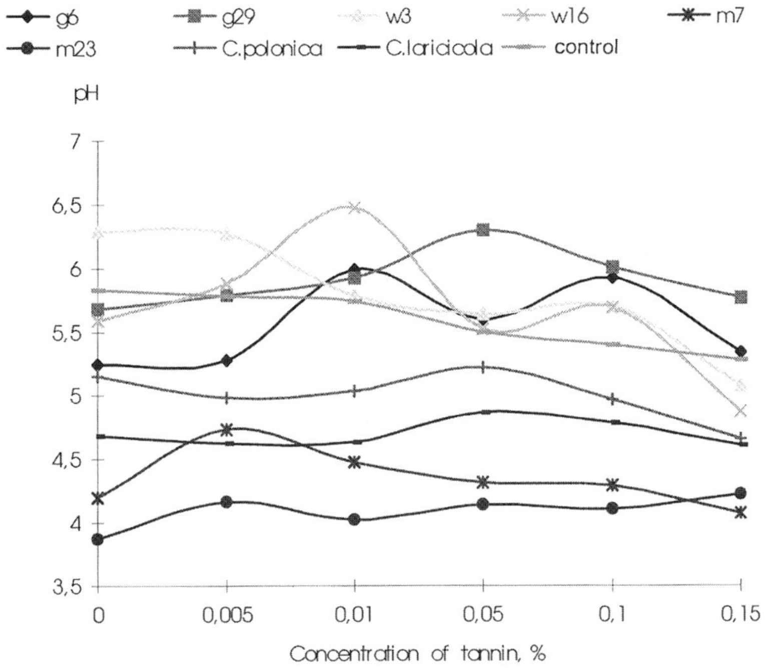

Figure 2. Regulation of pH by blue-stain fungi after 10 days growth on liquid media with different tannin concentrations. Control is measurement of pH in media incubated without fungi. Data are means of three replicates for each treatment of the following isolates: *Leptographium* sp. (g6 and g29), *Ophiostoma minus* (m7 and m23), *Ophiostoma* sp. (w16 and w3), and means of six replicates for *Ceratocystis laricicola* (l1+ l5) and *C.polonica* (p9+ p23)

Table 2. F statistics from ANOVA of effects of tannin concentration (TC) and species of blue-stain fungi (FS) on change of pH in media

Source	SS	df	MS	F	% Total variability
Tannin concentration (TC)	3,33	5	0,67	13,75***	4,2
Fungus species (FS)	62,63	4	15,66	323,02***	79,2
Interaction TCxFS	5,82	20	0,29	6,00***	7,4
Error	7,27	150	0,05		9,2
Total	79,06	179			100

*,P<0,05; **, P<0,01; ***P<0,001

The results obtained show that blue-stain fungi are tolerant to tannin. The isolates investigated were capable of growing even at the tannin concentrations of 0.15%. It can be suggested that the species *Leptographium sp.*, *Ophiostoma sp.*, and *C. polonica* possess some mechanism of tolerance to tannin, which is effective at high concentrations of the inhibitor. High resistance to tannin of *Leptographium sp.* isolates suggests that this species can directly affect plant phenols. There are some evidences in favour of this suggestion concerning this species (Polyakova *et al.*,1995) and the species *C. polonica* (Brignolas *et al.*,1995).

Tolerance to conifer resin

Lesion resin of conifers inhibited growth of blue-stain fungi, but the level of inhibition varied for different combinations of fungal species and host species. The effect of both factors and their interactions was proved to be true by the analysis of variance, Table 3.

Table 3. F statistics from ANOVA of effects of lesion resin of different tree species (TS) and different fungus species (FS) on fungal radial growth rate

Source	SS	df	MS	F	% Total variability
Tree species (TS)	8,18	4	2,05	55,95***	55,0
Fungus species (FS)	2,23	3	0,74	20,35***	15,0
Interaction TSxFS	3,00	12	0,25	6,83***	20,2
Error	1,46	40	0,04		9,2
Total	14,87	50			100

*,P<0,05; **, P<0,01; ***P<0,001

The strongest inhibitory effect on the growth of all the fungi studied was produced by fir resin, Fig.3. Pine resin did not inhibit the growth of the *C. polonica* and *Leptographium sp.* isolates and reduced the growth of the *C. laricicola* and *O.*

minus isolates. Spruce and larch resins inhibited the linear growth of the fungi of the genus *Ceratocystis* but their effect on the growth of *Leptographium sp.* and *O.minus* was little, if any, Fig.3.

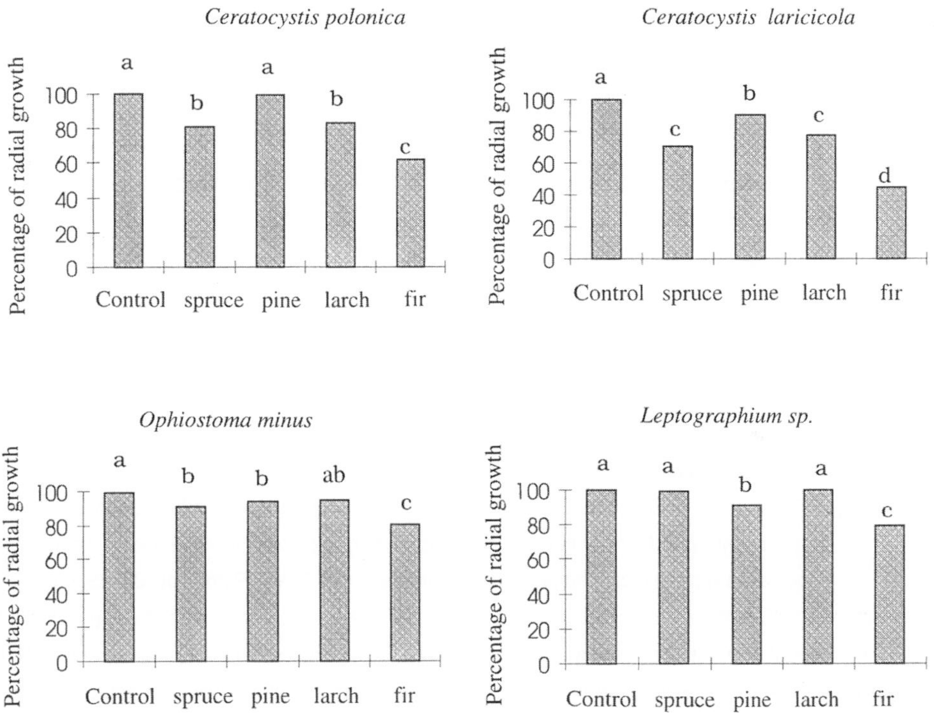

Figure 3. Effect of lesion resin of different conifers on radial growth of blue-stain fungi. Date are means of fungal growth rate for 3 replicates of each treatment expressed as a percentage of radial growth in control. Columns with the same letters indicate means are not significantly different at $P<0,05$ level, t-test.

The data given in Figure 3 show that the smallest growth decline and the highest tolerance to certain resins were recorded in the *Leptographium sp.* and *O. minus* isolates. The linear growth rate decrease was not very significant and, as a rule, did not exceed 20 - 30%, which suggests tolerance of the fungi to this factor.

The fungi of the genus *Ceratocystis* proved to be less tolerant, their growth falling to 50 - 60% in the experiments with fir resin, Fig. 3. The date obtained did not confirm the assumption of specific interrelations between the fungus, the primary invader, and its host plant.

The results generally agree with those of other investigations, which showed that inducible chemicals of conifers may inhibit growth of blue-stain fungi in bioassays but do not appear to be fungicidal (Shrimpton, Whitney, 1968; Wong, Berryman, 1977; Raffa *et al.*, 1985; Solheim, 1991). They also support to the view that blue stain fungi have ability to adapt to defensive phytochemicals.

REFERENCES

BRIDGES J.R., 1987. Effects of terpenoid compounds on growth of symbiotic fungi associated with the southern pine beetle. *Phytopathology,* 77, 83-85.

BRIGNOLAS F., LIEUTIER F., YART A., 1995. Phenolic content of Norway spruce phloem and resistance to *Ophiostoma polonicum. Actuelt fra skogforsk,* 6, 29-30.

BRIGNOLAS F., LIEUTIER F., SAUVARD D., YART A., DROUET A., CLAUDOT A.C., 1995. Changes in soluble phenol content of Norway spruce (*Picea abies* Karst.) phloem in response to wounding and inoculation with *Ophiostoma polonicum. European J. of Forest Pathology,* 25, 253-265.

CHRISTIANSEN E. 1985. *Ceratocystis polonica* inoculated on Norway spruce: blue-staining in relation to inoculation density, resinosis and tree growth. *European J. of Forest Pathology,* 15, 160-167.

COOK S.P., HAIN F.P. Four parameters of the wound response of loblolly and shortleaf pines to inoculation with the blue-staining fungus associated with the southern pine beetle. *Can. J. Bot.*, 65, 2403-2409.

COBB F.W.Jr., KRSTIC M., ZAVARIN E., BARBER H.W.Jr., 1968. Inhibitory effects of volatile oleoresin components on *Fomes annosa* and four *Ceratocystis* species. *Phytopathology,* 58, 1327-1335.

DELORME L., LIEUTIER F., 1990. Monoterpene composition of the preformed and induced resins of Scotch, and their effect on bark beetles and associated fungi. *European Journal of Forest Pathology,* 20, 304-316.

GOTTSTAIN D., GROSS D. 1992. Phytoalexins of woody plants. *Trees,* 6 , 55-68.

HEMINGWAY R.W., MCGRAW G.W., BARRAS S.J. 1977. Polyphenols in *Ceratocystis minor* infected *Pinus taeda*: fungal metabolites, phloem and xylem phenols. *Agriculture and Food Chemistry J.* 25, 717-722.

PAINE T.D., RAFFA K.F., HARRINGTON T.C., 1997. Interactions among scolytid bark beetles, their associated fungi, and live host conifers. *Annu. Rev. Entomol.*, 42, 179-206.

POLYAKOVA G.G., VETROVA V.P., PASHENOVA N.V., OSIPOV V.I., 1995. Role of Proanthocyanidins and Lignin in the Defence Response of Siberian Fir to Inoculation with Micromycetes. *Russian Journal of Plant Physiology*, 42, 4, 552-557.

RAFFA K.F., BERRYMAN A.A. 1982. Accumulation of monoterpenes and associated volatiles following inoculation of grand fir with fungi transmitted by the fir engraver, *Scolytus ventralis (Coleoptera: Scolytidae)*. *Can. Entomol.* 114, 797-810.

RAFFA K.F., BERRYMAN A.A., 1983. Physiological aspects of lodgepole pine wound responses to a fungal symbiont of the mountain pine beetle, *Dendroctonus ponderosae. Can. Entomol.*, 115, 723-734.

RAFFA K.F., BERRYMAN A.A., SIMASKO J., TEAL W., WONG B.L, 1985. Effects of grand fir monoterpenes on the fir engraver *Scolytus ventralis (Coleoptera: Scolytidae)*, and its symbiotic fungus. *Environ. Entomol.*, 14, 552-556.

SHRIMPTON D.M, 1973. Extractives associated with wound response of lodgepole pine attacked by the mountain pine beetle and associated microorganisms. *Can. J. Bot.,* 51, 527-534.

SHRIMPTON D.M., WHITNEY H.S. 1968. Inhibition of growth of blue stain fungi by wood extractives. *Can. J. Bot.* ,46, 757-761.

SOLHEIM H., 1991. Oxygen deficiency and spruce resin inhibition of growth of blue stain fungi associated with Ips typographus. *Mycolog. Res.*, 95, 12, 1387-1392.

STAFFORD H.A. 1988. Proanthocyanidins and the lignin connection. *Phytochemistry,* 27 , 1-6.

VETROVA V.P., POLYAKOVA G.G., MATRENINA R.M., PASHENOVA N.V, OSIPOV V.I. 1995. Accumulation of condensed tannins and lignin in fir and larch phloem induced by blue-stain fungi and their elicitors. *Actuelt fra skogforsk* , 6, 18-19

Chapter 4

Effect of the Aggressors on the Host Tree

Physiology and Genetics of Tree-Phytophage Interactions
Gujan (France), August 31 - September 5, 1997
Ed. INRA, Paris, 1999 (Les Colloques, n°90)

Some fungi associated with *Platypus cylindrus* F. (Coleoptera : Platypodidae) on *Quercus suber* L.: toxicity bioassays

E. M. R. SOUSA [1], M. E. M. GUEDES [2]

[1] *Estação Florestal Nacional, Departamento de Protecção Florestal*
Quinta do Marquês 2780 Oeiras, Portugal
[2] *Instituto de Investigação Científica e Tropical, Centro das Ferrugens do Cafeeiro*
Quinta do Marquês 2780 Oeiras, Portugal

RESUME

Recently, new fungi symbiosis were detected in association with high population levels of *P. cylindrus* in portuguese cork oak stands. The toxicity of these fungi was assessed by a bioassay method, with a dense suspension of *Cladosporium cucumerinum* ELL. et Art, however only *Nodulisporium* sp. has shown the presence of a biocidal compound.

INTRODUCTION

In several species of scolytids and platypodids a direct correlation between their presence in the host and the appearing of serious diseases on trees has been verified (Beaver, 1989). This symbiosis between the insects and the pathogenic fungi plays an important role, specially when the colonised tree is healthy (Berryman, 1972).

P. cylindrus is an ambrosia beetle known for attacking mainly dead and dying trees (Baker, 1963). However, the new outbreak in population levels led to the establishment of new relationships such as associations with other fungi (*Acremonium* sp, *Nodulisporium* sp., *Fusarium solani* (Mart.) Sacc. and *Raffaelea ambrosia* v. Arx & Henneb.). Some of these new symbiosis may contribute to the weakness of the host and may create the ideal conditions for the establishment of insects (Sousa *et al.*, 1997).

In this study we intend to evaluate if some of the four fungi carried by P. *cylindrus* (with the probability of being pathogenic to the cork oak) may synthesise some toxic compounds to the host.

MATERIAL AND METHODS

Pure cultures of the four fungi (*Acremonium* sp., *Nodulisporium* sp. - IMI number 366325, *Fusarium solani* and *Raffaelea ambrosia*) were obtained from successive replications in malt from samples of the *P. cylindrus* galleries. In a second step these fungi were developed in 250 ml Erlenmeyer balloons (in each one 3 inoculation samples of 0,5 cm^2 were placed) in two liquid mediums: one with cork oak wood fragments that had gone through a riddle number 6 (10g of wood / 100ml of water; one of malt (40g of malt / 1000ml of water).

Four repetitions of each of these cultures were successively filtered (filter of a porous membrane with 45 µm of diameter) after 10 and 20 days of growth in an incubator at 25°C (dark conditions). The filtrations (around 250ml of the total) were then frozen (-4°C) for 24h. The filtrations were placed (10 µl) on thin layer chromatography plates and eluated with chloroform: methanol (99:5, v/v). The presence of antifungal compounds in extracts was assessed by spraying developed TLC plates with a dense spore suspension of *Cladosporium cucumerinum* ELL et Arth. (Allen & Kúc, 1968) and incubated in the dark at 25°C in a humid environment.

RESULTS

Based on cultures developed in a liquid medium composed of water and fragments of cork oak wood, we verified that several spots of inhibition growth were seen at different stages after inoculation at 10 and 20 days (Fig 1-A). The biggest inhibition spots of the fungus were found in 10 day cultures of *Nodulisporium* sp. The existence of these spots does not prove that there is a synthesis of inhibitory compounds made by the fungi. In fact, since the control itself shows spots of inhibition (R_F 0.37, 0.50, 0.74, 0.85), the first ones may result from derivatives of the initial substances of the wood.

Aiming to verify if the fungi still form spots of inhibition when they develop in the absence of cork oak wood, some TLC plates were prepared with fungi that had grown in a liquid malt medium (Fig. 1-B). In these TLC plates the control has not an inhibition role and therefore all the inhibition spots of the fungi cultures were provoked by the compounds they have synthesised. It was verified that the fungi *Nodulisporum* sp., once again, showed the biggest inhibition spots to the *C. cucumerinum* growth.

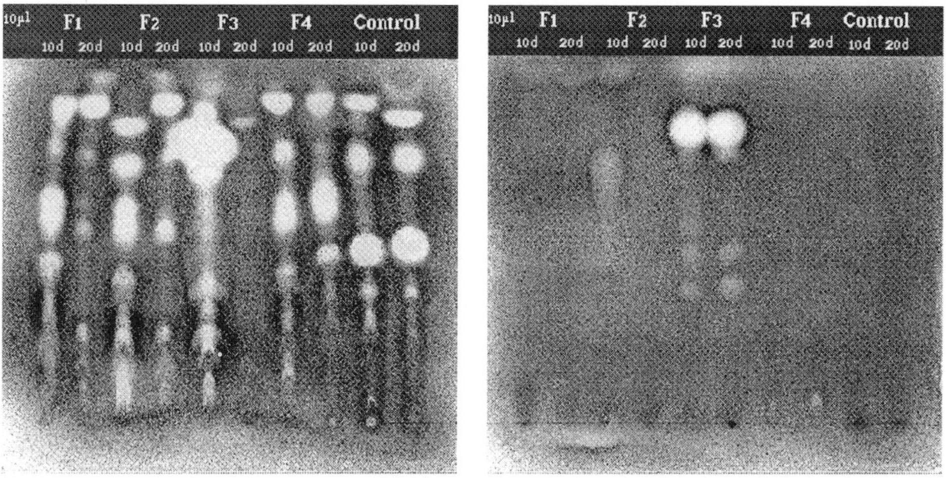

A B

Figure 1 - TLC plates eluated with chloroform : methanol (95/5, v/v) of fungi cultures extracts (F1 - *Fusarium solani*, F2 - *Acremonium* sp., F3 - *Nodulisporium* sp., F4 - *Raffaelea ambrosia*) sprayed with a spore suspension of *Cladosporium cucumerinum* and then incubated. White stripes of the chromatogram correspond to inhibition spots after inoculation. A - developed in a liquid medium of cork oak wood fragments (F1 - 10 days R_F 0.44, 0.58, 0.75, 0.88; F1 - 20 days R_F 0.54, 0.75, 0.88; F2 - 10 days R_F 0.55, 0.71, 0.82; F2 - 20 days R_F 0.53, 0.88; F3 - 10 and 20 days R_F 0.76; F4 - 10 days R_F 0.43, 0.59, 0.75, 0.89; F4 - 20 days R_F 0.47, 0.62, 0.89). B - developed in a liquid medium of malt (F2 - 10 days R_F 0.70; F3 - 10 days R_F 0.78; F3 - 20 days R_F 0.77).

DISCUSSION

The *Nodulisporium* sp. fungus showed a compound with fungitoxic activity to *C. cucumerinum* when the fungus grew in a malt medium as well as when it developed in the extract of cork oak wood. Nevertheless only the tests of artificial inoculations in seedling or cork oak trees, will make a conclusion about the pathogenicity of this compound.

In almost all plant diseases, it is possible to detect metabolites produced by the pathogenic fungus. These phytotoxins vary immensely in their structures and biosynthetic origins from polyketides and terpenoids to peptides and quinones (Harborne, 1993). At the present and in what concerns the *Nodulisporium hinnuleum* Smith we know that it synthesizes two fungitoxic substances - demethoxyviridin and desmethoxyviridiol (Stoessl, 1981).

On the other hand, the presence of this new fungus (*Nodulisporium sp.)* associated with *P. cylindrus*, with the possibility of it being pathogenic to the cork oak, will corroborate the hypothesis already established (Sousa *et al.*, 1997) that the existence of new insect symbiosis may represent an important factor to a higher effectiveness in its attack strategies of the host. However, in some cases of fungi vection by insects, this evidence is circumstantial and, it could be argued that the pathogenic fungi confer no benefit to the beetle and, indeed, may be detrimental to the development of beetle brood (Harrington, 1993).

CONCLUSIONS

The presence of this new fungus (*Nodulisporium* sp.) associated to *Platypus cylindrus* may probably be part of a complex attack strategy. In fact, it was possible to verify that *Nodulisporium* sp. fungus shows a compound with fungitoxic activity to *C. cucumerinum.* However its chemical structure and its effects in artificial inoculations must be evaluated.

ACKNOWLEDGEMENTS

We thank Sofia Basto and Ana Bela Carvalho for chemicals and Mónica Moreira, Luís Bonifácio, Luís Monteiro and Vítor Gonçalves for their kindly cooperation.

REFERENCES

ALLEN E. H., KÚC J., 1968. α-solanine and -chaconine as fungitoxic compounds in extract of irish potato tubers. *Phytopathology*, 58, 776-781.

BAKER J. M., 1963. Ambrosia beetles and their fungi, with particular reference to *Platypus cylindrus* Fab. *Symp. Soc. General Microbiol.*, 13, 323-354.

BEAVER R. A., 1989. Insect-fungus relationships in the bark and ambrosia beetles. In: Wilding N., Collins N. M., Hammond P. M., Webber J. F. (Eds) : *Insect-Fungus Interactions.* Academic Press, London, p. 121-143.

BERRYMAN A. A., 1972. Resistance of conifers to invasion by bark beetle-fungus associations. *BioScience*, 22, 598-602.

HARBORNE J. B., 1993. Advances in chemical ecology. *Natural Products Reports*, 327-348.

HARRINGTON T. C., 1993. Diseases of conifers caused by species of Ophiostoma and Leptographium. In: Wingfield M. J., Seifert K. A., Webber J. (Eds) : *Ceratocystis and Ophiostoma. Taxonomy, ecology, and pathogenicity.* APS Press, Minnesota, p. 161-172.

SOUSA E. M. R., TOMAZ I. L., MONIZ F. A., BASTO S., 1997. La répartition spatiale des champignons associés à *Platypus cylindrus* Fab. (Coleoptera : Platypodidae). *Phytopathologia Mediterranea*, 36, 145-153.

STOESSEL A., 1981. Structure and Biogenetic relations : Fungal nonhost-specific. In : Durbin R. D. (Ed) : *Toxins in Plant Disease.* Academic Press, New York, p. 109-219.

Physiology and Genetics of Tree-Phytophage Interactions
Gujan (France), August 31 - September 5, 1997
Ed. INRA, Paris, 1999 (Les Colloques, n°90)

Cork Oak - *Hypoxylon mediterraneum* de Not.: pathogenicity tests

MARIA NATÉRCIA SOUSA SANTOS

Estação Florestal Nacional, Departamento de Protecção Florestal
Quinta do Marquês, 2780 Oeiras, Portugal

RESUME

Hypoxylon mediterraneum (de Not.) Mill. is a fungus closely associated with cork oak trees in the last stage of decline. This fungus has frequently been considered a strong contributory factor to cork oak decline. Observations and experiments conducted under field conditions, raise doubts about the role of the fungus even in late stages of decline. To clarify this situation several attempts were made to assess fungus pathogenicity. The results obtained confirmed that the fungus develops on previously killed tissues, leading to the hypothesis that *H. mediterraneum* probably functions as a saprophyte.

INTRODUCTION

Since the end of the nineteen century, several cases of cork oak mortality have been periodically observed in Portugal (David *et al*, 1992). Efforts developed to understand this phenomenon did not reach any specific conclusion. Multiple biotic and abiotic stress factors, occurring simultaneously or in succession and changing from region to region, have been found in close association with cork oak stand decline (Cabral & Sardinha, 1992; Yousfi, 1995).

Among these factors, insects and fungi seem to be involved with mortality of trees previously weakened by other environmental stress factors, as it has been frequently pointed out regarding *H. mediterraneum* (Azevedo, 1958; Macara, 1975; Torres-Juan, 1985). However, no conclusive work in the pathogenicity of this fungus has been presented (Oliveira, 1931; Barbosa, 1958; Azevedo & Macara, 1963).

The objective of this paper is to provide a better understanding of the relationships between this fungus and its prefered host - the cork oak.

MATERIAL AND METHODS

Sixty three-year-old plants were grown in pots (volume 70 cm x 70 cm x 80 cm) containing sandy soil, and kept in a greenhouse. Two blocks, each with 30 plants, were established. Half of these plants were supplied with 8 x 10^3 ml of water, twice a week, and half were subjected to water stress by providing only 2 x 10^3 ml once a week. These watering regimes started one month before the inoculation tests. In each group of 15 plants (stressed and unstressed), 10 plants were inoculated, in early April, with mycelium obtained from two-week-old colonies of *H. mediterraneum* grown on Malt Agar medium at 25 ± 2°C, and with stroma removed from an infected cork oak tree. Mycelium and a small piece of stroma were inserted under the bark through a longitudinal cut (1.0 cm x 0.2 cm) that was covered with wet cotton and cellophane paper for 10 days. The remaining 5 plants were inoculated with sterile Malt Agar medium as control. In the beginning of the third year, a lower branch was detached from each plant and cut into 0.7 cm sections which remained in the same greenhouse conditions. One Petri dish per pot, containing 2 sections was put at soil level. Two months later one section was inoculated and the other one used as a control. The inoculations were made using the same method above described for plant inoculation. Fungus re-isolation was made monthly by removing aseptically 0.2 mm pieces (one per wound) from tissues at level of inoculated zones, at the end of the first five months after inoculation. Each piece was put in a Petri dish containing Malt Agar amended with 100 ml/l of Penicillin and 100 ml/l of Streptomycin and incubated at 25° ± C. It was considered as positive results the development of a characteristic dark stroma (thick, compact, friable) containing fungus perithecia.

The height of all plants was measured at the end of the three years of tests and any disease symptoms or signs were recorded. The relative humidity in the greenhouse was maintained between 70% and 80%, during the first 60 days after the inoculation.Statistical significance was determined by Student t - test and χ^2 using Statview Aboars Concepts, Inc. ABACUS software.

RESULTS AND DISCUSSION

The results of the pathogenicity tests are sumarised in table 1.

After cotton removal, a darkening of the superficial tissus in contact with the inoculum was observed on all inoculated stressed and unstressed plants. Tissues around inoculation zones were not necrotic. Two months after inoculation, it was verified the development of callus around inoculation zones and the healing of the wounds on all inoculated plants and controls.

Plants subjected to water stress presented slight discoloration and growth reduction. There was significant height difference between stressed and unstressed plants. As there were no differences on discoloration and height between inoculated plants and controls, these symptoms were probably induced by low water supply.

A longitudinal spread of dark lesions was observed on 15% of the inoculated branch sections and four months later these lesions developed characteristic stroma containing perithecia of *H. mediterraneum.*In spite of the low percentage of such material, the fungus presented a prevailing ability to develop on dead tissues, confirming previous field results (Santos, 1992).

Re-isolation frequency (positive re-isolation per number of re-isolations attempts), was 90%, 43% and 25% respectively at the end of the first, second and third months and 0% at the end of the fourth and fifth months after inoculation.

No significant differences on results were observed between the two blocks (P< 0.05)

TABLE 1- Artificial inoculations of *Hypoxylon mediterraneum* on cork oak (*Quercus suber* L.) plants subjected to different water regimes and on detached branch sections

Stressed plants		**Unstressed plants**		**Branch sections**	
Innoculated (19)	**Control (10)**	**Innoculated (20)**	**Control (10)**	**Innoculated (60)**	**Control (60)**
++	+	+++		++++ (9 positive results)	(0 positive results)
* 74.53 ± 16.88 (a)	* 72.20 ± 6.51 (a)	* 103.90 ± 14.51 (b)	* 107.10 ± 12.47 (b)	(c)	(d)

( ) Number of replicates
+ Leaf discoloration and growth reduction
++ Leaf discoloration, growth reduction and fungus re-isolation
+++ Fungus re-isolation
++++ Development of stroma and perithecia and fungus re-isolation
* Mean height and standard deviation
(a);(b) values followed by the same letter do not differ significantly; values with different letters differ significantly at 5% significance level.
(c); (d) significantly different at 2% significance level

A general review of artificial inoculation tests to assess susceptibility on cork oak (Oliveira, 1930; Barbosa,1958; Azevedo & Macara, 1963) and also on other species of *Quercus* (Luisi *et al*, 1992; Vannini, 1991,1996) allowed to conclude that host susceptibility level was determined by presence and size of the lesions produced around inoculation zones and fungus re-isolation but the development of other external disease symptoms and signs of *H. mediterraneum* e. g. characteristic stroma and perithecia were, not recorded.

It is widely reported that *H. mediterraneum* is closely associated with cork oak trees in late decline stage - level 3 of an international scale (EC, 1989). The main symptoms of declined cork oak trees are crown transparency and dark soaked stem patches extruding a viscous liquid. These exudates have been often considered as the first symptom of *H. mediterraneum* establishment (Malençon, 1951; Azevedo, 1958; Barbosa, 1958). Attempts to confirm this hepothesis were not successful (Belisario *et al*, 1992). This author did not find any correlation between this symptom and micoflora isolated from exudates or active bleeding tissus of *Quercus cerris* L. The same author pointed out that *H. mediterraneum* was rarely isolated from those exudates and active bleeding tissues.Similar results also were obtained on cork oak by Santos (1992). Other species e. g. *Fagus* spp (Kowalski, 1991), poplar (Naidenov, 1984; Cellerino, 1992), eucalyptus (Santos unpublished) also present similar symptom under unfavourable environmental conditions but no correlation was found between exudates and isolated harmful microorganisms.

CONCLUSIONS

Two main points require emphasis; *Hypoxylon mediterraneum* seems to have a prevailing ability to develop on dead tissues since characteristic stroma containing fungus perithecia only developed on detached branch sections; Leaf discoloration and growth reduction only occurred on trees (inoculated and controls) subjected to water stress. As such, these symptoms are probably induced by water stress and not by fungus activity.

In spite of these results data are not sufficient to conclude that *Hypoxylon mediterraneum* is strictly saprophyte but clearly indicate that a more thorough investigation is needed to clarify relationships between this fungus and cork oak and interaction with other site factors and organisms involved.

REFERENCES

AZEVEDO F.S., 1958. O carvão do entrecasco do sobreiro. *Publicações dos Serviços Florestais e Aquicolas* 25:159-179.

AZEVEDO N.F.S.,MACARA A.M., 1963. Quelques observations sur la pathogénicité du "charbon du liber". FAO/SCM/LG/63. Annexe IV.

BARBOSA, M.A.F., 1958. *O carvão do entrecasco. Hypoxylon mediterraneum (de Not.) Ces. et de Not. Contribuição para o seu estudo. Publicações da Direcção dos Serviços Florestais e Aquicolas,* 25 : 93-132.

BELISARIO, A.; MOTTA, E., BIOCCA, M., 1992. Occurrence and role of exsudations in turkey oak decline in central Italy. *Proceedings of an International Congress "Recent Advances in Studies on Oak decline".* Selva di Fasano (Brindisi) Italy, p. 149-154

CABRAL M.T., SARDINHA R.M.A., 1992. Perspectiva integrada do declinio dos montados de sobro. *Actas do 2º Encontro sobre os montados de Sobro e Azinho.* Évora, Portugal, p. 217-231.

CELLERINO J. P., 1982. Situation sanitaire des salicaceae en Italy. *Session du Groupe d'Étude sur les Maladies du Peuplier, FAO/CIP.* Casale Monferrato, Italie.

DAVID T.S., CABRAL M.T., SARDINHA R.M.A., 1992. A mortalidade dos sobreiros e a seca. *Finisterra,* 27: 17-24.

EC, 1989. *Global Environmental Monitoring System - Forest Damage and Air Pollution Draft Report on the 1988 Forest Damage Survey in Europe.* Project FP/9/01 -86 - 05 ECE/Unep, Geneve.

KOWALSKI, T., 1991. Oak decline, fungi associated with various disease symptoms on overground portions of middle aged and old oak. *European Journal of Forest Pathology, 21: 136 - 14*

LUISI N., MANICONE R.P., SICOLI G., LERARIO P., 1992. Pathogenicity tests of fungi associated with oak decline on *Quercus* spp. seedlings grown at different water regimes. *Proceedings of an International Congress "Recent Advances in Studies on Oak decline".* Selva di Fasano, Italy, p. 85-93.

MACARA, A.M., 1975. Estimativa em 1975 dos prejuizos causados pelas principais doenças do sobreiro na Região Alentejana. *Boletim do Instituto dos Produtos Florestais. Cortiça,* 444: 205-212.

MALENÇON, G. & MANION, J., 1951. Les modalités épidémiologiques de *l'Hypoxylon mediterraneum* (D. Ntrs.) Ces, & E. Ntrs en Afrique du Nord. *Extrait du Fascicule IV du 70º Congrès de l'AFAS.* Tunis.

NAIDENOV Y., 1984. Les liaisons entre la dynamique de l'attaque de la maladie des taches brunes et la densité des cultures de peupliers. *XII Session du Groupe sur les Maladies du Peuplier. FAO/CIP.* Ottawa, Canada.

OLIVEIRA A.B., 1931. Apontamentos para o estudo de duas doenças do sobreiro. *Revista Agronómica,* 19: 37-56.

SANTOS M.N.S., 1992. Microflora do entrecasco de sobreiros em declíneo. *Actas do 2º Encontro sobre os montados de Sobro e Azinho.* Évora, Portugal, p.211-216.

TORRES-JUAN J., 1985. El *Hypoxylon mediterraneum* (de Not.) Mill. y su comportamiento en los encinares y alcornocales andaluces. *Boletim Servicio de Defesa Contra Plagas e Inspeccion Fitopatologica,* 11: 185-191.

VANNINI A., 1991. Susceptibility of *Quercus cerris* to *Hypoxylon mediterraneum* at different levels of water stress. *Proceedings of an International Symposium: "Oak decline in Europe".* Kórnik, Poland, p. 165-172.

VANNINI, A., 1996. Impact of drought and *Hypoxylon mediterraneum* on oak decline in the Mediterranean region. *Annales des Sciences Forestières,* 53: 753-760

YOUSFI, M., 1995. Les contraintes exercées sur le chêne liège au Maroc. Exemple de la Mamora. *Bulletin IOBC,* 18: 43-49.

Chapter 5

Effects of External Factors on Tree/Aggressor Interactions and resistance expression

Chapter

Physiology and Genetics of Tree-Phytophage Interactions
Gujan (France), August 31 - September 5, 1997
Ed. INRA, Paris, 1999 (Les Colloques, n°90)

Effect of defoliation on resistance response of *Abies sibirica* Ledeb. to inoculation with blue-stain fungi

V.P. VETROVA [1], V.V. STASOVA [2] AND N.V. PASHENOVA [3]

[1] *Institute of Forest, Russian Academy of Sciences, Laboratory of Forest Zoology 660036 , Krasnoyarsk , RUSSIA*

[2] *Institute of Forest, Russian Academy of Sciences, Laboratory of Plant Physiology 660036 , Krasnoyarsk , RUSSIA*

[3] *Institute of Forest, Russian Academy of Sciences, Laboratory of Microbiology 660036 , Krasnoyarsk , RUSSIA*

RESUME

Effect of defoliation on resistance response of Siberian fir , *Abies sibirica* Ledeb., to fungal inoculation was investigated within three even-aged fir stands damaged by Siberian moth, *Dendrolimus superans sibiricus* Tschetw., and located in the Krasnoyarsk Territory (Central Siberia). Histological changes in tissues, accompanying the resistance response were examined in 30 fir trees (90-130 years old) of different defoliation degree (50, 75, 100 %) six weeks after single inoculation with *Leptographium sp.* vectored by *Monochamus urussovi* Fisch. (*Coleoptera: Cerambycidae*). It was recorded that the rate and intensity of defence response of phloem and xylem tissues to inoculation as well as percent of trees infested by the insect-vector differed significantly in dependence of defoliation degree. Trees of 50 percent defoliation significantly differed from trees of more severe defoliation in all parameters of defence response and percentage of colonisation by the beetle. The trees defoliated to 75 and 100% did not differ significantly in defence response activity and the number of the trees attacked by *M. urussovi.* Strong difference in resistance to inoculation and colonisation by the beetle was recorded between trees defoliated in the current year and in the previous year. All infested by *M. urussovi* trees were characterised by the epidemic level of frequency of blue-stain fungi associated with this insect. The tendency was recorded to a decreased frequency of the pathogenic *Ophiostoma sp.* and a more frequent occurrence of the saprophyte *O. curvicollis* in trees defoliated in previous year which lost ability to defend against wounding and fungal infection.

INTRODUCTION

The resistance response of conifers to inoculation with blue-stain fungi involves necrosis of the tissue in the infested area , impregnation of a reaction zone with phenolics and resin, periderm and callus formation at the periphery of the lesion (Shrimpton, 1973; Berryman, 1972; Wong and Berryman, 1977). The hypersensitive response is non specific reaction induced by pathogens in resistant plants (Berryman, 1972; Hain *et al.*, 1983). Under stresses the reaction is disturbed which may lead to pathogen invasion into plant tissues. The activity of hypersensitive reaction to inoculation with blue-stain fungi is usually used as a test of conifer tree vigour and resistance to attacks of insect-vectors.

Defoliation of conifers by phytophagous insects causes widespread tree death resulting from a decrease in plant resistance to insect/fungal invasion . The influence of defoliation on resistance response in conifers to blue-stain fungi has been little studied. There are data only on defoliation-related biochemical alterations in the reaction, specifically changes in monoterpene composition and accumulation dynamics as well as in inner bark carbohydrate concentrations (Wright *et al.*, 1979) . Anatomical alterations in the defence reaction related with defoliation have not been studied.

The present histological investigation was designed to assess the effect of defoliation on the resistance response of Siberian fir, *Abies sibirica* Ledeb., to inoculation with blue-stain fungus *Leptographium sp.* transmitted by the fir sawyer beetle *Monochamus urussovi* Fisch. (*Coleoptera: Cerambycidae*). The study was carried out in the centre of an outbreak of the Siberian moth, *Dendrolimus superans sibiricus* Tschetw. Recurrent outbreaks of the Siberian moth and associated outbreaks of *M. urussovi* periodically spread to many hundred thousand hectares of boreal coniferous forests in North-Eastern Russia (Isaev *et al.,* 1988). Outbreaks of *M. urussovi* cause widespread mortality in stands of Siberian fir and Siberian spruce *Picea obovata* Ledeb., defoliated by *D. superans sibiricus.* Siberian fir is the preferred host of the fir sawyer beetle. *M. urussovi* transmits some species of fungi which can cause vascular mycosis and blue-staining of sapwood in conifers (Isaev *et al.*, 1988; Pashenova *et al.*, 1994). The blue-stain fungus *Leptographium sp.* is frequently associated with this beetle in Siberian fir (Pashenova *et al.*, 1994).

We have studied the hypersensitive response of Siberian fir to inoculation with blue-stain fungi, associated with the fir sawyer beetle *M. urussovi*, on healthy trees and found that the necrotic lesion usually forms 3-4 weeks after inoculation (Polyakova *et al.*, 1995). Necrosis of cells in the infected area is accompanied by active accumulation of tannins and lignin in the reaction zone of phloem (Polyakova et al., 1995). Callus forms 4 weeks after inoculation sealing the necrotic infected area. Necrophylactic periderm formation is usually completed 6 weeks after inoculation.

This investigation involved studying of anatomical changes in defence response to infection in trees of various defoliation degrees. The purpose of this study was to find indicators of plant resistance to colonisation by the fir sawyer beetle and the associated blue stain fungi, using histological parameters of the defence response to fungal inoculation.

MATERIAL AND METHODS

The influence of defoliation on resistance response of fir stem tissues to fungal infection was studied in July-August 1996 in even-aged fir stands near Taseevo (The Krasnoyarsk Territory). The region of study is characterised by the availability of large areas of defoliated stands (more than 500 hectares). The territory belongs to south taiga region of boreal dark coniferous and larch- pine forests. The three plots were chosen in the stands growing in similar conditions. The stands were damaged by Siberian moth in 1995 and 1996. In the plots the time and the degree of defoliation as well as refoliation were taken into account. Field data collected on each plot included percentage of trees infested by *M. urussovi* in relation to tree defoliation degree. The percent of trees colonised by the fir sawyer beetle was determined among 100 fir trees of different defoliation degrees taken at each plot. For microbiological analysis, 50 samples of phloem and sapwood with laid eggs and larval galleries of the fir sawyer beetle were collected from the category of trees that was dominating on each plot. The species of fungi were identified on the basis of typical morphological signs of anamorphes and teleomorphes (Olchowecki and Reid, 1974; Solheim, 1986) by examining the collected samples.

For histological analysis, at the beginning of July (swarming time for *M. urussovi*) 30 fir trees of various defoliation degree - 50, 75 and 100 % defoliated in the current year and completely defoliated in the previous year, each about 25 cm diameter at breast height, were inoculated with *Leptographium sp.*, using the cork borer technique (Wong and Berryman, 1977). The age of the trees sampled ranged from 90 to 130 years, but most samples were taken from 100-120 year-old trees. The trees were inoculated with 2-week-old cultures of *Leptographium sp*, the holes were made using a 7-mm cork borer into the trunk to the sapwood. After 6 weeks, samples of bark and sapwood , consisting of the brown reaction zone and 5-mm surrounding tissue, were removed with a chisel. In all samples, the length of the phloem necrotic lesion and size of the resin cavity were measured. For sectioning, razor blades were used to cut transverse sections of phloem and xylem tissues. The transverse sections were made at the middle of the necrotic lesion. Cupric acetate was used to test tissue from the reactive zone for resin (Wong and Berryman, 1977).

For each sample, the following parameters of defence response were estimated: the stage of wound periderm development: in grades: 1) absence of periderm, 2) non-coloured periderm, 3) completely formed coloured periderm ; the number of traumatic resin ducts (per 1mm of transverse section) and percentage of resin ducts filled with resin; formation of callus and its size; percentage of phloem cells and tracheids filled with resin.

Data within and among groups were subjected to an ANOVA statistical analysis. For each group of trees, the means of the histological parameters of the defence response were calculated. Comparison of the means of quantitative parameters of defence response and percentage of colonisation by the fir sawyer beetle between trees with different defoliation degree were made using a two-sample t-test. Significance of difference was tested at the 0.05 level. Statistical analysis of histological data included the estimation of correlation between all defence response parameters.

RESULTS

Histological analysis

In all samples, a typical elliptical necrotic lesion was visible in the phloem. The length of the necrotic zone in phloem varied from 25 to 180 mm. Removal of the phloem usually showed a resin cavity. The size of the resin cavity was similar to or smaller than the necrotic zone of phloem. At transverse sections, formation of callus and periderm at periphery of the necrotic lesion was recorded. The phloem of the necrotic lesion was usually weakly soaked with resin. Resin was observed in the lumina of sieve cells, the resin containing sieve cells were usually found in close proximity to the resin cavity and along fissures of necrotic phloem. Both young and old phloem seemed to be equally resin impregnated. The sapwood response to inoculation was characterised by formation of resin ducts and a cavity , and the presence of resin in the tracheid lumina. In *Abies* genera, trees do not normally produce resin ducts. Inoculation of the stem causes formation of so called traumatic resin ducts. The number of resin ducts varied from 6 to 12 per 1 mm of transverse section, their filling with resin ranged from 0 to 100%. The resin cavity formed on the boundary of phloem and xylem on the line of resin duct gaps. Resin in tracheid lumina was recorded mainly in two last annual rings. Resinosis of early and late tracheids was similar. Resin filled tracheids were not associated with rays or resin ducts.

The correlation analysis showed that the size of resin cavity was negatively related to the length of necrotic lesion ($r=-0.62$; $p=0.01$). No resin cavities were found

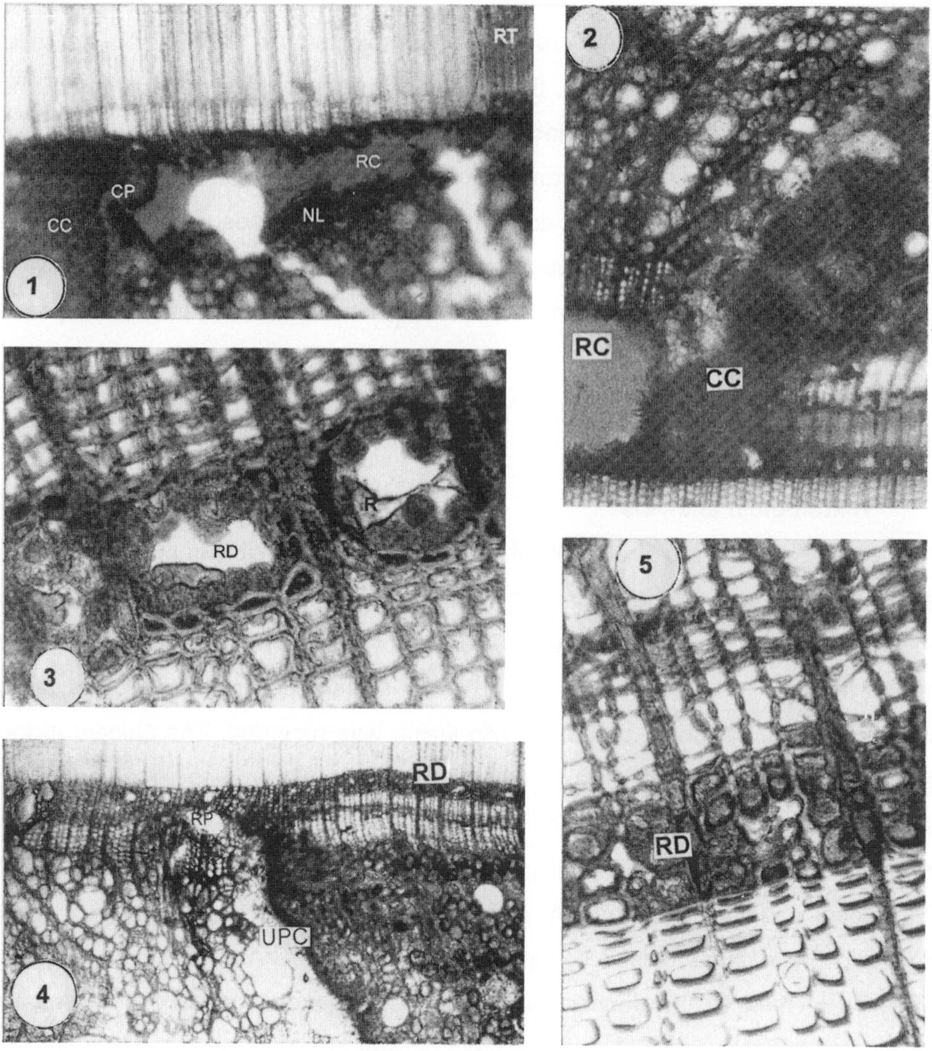

Fig. 1 to 3. Transverse sections through the phloem and xylem at the middle of reaction zone from trees of 50% defoliation .

Fig. 1. Transverse section showing necrotic lesion of phloem (NL), resin cavity (RC), resin soaked tracheids (RT), pad of poorly differentiated callus cells (CC) and coloured phellem (CP) of periderm derived from phellogen that have been developed in the outer layers of callus cells. x 40.

Fig. 2 Transverse section showing well developed resin cavity (RC) filled with resin, and mass of undifferentiated callus cells (CC) supposedly derived from divisions of phloem parenchyma cells. x 40.

Fig. 3. Showing mature traumatic resin ducts (RD) filled with resin (R). x 100.

Fig. 4. Transverse sections through phloem and xylem tissue from a tree of 75% defoliation showing necrophylactic periderm with layers of uncoloured phellem cells (UPC), resin ducts (RD) and resin pockets (RP) Note absence of resin cavity. × 40.

Fig. 5. Transverse section through xylem from a tree of 100% defoliation showing incompletely differentiated resin ducts (RD). × 100.

under necrotic lesions longer than 80 mm. From the physiological point of view, it may be interpreted as the absence of defence response of the tree that doesn't resist infection spreading. This is supported by the strong negative correlation between the length of necrotic lesion and the development of wound periderm (r=-0.76; p=0.01), as well as with the number of traumatic resin ducts (r=-0.42; p=0.05). A strong positive correlation was recorded between callus development and periderm formation (r= 0.56; p=0.01).

The rate and the intensity of defence response of fir stem tissues to infection differed for the trees of various defoliation degrees . With the defoliation up to 50% defence response was very active. In this case, the small necrotic lesions (average length 40 mm) were completely isolated by necrophylactic periderm that had red colour that is characteristics of freshly formed phellem (Fig. 1). There was well developed callus, which suggested that the wound lesion was healing, and the inoculated pathogen had been completely suppressed (Fig. 1, 2). In xylem a tangential band of mature traumatic resin ducts formed (Fig. 3). The number of traumatic resin ducts reached 12/mm, they were full of resin. A well developed resin cavity was recorded (Fig. 1, 2). Active callus formation was observed along the border of the necrotic phloem zone, due to division of tangential band parenchyma (Fig. 2). This observation is similar to those noted by P.R. Larson (1994): in most wounds callus tissue is usually derived from the rays, vascular parenchyma and undifferentiated xylem and phloem derivatives, and is parenchymatous in nature.

In the 75% defoliated trees defence response to inoculation slowed down leading to an increase in the number of infected phloem cells; the length of the lesion reached 70-80 mm. Because of delay in formation, the wound periderm was less pronounced and non-coloured, callus was slightly developed (Fig. 4). Resinosis appeared to be less active - resin pockets rather than a resin cavity were found (Fig. 4). Complete defoliation disturbed periderm formation around infected phloem and decreased the activity of traumatic resinosis - resin ducts were poorly differentiated (Fig. 5), no resin cavity was formed in these trees.

Even more pronounced disturbances of defence response were recorded in trees defoliated in the previous year. In this case, enormous phloem necroses with the length reached 180 mm were found in the inoculation zone. Callus and necrophylactic periderm were absent (Fig. 6). Traumatic resin ducts didn't form (Fig. 7). The defence response disturbance resulted in infection spreading over sapwood tissues of these trees (Fig. 7).

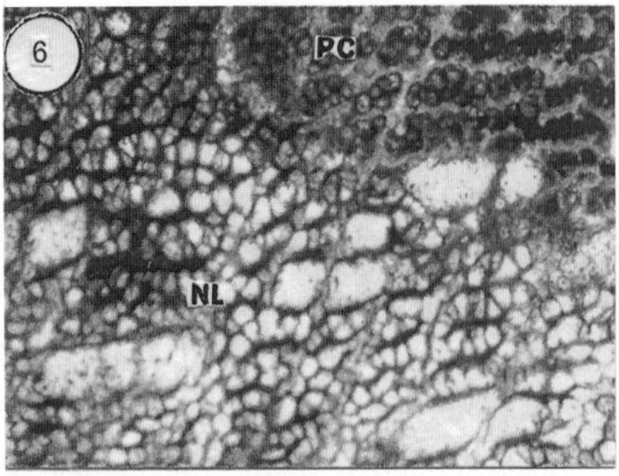

Fig. 6. Transverse sections through phloem of reaction zone from a tree full defoliated in previous year showing necrotic lesion (NL) and adjacent to lesion enlarged parenchymatous cells (PC) . Note absence of callus and periderm at the periphery of necrotic lesion. × 40.

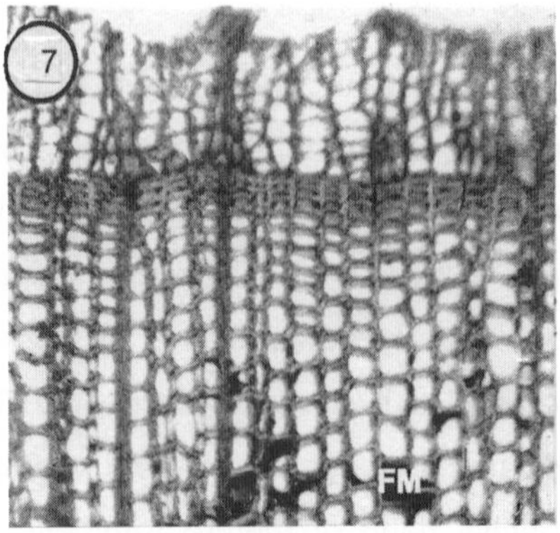

Fig. 7. Transverse section through xylem of inoculation zone showing tracheids filled with fungal mycelium (FM). Note absence of resin ducts. × 90.

The comparison of quantitative parameters of defence response showed a significant difference of trees with 50% defoliation from trees with stronger defoliation (Table 1).

Trees with 75% defoliated crown and completely defoliated ones did not significantly differ from each other either in the size of necrotic lesions which developed in response to inoculation or in the activity of traumatic resinosis (Table 1). Significant differences in all quantitative parameters of the defence response were found between trees completely defoliated in the previous year and trees completely or 75% defoliated in the current year.

Table 1. Mean of defence response parameters (± SD) for trees of different defoliation degree.

Parameters of response	Defoliation degree 50 % (n=5)	75% (n=5)	100% (n=10)	100% (1995 year) (n=10)
Length of necrotic lesion (mm)	40.2±11.6 (a)	55.7±13.7 (b)	60.2±13.8 (b)	103.7±47.5 (c)
Periderm formation	3.0±0.1 (a)	2.3±0.5 (b)	1.7±0.9 (b)	1.0±0 (c)
Width of callus (mm)	0.76±0.13 (a)	0.12±0.08 (b)	0 (c)	0 (c)
Number of resin ducts (per 1 mm)	11.0±1.2 (a)	8.2±1.8 (b)	8.1±1.9 (b)	3.3±3.0 (c)
Percent of resin ducts filled with resin	100.0±0.4 (a)	71.7±31.3 (b)	64.4±33.6 (b)	25.0±35.3 (c)

* Means followed by the same letter within a line are not significantly different at P=0.05, t-test

Field observation

It was found that there is a relation between defoliation degree and the resistance of fir trees to the attack of the sawyer beetle and invasion of blue-stain fungi transmitted by this insect. Among trees with 50% defoliation, the mean percentage of trees infested by the fir sawyer beetle didn't exceed 7%, for trees with strong and complete defoliation this value increased to 45%. The highest colonisation percentage (75%) was recorded for trees completely defoliated in the previous year. The total frequency of blue-stain fungi in the trees infested by the fir sawyer beetle reached 100% (Table 2).

Table 2 . Frequency of the blue-stain fungi in *M.urussovi* galleries

N° of Plot	Year of defoliation	Degree of defoliation of sampled trees (%)	Percentage of samples with blue-stain fungi * Total	*Leptographium sp.*	*Ophiostoma sp.*	*O.curvicollis*
1	1996	75	100 (100)	88(100)	52(36)	12(5)
2	1996	100	100(100)	100(100)	63(50)	25(0)
3	1995	100	96(100)	68(100)	28(22)	60(11)

*Data for phloem samples are without brackets, data for sapwood samples are enclosed in brackets

It was shown that in defoliated stands the fir sawyer beetle transmitted the complex of blue-stain fungi, consisting of the species *Ophiostoma curvicollis*, *Ophiostoma sp.* and *Leptographium sp.* For the trees which were defoliated in the previous (1995) year and lost the ability to defend against wounding and infection we recorded the tendency to a decreased frequency of the pathogenic species *Ophiostoma sp.* and a more frequent occurrence of the saprophyte *O. curvicollis*, in comparison with trees defoliated in the current year (Table 2).

CONCLUSION

The rate and the intensity of defence response of phloem and xylem tissues to fungal inoculation appear to decrease with a higher defoliation degree of Siberian fir. The defence response was active in medium-defoliated trees (50% of crown). These trees were shown to be resistant to colonisation by the fir sawyer beetle. In severely defoliated trees some defence activity was observed, although it was not efficient enough to prevent colonisation. The response of these trees to infection was characterised by weak traumatic resinosis, disturbance of callus and periderm formation. These disturbances of defence response may have resulted from sharp energy deficit in stem tissue of defoliated trees. This supposition could be confirmed by the experimental data on significant decrease of starch and soluble carbohydrate content in phloem and xylem tissues of conifers under full defoliation of crown (Wright et al., 1979; Girs, 1982; Romanova and Sudachkova, 1990).

The recorded relation between the activity of defence response to fungal infection and plant resistance to colonisation by *M. urussovi* allows the method of inoculation to be used in defoliated stands for assessment of fir resistance to the attack of the fir sawyer beetle and to wound infection.

REFERENCES

BERRYMAN A.A.1972. Resistance of conifers to invasion by bark beetle-fungus associations. *BioScience*, 22(6), 598 -602.

GIRS G.I. 1982. *Physiology of weakened tree*. Nauka, Novosibirsk, 253 p. (in Russian).

HAIN F.P., MAWBY W.D., COOK S.P., ARTHUR F.H. 1983. Host conifer reaction to stem invasion. *Z. Ang. Entomol.*, 96, 247-256.

ISAEV A.S., ROZKOV A.S., KISELEV V.V. 1988. *Fir sawyer beetle*. Nauka: Novosibirsk, 212 p. (in Russian).

LARSON P.R. 1994. *The vascular cambium: development and structure*. Springer-Verlag: Berlin; London, 705 p.

OLCHOWECKI A., REID J. 1974. Taxonomy of the genus *Ceratocystis* in Manitoba.*Canad. J. Bot.*, 52 (7), 1675-1711.

PASHENOVA N.V., VYDRYAKOVA G.A., VETROVA V.P. 1994 . Phytopathogenic microscopic fungi associated with the black fir sawyer beetle. *Lesovedenie*. 3: 39-47 (in Russian).

POLYAKOVA G.G., VETROVA V.P., PASHENOVA N.V., OSIPOV V.I.,1995. Role of Proanthocyanidins and Lignin in the Defense Response of Siberian Fir to Inoculation with *Micromycetes. Russian Journal of Plant Physiology*, 42, 4, 552-55.

ROMANOVA L.I., SUDACHKOVA N.E. 1990. Effect of defoliation on carbohydrate level and annual ring structure of Scotch pine. *Lesovedenie*, 2: 54-60 (in Russian).

SHRIMPTON D.M. 1973. Extractives associated with wound response of lodgepole pine attacked by the mountain pine beetle and associated microorganisms. *Can. J. Bot.*, 51(3), 527-534.

SOLHEIIM H. 1986. Species of *Ophiostomataceae* isolated from *Picea abies* infested by the bark beetle *Ips typographus. Nord. J. Bot.*, 6(2), 199-207.

WRIGHT L.C., BERRYMAN A.A., GURUSIDDAIAH S.1979. Host resistance to the fir engraver beetle, *Scolytus ventralis (Coleoptera: Scolytidae)*: 4. Effect of defoliation on wound monoterpene and inner bark carbohydrate concentrations. *Can. Entomol.* 111, 1255-1262.

WONG B.L., BERRYMAN A.A. 1977. Host resistance to the fir engraver beetle. 3. Lesion development and containment of infection by resistant *Abies grandis* inoculated with *Trichosporium symbioticum. Can. J. Bot.* 55: 1358-1365.

Physiology and Genetics of Tree-Phytophage Interactions
Gujan (France), August 31 - September 5, 1997
Ed. INRA, Paris, 1999 (Les Colloques, n°90)

Susceptibility of fire-damaged Scots pine (*Pinus sylvestris* L.) trees to attack by *Tomicus piniperda* L.

BO LÅNGSTRÖM [1], CLAES HELLQVIST [1] AND BENGT EHNSTRÖM [2]

[1] Swedish University of Agricultural Sciences, Department of Entomology, Division of Forest Entomology; P. O. Box 7044, S-75007 Uppsala, Sweden

[2] Swedish University of Agricultural Sciences, Swedish Threatened Species Unit; P. O. Box 7007, S-75007 Uppsala, Sweden

RESUME

The susceptibility of fire-damaged Scots pine trees to attack by the common pine shoot beetle, *Tomicus piniperda*, was followed during 3 years in seven reserves of burned forests that were established in south and central Sweden following extensive forest fires in the summer of 1992. Fire-damaged pine trees were susceptible to beetle attack, mainly during the first two years after the fire. Colonization attempts by *T. piniperda* were successful in trees having less than 25 % intact foliage and failed in trees carrying ca 40 % of full foliage, whereas trees with at least half of their foliage left were not attacked at all. Altogether, ca 60 % of the 446 study trees were attacked, and most of them died. A few trees sustained beetle attack in two or even three years.The attack density of *T. piniperda* increased from the first to the second year, and fell again in the third year. Many new beetles developed in the two first years but brood production was low in the third year. Thus, fire-damaged stands may produce large numbers of pine shoot beetles during a few years when susceptible trees are abundant.

INTRODUCTION

The pine shoot beetles *Tomicus piniperda* (L.) and *Tomicus minor* (Hart.) are the most important bark beetles on Scots pine (*Pinus sylvestris* L.) in Scandinavia. These beetles may cause substantial growth losses by their devastating shoot-feeding in the pine crowns (Nilsson 1976, Långström & Hellqvist 1991). Healthy pine trees are generally resistant to stem-attacks by these beetles, which normally reproduce in fresh pine timber. Weakened trees may, however, be killed by *Tomicus*-attack, and suppressed trees in unmanaged pine stands are not seldom killed by pine shoot beetles (or other stem-attacking insects, like *Pissodes pini* L.). Extensive tree mortality due to *Tomicus*-attack has been rare in northern Europe, and is always preceeded by substantial needle losses (for references, see Långström & Hellqvist 1993). In warmer climates, stem-attacks and subsequent tree mortality seem to occur more frequently (Triggiani 1984, Li et al. 1993, Ye & Li 1996).

In Scandinavia, pine stands normally survive one year of severe defoliation, but the needle loss may render these trees susceptible to secondary attacks by stem-attacking insects, mainly pine shoot beetles. On the other hand, empirical evidence as well as experimental data (Långström et. al. 1992, and references therein) indicate that Scots pine, at least at Scandinavian latitudes, retains a substantial defensive capacity even after severe defoliation, i.e. that almost total defoliation is needed before stem-attacking insects succeed in killing the trees. The defense systems in conifers against bark beetles have been intensively studied in the last decades, but the underlying physiological and chemical processes are still poorly understood (for overviews, see Christiansen et al. 1987 and Raffa 1995). As the availability of carbohydrates is thought to play an important role in the defense chemistry, all kinds of needle losses should hence increase the susceptibility of the trees to beetle attack.

Fire-damaged trees often loose a substantial part of the foliage, but the stem phloem and the roots may also be damaged by the fire. Although Scots pine is known to be fairly resistant to forest fires (Kolström & Kellomäki 1993), surviving trees may be substantially weakened and become colonized by stem-attacking insects (Wikars 1997, and references therein). Among these, the pine shoot beetles are likely to be among the first invaders.

Frequent forest fires in 1992 lead to the establishment of a number of protected reserves, where fire-damaged areas were left for free development in order to promote biological diversity. In 1993, study plots were established in seven of these reserves in order to study the early colonization of fire-damaged trees by insects, and especially to evaluate the risk for bark beetle outbreaks developing in these reserves. The methodology and first-year-results have been described by Ehnström et al. (1995). In the present paper, we report on the susceptibility of the fire-damaged pine trees to pine shoot beetle attack, and relate this to the remaining foliage and beetle performance.

MATERIAL AND METHODS

The study areas and the plots as well as the general procedures of the present study have been described in detail by Ehnström et al. (1995). In summary: the seven forest fires that were included in this study were situated in south and central Sweden and varied in size from a few to more than 1000 hectares. The reserved areas varied correspondingly (7-300 ha). Most of the reserves were fully-stocked conifer forests dominated by Scots pine, but some of them also contained burned peatlands with a sparse forest cover. The tree size varied from pole-sized to mature trees, and all levels of fire-damage occurred in all areas. The earliest fire took place on 10 June and the latest on 23 July 1992.

In spring 1993, circular plots were laid out in the burned stands (except at Torsburgen and Gimo, where plots were established in the autumn 1993). The plot sites were selected to cover the range of fire damage and tree vitality of the dominating tree species in the area. The number of plots varied from 3 to 12 depending on the size and variability of the fire area in question. Plot size was 100, 200 or 300 m^2 (radius: 5.64, 7.98 and 9.78 m) depending on the stocking, and was selected to yield 10-15 trees per plot. On each plot, each tree exceeding 5 cm in diameter at 1.3 m stem height ("breast height") was numbered and its species and diameter was recorded. The vigour of each tree was also noted according to the estimated amount of green foliage left on the tree using the following classes: 0, 1-10, 11-20, 21-40, 41-60, 61-80, 81-100 per cent of full foliage. After classifying tree vigour, all trees were inspected for the presence or absence of pitch tubes or boring dust on the lower stem, indicating current stem-attack by *T. piniperda*.

In the autumn 1993, all trees were re-inspected and re-classified with regard to the percentage of healthy foliage. All trees were checked for presence/absence of exit holes indicating successful bark beetle colonization. On every third tree, a bark sample (10 cm wide and 30 cm high) was inspected at knee height, breast height and three metres above the ground. In principle, the samples were taken on the side of the tree facing the plot centre, but the aspect was sometimes modified for practical reasons. All exit holes of pine shoot beetles were counted before the bark was removed. The number of gallery systems of each occurring species was counted, and the developmental stages present in the galleries were recorded. We also measured the lengths of the egg galleries of the pine shoot beetles. Finally, the bark type was recorded as rough, intermediate or smooth, and the phloem vitality as dead (brown and dry), dying (dry and white - brownish) and fresh (white and moist). When appropriate, the tree's deviation from an erect position was recorded.

The sample plots were visited each spring 1994-96 when all living trees were re-inspected for current stem attacks by *T. piniperda*, and were classified according to the amount of green foliage as described above. All sample plots were also inspected in the autumns of 1994 and 1995, when a new third of trees was inspected as described above for autumn 1993. At these later inspections, the beetle attacks had to be dated according to the year(s) of attack, i.e. trees inspected in 1995 could have been attacked in 1993, 1994 or 1995. Current attacks were easy to recognize each year, whereas one-year-old galleries in 1995 were separated from two-year-old ones by the general appearance of the gallery and the surrounding bark structure. Since one third of the trees was inspected each autumn, attack data for 1993 was obtained from all trees, whereas data for attacks in 1994 and 1995 were obtained from two thirds and one third of the trees, respectively. In addition, live sample trees from previous inspections were re-inspected each autumn, and a few of these displayed attacks by pine shoot beetles from more than one year.

A preliminary analysis of the data indicated that if a tree was attacked by *T. piniperda* galleries often occurred on all three sampled stem heights. Thus, data from the three bark samples were pooled for each tree. Results were analysed using the SAS statistical program (SAS 1987). Means were compared by one-way analysis of variance followed by Tukey's test for multiple comparisons, and considered significant at the 5% level (Zar 1984).

RESULTS

Tree survival and beetle attack patterns

Of the 446 pine trees followed in this study, 204 were alive and not attacked by pine shoot beetles in the autumn 1993 (Figure 1). Of these, 89 were still alive in 1996, and had remained unattacked through the study period. On the other hand, 100 trees were recorded dead in 1993 without any signs of pine shoot beetle attack that spring. Of the remaining trees, 98 were successfully attacked (i. e. had exit holes indicating brood production) and killed in 1993, whereas one tree was classified as dead after being unsuccessfully attacked (galleries but no exit holes). Nine trees survived unsuccessful attacks and 34 trees were recorded as living despite successful attack in 1993.

In 1994, 27 trees in the last mentioned group of 34 trees died without further attack, 6 were re-attacked and killed and 1 tree escaped further attack and survived to spring 1996. Two of the nine trees that were unsuccessfully attacked in 1993, became re-attacked in 1994 but survived and was not attacked later on; one tree escaped attack in 1994 but died anyway in 1995; six were successfully re-attacked in 1994, 4 of which died in the same and two in the following year.

The flow chart also shows that the 204 live trees that escaped attack in 1993 were next year distributed among all categories mentioned above. Half of the previously unattacked live trees remained unattacked and alive in 1994. Fourtyfour trees died as a result of *Tomicus*-attack, 15 trees were successfully colonized but still alive, while the attacks failed in 29 trees. Eleven trees died from other causes and one of these was also attacked by *T. piniperda*.

The next year (1995), *Tomicus*-attack occurred in 10 of the previously unattacked (105) and in 4 of the previously attacked (29+15) trees. Two of these survived, and one was re-attacked in 1996 for the third time. In this last year, only 2 more trees were attacked, both of them for the first time. Two trees were recorded dead in this spring. One of them was attacked in the previous year, and the other was never attacked.

Thus, *Tomicus*-attack occurred in all four years, but the proportion of attacked trees decreased over time, and was 41, 42, 11 and 2 % of the trees alive in spring 1993, 1994, 1995 and 1996, respectively (i. e. 142 /346, 103/247, 16/155 and 3/128). As mentioned above, one tree was still alive in spring 1996 after 3 years of consecutive attacks. Two trees survived

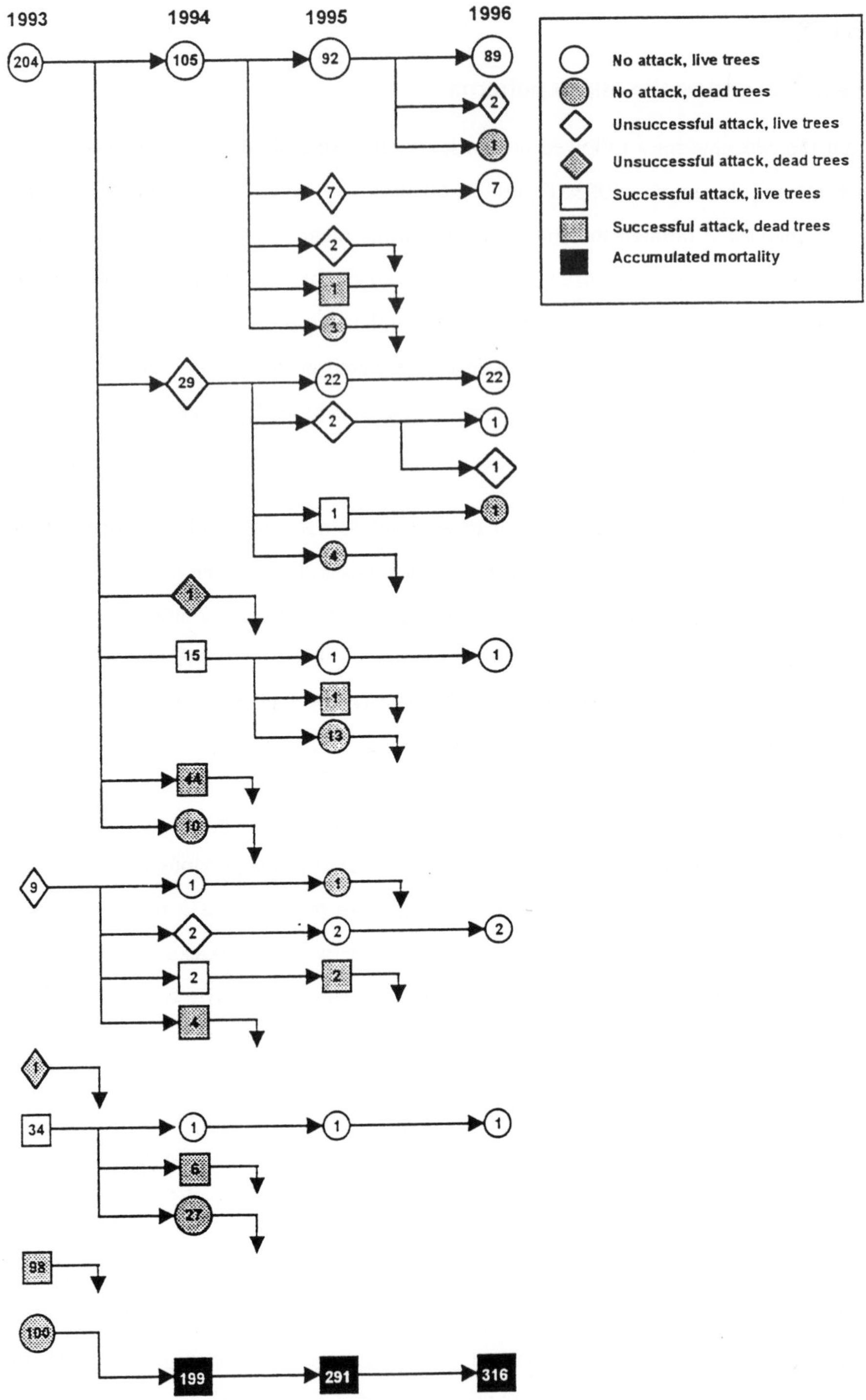

Figure 1. Flow chart showing the fate of the 446 pine trees followed in the study (all sites pooled); numbers in symbols indicate the number of trees in the actual category in the autumn of a given year. Down-arrows indicate that dead trees, regardless of mortality cause, were accumulated at the bottom of the graph.

attacks in 1993 and 1994, and 24 trees that were attacked in 1993 survived and escaped further attacks.

All 99 trees that died in 1993 were attacked by *T. piniperda*. In addition, 27 of the trees that died the following year had been successfully attacked in 1993. Considering these trees to be beetle-killed together with the 55 successfully attacked trees, means that *T. piniperda* was involved in 89 % (27+55/92) of that year's mortality. The corresponding figure for 1995 was 68 % (13+4/25), and in spring 1996 one more beetle-attacked tree had died. In all, 63 % of all dead trees (199/316+1+1) were attacked by *T. piniperda* in the year of, or prior to their death.

Foliage changes

In all years, trees that were successfully colonized by the pine shoot beetles, carried significantly less green needles at the time of attack than unattacked trees, or trees where the attacks failed (Table 1). The two latter groups did not differ significantly concerning the remaining foliage. The estimated needle biomass remained at the same level for each attack category during three years, indicating little recovery or decline in foliage during the study period. The means derived from the defoliation classes may, however, not reflect foliage changes for individual trees that rendered them susceptible or resistant from one year to another.

Performance of *T. piniperda*

The attack density, i. e. the number of egg galleries per m^2 (averaged for the 3 bark samples from different stem heights) of *T. piniperda* increased from the first to the second year at all sites, except Galtabäck and Skir (Table 2). In the third year it fell again, except at Vakö myr. At Galtabäck+Skir and Gimo, where there were no attacks at all in 1995. Attack densities exceeding 100 egg galleries per m^2 were not rare, and at Brattforsheden it was above 200 in 1994.

The mean gallery lengths varied between years and sites ranging from 30 to 120 mm in length (Table 2). As the means include very short galleries from failed attacks as well as successful ones resulting in long galleries, the figures are difficult to interpret. Obviously,

Table 1. *Tomicus*- attack in the years 1993-1995 as related to the average needle biomass (mean and SD) at the time of attack in each year (N = number of live trees each year). Means within columns followed by the same letter were not significantly different (Tukey's test)

Status of *Tomicus*- attack	Estimated needle biomass at the time of attack								
	1993 1)			1994			1995		
	mean	SD	N	mean	SD	N	mean	SD	N
No attack	47,0 *a*	24,7	118	50,7 *a*	23,5	116	49,4 *a*	22,4	124
Failed attack	36,0 *a*	19,6	10	47,2 *a*	19,0	32	36,4 *a*	29,1	11
Successful attack	15,7 *b*	16,3	79	22,7 *b*	13,7	71	23,3 *a*	5,8	3
P-value	0,0001			0,0001			0,0364		

1) Gimo and Torsburgen are excluded from the analyses in 1993 because spring needle biomass is not known for that year

Table 2. Performance of *T. piniperda* on trees attacked in 1993-1995 at the different study sites (data for sample sections 1-3 pooled within trees before calculating means and *standard deviations*)

Site	Year	Egg galleries / m^2		Mean gallery length, mm		Brood / m^2		Brood / gallery		Number of trees attacked	total 1)
Brattfors	1993	103,8	*70,5*	97,8	*46,7*	881,8	*883,1*	8,6	*6,8*	44	92
	1994	239,1	*132,8*	67,7	*42,6*	450,7	*553,9*	2,5	*3,0*	23	
	1995	144,4	*50,9*	70,9	*54,5*	366,7	*384,4*	2,1	*1,9*	3	
Galtabäck + Skir	1993	126,7	*68,3*	118,0	*51,0*	833,3	*495,5*	7,6	*7,1*	5	25
	1994	66,7	*47,1*	110,5	*31,5*	516,7	*611,9*	6,1	*4,5*	4	
	1995	0,0	-	-	-	0,0	-	-	-	0	
Gimo	1993	66,7	*47,1*	110,3	*42,6*	430,8	*459,0*	7,4	*6,5*	11	85
	1994	98,4	*78,5*	43,1	*35,3*	212,7	*337,3*	2,0	*3,1*	21	
	1995	0,0	-	-	-	0,0	-	-	-	0	
Lenhovda	1993	77,2	*47,2*	108,4	*32,0*	408,8	*371,8*	5,8	*4,7*	19	75
	1994	111,1	*83,3*	123,3	*34,6*	913,3	*849,3*	9,5	*8,7*	15	
	1995	66,7	-	17,5	-	0,0	-	0,0	-	1	
Torsburgen	1993	44,4	*30,6*	106,6	*29,1*	488,0	*361,7*	11,2	*6,6*	24	130
	1994	100,0	*55,3*	105,8	*32,8*	985,2	*993,8*	10,1	*9,0*	9	
	1995	66,7	*0,0*	43,5	*56,2*	55,5	*96,2*	0,8	*1,4*	3	
Vakö myr	1993	46,7	*29,8*	104,5	*35,1*	146,6	*130,4*	3,3	*3,4*	5	39
	1994	133,3	*73,0*	94,5	*18,9*	1027,8	*604,6*	8,1	*4,7*	6	
	1995	144,4	*107,2*	30,0	*18,9*	0,0	-	0,0	-	3	

1) Number of live trees (in spring) available for attack each year

many attacks must have failed at Gimo in 1994 and at Torsburgen, Lenhovda and Vakö myr in 1995.

Brood production was very low at Torsburgen and nil at the two last-mentioned sites in 1995 (Table 2). In contrast, close to 1000 beetles emerged per m^2 bark area in the previous year. At half of the sites brood production peaked in the first, and for the other half in the second year. The same pattern is also evident from the brood/gallery figures, ranging from 0 to 11 exit holes per gallery. Assuming a balanced sex ratio, the figures should be divided by 2 to express the rate of population increase (i. e. new females per old female).

DISCUSSION

The susceptibility of the pine trees exposed to the fire clearly varied with the level of fire-damage. Some of the badly burned trees had no live phloem left for the beetles to colonize, and were hence not attacked at all by the pine shoot beetles. These were mainly small trees (for data, see Ehnström et al. 1995; Table 2). On the other hand, many trees survived the fire and were never attacked by the pine shoot beetles during the entire study period. These trees were characterized by having about half of full foliage left in all three years of inspection. These two groups of unattacked trees constituted ca 40 % of the total number of trees studied. It must be noted, however, that study plots were laid out to cover the range of fire-damage in each area, and do not necessarily reflect the proportions of different fire-damage levels in the stands. A true picture of how different stands were affected by the fire would have required a larger number of plots and a different study design.

The main finding of the present study was the fact that successfully colonized trees in all years carried less foliage than did the trees where the attacks failed, which in turn had less foliage than the unattacked ones. On an average, trees having less than about 25 percent of full foliage were unable to withstand the attacking pine shoot beetles, and this pattern was true for all three years. This observation is consistent with the experience that severe defoliation may render trees susceptible to secondary beetle attacks (Butovitsch 1946, Lekander 1953, Mihkelson 1986, Speight & Wainhouse 1989).

The critical level of foliage loss for successful beetle attack has not been determined, and it may obviously vary from time to time depending on e. g. tree vigour prior to defoliation and beetle population levels. As secondary beetle attacks seldom occur after severe defoliation by *Neodiprion sertifer* (Geoffr.), and since this sawfly species normally leaves the current needles intact, it seems as the new needles (corresponding to 20-30 % of the total foliage) give enough resistance to pine shoot beetle and other stem-attacking insects. Current work in pine stands severely defoliated by *Diprion pini* (L.) indicates that 10 % remaining foliage may be enough to save the trees from the pine shoot beetles (Annila et al. 1993, 1998). For snow-broken pine trees, Schroeder and Eidmann (1993) noted that broken trees having more than five live branches were not attacked at all by stem-boring insects, whereas all snow-breaks without live branches were attacked. Pruning experiments have also demonstrated that removal of half of the crown did not render trees susceptible to *Tomicus*-attack whereas trees with less than 20 % foliage left were killed (Långström & Hellqvist 1988), Thus, the fire-damaged Scots pine trees seem to be somewhat more susceptible to beetle attack than defoliated or pruned ones.

It has also been suggested that the beetles themselves could predispose trees to stem attack by their own shoot-feeding activity in the pine crowns (Li et al. 1993). That would, however, require massive shoot losses and this phenomenon hardly occurs in Scandinavia (Långström & Hellqvist 1993, and references therein). In the present study, we recorded modest shoot losses (data will be published elsewhere), and they did neither predispose trees to attack, nor explain the observed slow recovery of the foliage.

In this study, tree susceptibility was not analysed by tree size, but there is some evidence indicating that defoliated small trees are generally more susceptible to beetle attack than larger ones (Butovitsch 1946, Lekander 1953, Annila et al. 1993, 1998). As no chemical analyses were included in this study, it is not meaningful to discuss the host defense systems in any detail here. It is widely accepted that conifers rely on a resin-based defense strategy involving a primary resin flow followed by an induced defense reaction aiming at containing the attacking beetles and their associated blue-stain fungi in resin-soaked lesions (for a review and references; see Christiansen et al 1987). It is also widely accepted that the supply of energy (i.e. carbohydrates) is critical for these defense reactions (e.g. Lorio 1988), and that vigourous trees hence should be able to mobilize more resistance than less vital ones. As defoliated trees are deprived of most of their photosynthetic capacity, it is obvious that their susceptibility should increase with increasing needle loss. Actually, it is surprising that 10-20 percent remaining needles still may be enough to prevent beetle colonization.

The results showed that *T. piniperda* was strongly involved in the tree mortality. Altogether, about 60 % of the pine trees were attacked during the study period, and most of them died, probably as result of the attack. Other stem-attacking species may of course also have been involved, but since *T. piniperda* was the dominating species, and the only one (together with the less common Arhopalus rusticus (L.)) that showed some aggressivess in its occurrence (Ehnström et al. 1995), it is reasonable to assume that the pine shoot beetles were the main challenge to the host resistance mechanisms. In Siberia, pine shoot beetles are important colonizers of fire-damaged trees (Prosorow 1929), and in southern Europe they cause substantial mortality in such stands (Triggiani 1984).

Each year, the pine shoot beetles attacked previously unattacked trees as well as trees that had sustained attack in one or several years before. The proportion of *Tomicus*-attacked trees decreased over time from 41 to 2 % of the trees that were alive in spring 1993 and 1996, respectively. This decline in beetle attack cannot primarily be attributed to increased host resistance, as foliage levels of attacked and unattacked trees did not differ between the years (cf. Table 1). It is more likely that it reflects a declining beetle population with increasing difficulties to find new susceptible hosts to colonize.

The local beetle populations in the study areas are difficult to estimate, but the observed attack densities were generally low (means below 150 egg galleries per m^2 bark area, except at Brattforsheden in the second year where it was close to 240, cf. Table 2). Other studies have showed that attack densities of 150-300 egg galleries per m^2 bark area are necessary to overcome the host resistance, even in weakened pine trees (Schroeder & Eidmann 1987; Långström & Hellqvist 1993). Thus, the fire-damaged trees were weak despite the fact that they had a considerable amount of green needles. Possibly, the fire had damaged the root systems and impaired the water uptake and the defensive capacity of the trees.

At most sites, the attack density increased from the first to the second year, and then decreased again (being zero at some sites; cf. Table 1.) In the fourth year, only occasional attacks were recorded. Thus, the pine shoot beetles were mainly able to utilize the trees during the two first years following the fire. The beetles were, however, opportunistic and tried in all years to attack healthier trees than they could conquer. Failed attacks are not unusual at high population levels (Köhler 1986; Långström & Hellqvist 1993). As no attack attempts were seen on the most vigourous trees (having more than 50 % foliage left), it seems likely that the beetles can discriminate between unsuitable and possible host material at an early stage, or even in flight (Byers et al. 1989)

Attack densities between 50 and 100 egg galleries per m^2 bark area are high enough to fully exploit the host material, and produce a substantial brood (see e.g. Saarenmaa 1983, Sauvard 1989). Average brood figures reaching 1000 exit holes per m^2 bark area and 10 callow adults per gallery indicate that fire-damaged trees may be as good host material for *T. piniperda* as storm-felled trees (Långström 1984, and references therein). Thus, the pine shoot beetles occupied most of the available phloem, and were therefore the main colonizers of the lower stem (see also Ehnström et al. 1995). The possible interaction between these beetles and other stem-attacking insects will be treated elsewhere.

ACKNOWLEDGEMENTS

We thank "Stiftelsen Oscar och Lili Lamms minne" for financial support, the landowners and the county government boards for permission to work in the forest reserves, Rune Axelsson for field assistance, Erkki Annila and an anonymous reviewer for comments and Carolyn Glynn for improving the English.

REFERENCES

ANNILA, E., VARAMA, M., LÅNGSTRÖM, B., & NIEMELÄ, P. 1993. Pilkkumäntypistiäistuhojen vaikutus männyn elinvoimaisuuteen. *Metsäntutkimuslaitoksen tiedonantoja* 46, 27-33. (In Finnish only)

ANNILA, E., LÅNGSTRÖM, B., VARAMA, M., HIUKKA, R. & NIEMELÄ, P. 1998. Susceptibility of defoliated Scots pine to spontaneous and induced attack by *Tomicus piniperda* and *T. minor. Silva Fenn.*, submitted.

BUTOVITSCH, V. 1946. Redogörelse för flygbekämpningskampanjen mot tallmätaren under 1944-1945 (Bericht über die Flugzeugbestäubung gegen den Kiefernspanner in den Jahren 1944-1945 *Medd. Statens Skogsforskn.* 35:9, 108 pp.

BYERS, J.A., LANNE, B. S., LÖFQVIST, J. 1989. Host tree unsuitability recognized by pine shoot beetles in flight. *Experientia* 45, 489-492.

CHRISTIANSEN, E., WARING, R. H., BERRYMAN, A. A. 1987. Resistance of conifers to bark beetle attack: Searching for general relationships. - *For. Ecol. Manage.* 22, 89-106.

EHNSTRÖM, B., LÅNGSTRÖM, B., HELLQVIST, C. 1995. Insects in burned forests - forest protection and faunal conservation (preliminary results). *Entomol. Fenn.* 6, 109-117.

KOLSTRÖM, T., KELLOMÄKI, S. 1993. Tree survival in wildfires. *Silva Fenn.* 27, 277-281.

KÖHLER, U. 1986. Zur Problematik des Stehendbefalls durch den Grossen Waldgärtner, *Blastophagus piniperda* L. - *Anz. Schädlingskde Pflanzenschutz Umweltschutz* 59, 145-147.

LEKANDER, B. 1953. Über das Auftreten von *Blastophagus piniperda* und *Pissodes pini* im Wald vorher befallen von *Panolis*- und *Bupalus*-Raupen. *Medd. Statens Skogsforskn.* Inst. 44, 31 pp.

LÅNGSTRÖM, B. 1984. Wind-thrown Scots pines as brood material for *Tomicus piniperda* and *T. minor*. *Silva Fenn.* 18:187-198.

LÅNGSTRÖM, B., HELLQVIST, C. 1988. Scots pine resistance against *Tomicus piniperda* as related to tree vitality and attack density. - In: PAYNE, T. L., SAARENMAA, H. (eds) *Integrated control of scolytid bark beetles.-Proc.*, IUFRO working party and XVII Int. Congr. Entomol., Vancouver, BC, Canada, July 4 1988, 121-133.

LÅNGSTRÖM, B. HELLQVIST, C. 1991. Shoot damage and growth losses following three years of *Tomicus*-attacks in Scots pine stands close to a timber storage site. *Silva Fenn.* 3, 133-145.

LÅNGSTRÖM, B. HELLQVIST, C. 1993. Induced and spontaneous attacks by *Tomicus piniperda* and *T. minor* on young Scots pine trees: tree mortality and beetle performance. *J. appl. Ent.* 115, 25-36.

LÅNGSTRÖM, B., HELLQVIST, C., ERICSSON, A., GREF, R. 1992. Induced defence reaction in Scots pine following stem attacks by *Tomicus piniperda. Ecography* 15, 318-327.

LI, L.S., WANG, H.L., CHAI, X.S., WANG, Y.X., SHU, N.B., YANG, D.S. 1993. Study on the biological characteristics of *Tomicus piniperda* and its damage. *Forest Research* 6, 14-20 (In Chinese with English summary).

LORIO, P.L. JR 1988. Growth differentiation-balance relationships in pines affect their resistance to bark beetles (Coleoptera: Scolytidae). In: MATTSON W.J., LEVIEUX J., BERNARD-DAGAN C. (eds). *Mechanisms of woody plant defenses against insects*: *Search for Pattern*, New York Berlin Heidelberg, Springer Verlag, 73-92.

MIHKELSON, S. 1986. Mannivaksiku massilisest sigimisest Eestis. (Massive outbreaks of *Bupalus piniarius* in Estonia). *Metsanduslikud Uurimused*, Estonian SSR 21, 64-72.

NILSSON, S. 1976. Rationalization of forest operations gives rise to insect attack and increment. *Ambio* 5, 17-22.

PROSOROW, S.S. 1929. Die Brandflächen in Kiefernbeständen als Ansteckungsherde. *Rapport, Inst f Land- und Forstwirtschaft Sibiriens. Omsk 12, 1-54* (In Russian with German summary).

RAFFA, K.F. 1995. Bark beetles, fungi, trees and humans: four perspectives, four agendas. In: Christiansen, E. (Ed.). 1995. Bark beetles, blue-stain fungi, and conifer defense systems. Proceedings from a symposium held at the Norwegian Forest Research Institute (NISK) in Ås, Norway 31 July - 2 August 1995. *Aktuelt fra Skogforsk* 6, 7-9.

SAARENMAA, H. 1983. Modeling the spatial pattern and intraspecific competition in *Tomicus piniperda* (Coleoptera, Scolytidae). *Commun Inst For Fenn* 118, 40 PP.

SAUVARD, D. 1989. Capacités de multiplication de *Tomicus piniperda* L. (Col., Scolytidae). - *J. Appl. Entomol.* 108, 164-181.

SAS INSTITUTE INC. 1987. SAS/STAT Guide for Personal Computers, Version 6 Edition, 1028 pp.

SCHROEDER, L. M., EIDMANN, H. H. 1987. Gallery initiation by *Tomicus piniperda* (Col: Scolytidae) on Scots pine trees baited with host volatiles. - *J. Chem. Ecol.* 13, 1591-1599.

SCHROEDER, M., EIDMANN, H.H. 1993. Attacks of bark- and wood-boring Coleoptera on snow-broken conifers over a two-year period. *Scand. J. For. Res.* 8, 257-265.

SPEIGHT, M.R., & WAINHOUSE, D. 1989. *Ecology and management of forest insects.* Oxford Science Publications, 374 pp.

TRIGGIANI, O. 1984. *Tomicus (Blastophagus) piniperda* (Coleoptera, Scolytidae Hylesininae): biology, damage and control on the Ionic coast. *Entomologica* 19, 5-21. (In Italian with English summary).

WIKARS, L.-O. 1997. Effects of forest fire and the ecology of fire-adapted insects. *Acta Universitatis Uppsaliensis. Comprehensive summaries of Uppsala dissertations from the faculty of science and technology* 272, 35 pp.

YE, H., LI, L.S. 1996. Preliminary observations on the trunk attacks by *Tomicus piniperda* (L.) (Col., Scolytidae) on Yunnan pine in Kunming, China. *J. Appl. Ent.* 119, 331-333.

ZAR, J. 1974. *Biostatistical analysis*. Englewood Cliffs, 620 pp.

Physiology and Genetics of Tree-Phytophage Interactions
Gujan (France), August 31 - September 5, 1997
Ed. INRA, Paris, 1999 (Les Colloques, n°90)

Performance of beech caterpillar (*Syntypistis punctatella* (Motschulsky)) on water-stressed beech

NAOTO KAMATA[1], HIROMI TANABE[2]

[1] *Forestry and Forest Products Research Institute, Tohoku Research Center*
020-0123, Nabeyashiki 72, Shimokuriyagawa, Morioka, Iwate, Japan
[2] *Forestry and Forest Products Research Institute, Forest Environment Division*
305, Matsunosato 1, Kukizaki, Inashiki, Ibaraki, Japan

RESUME

The beech caterpillar, *Syntypistis* (=*Quadricalcarifera*) *punctatella* (Motschulsky) (Lepidoptera: Notodontidae), often causes serious defoliation of the Siebold's beech (*Fagus crenata* Blume) forests in Japan. We investigated the survivorship and body size of *S. punctatella* larvae raised on beech saplings grown under various levels of water availability over a three-year period to test the "water stress hypothesis" which proposes that the resultant increase in food quality due to water stress lowers mortality rates, enhances development, and increases body size. Beech saplings grew well under high water availability, but plant mortality was caused by both water stress and insect defoliation. Mortality tended to be highest under high water-stress conditions and with insect defoliation in the previous year. In water-stressed plants, foliar nitrogen was high but the rapid induced response (RIR) was weak: the increase of tannins was relatively small, even after the beech caterpillar consumed the foliage. Insect performance (i.e. survivorship and pupal weight) on water-stressed beeches was high. These results support the "water stress hypothesis". However, the delayed induced response (DIR) was completely different from the RIR; it tended to be strong in high-water stressed plants. In the year following defoliation, insect performance tended to be low because foliar nitrogen was low and tannins were high in high water- stressed plants.

INTRODUCTION

The beech caterpillar, *Syntypistis (=Quadricalcarifera) punctatella* (Motschulsky) is a foliage-feeding Lepidopteran species that is associated with beech, *Fagus crenata* Blume and *F. japonica* Maxim., in Japan. Outbreaks of this species are known to occur in Honshu and Hokkaido islands of Japan (Yanbe & Igarashi, 1983) and to occur synchronously among different areas at intervals of 8-11 years (Liebhold *et al.*, 1996). The moth populations exhibit 8-11 year cycles, widely synchronized both in outbreak and non-outbreak areas (Kamata & Igarashi, 1995b).

Synchrony among geographically disjunct populations has been observed in several forest insect populations (Martinat, 1987; Wallner, 1987; Myers, 1988). Although a variety of mechanisms have been proposed to explain this synchrony, they can be attributed to three major causes: 1) mass migration of the pest species (Hardy *et al.*, 1983; Wallner, 1987); 2) mass migration of a natural enemy of the pest species (Royama, 1984; Shepherd *et al.*, 1988; Myers, 1990); and 3) deviations in weather that are synchronous over large areas. Perhaps the most common explanation provided for simultaneous outbreaks is the concurrent occurrence of weather anomalies over large areas (Wellington, 1957; Martinat, 1987). The theory that weather anomalies simultaneously trigger outbreaks in disjunct forest pest populations has been advanced for *Hyphantria cunea* (Morris, 1964), *Choristoneura occidentalis* (Thomson *et al.*, 1984; Swetnam & Lynch, 1993), *C. fumiferana* (Wellington, 1952), *Malacosoma disstria* (Blais *et al.*, 1955), and several other important forest pests (Bodenheimer, 1930).

Kamata & Takagi (1991) analyzed a beech caterpillar outbreak time series and concluded that high June temperature and low July precipitation in the preceding 3 years were associated with the onset of outbreaks. They also indicated that variation in July precipitation is historically synchronous throughout N. Japan (see Kamata & Igarashi, 1995b). We hypothesize that this synchrony may be the cause of synchrony in *S. punctatella* populations, although population cycles themselves appear to be the result of intrinsic ecological relationships with host plants and/or natural enemy populations.

Three different ways in which successive years of dry summers trigger a gradual increase of the moth population were hypothesized: 1) abundant rainfall directly curtails feeding behavior of the larvae and has several influences on larval growth and mortality

(Kamata & Igarashi, 1994); 2) low rainfall indirectly reduces the mortality caused by fungal diseases in the soil because soil moisture is an important determinant of growth of fungi which are important mortality factors of *S. punctatella* pupae (Kamata in press); 3) the resultant increase in food quality due to water stress lowers mortality rates, enhances development, and increases body size (Mattson & Haack, 1987; Rhoades, 1985; White, 1974).

Kamata & Igarashi (1993) reared *S. punctatella* larvae on beech saplings grown under different levels of water availability by differing the frequency of the water supply and found that performance of *S. punctatella* was high in water-stressed beeches. This simple preliminary experiment suggests that the foliage became more nutritious to *S. punctatella* under water-stressed conditions.

Herein, we test the hypothesis that insect performance is enhanced on water-stressed plants by rearing larvae on beech saplings grown under a gradient of water availability. The saplings were irrigated daily by a drip irrigation system. Foliage nutrition (nitrogen and tannin levels) were compared among the treatments and so were constitutive defense, RIR, and DIR.

LIFE HISTORY

S. punctatella is a univoltine species (Igarashi 1975), overwintering as pupae in the forest floor and emerging as adults from late May to late July. Fecundity typically ranges from 300 - 400 eggs which are laid in masses of 20-100 eggs on the backs of beech leaves. Larvae undergo three to four molts which requires 30-60 days under typical field conditions. Final development is typically completed around mid-August.

MATERIALS AND METHODS

Plant response to water stress

Experiments were conducted for 3 years, from April 1994 to October 1996, in a greenhouse which had a vinyl covering to exclude natural rainfall and to allow control of internal temperature and light.

Tree height and diameter at 7 cm above ground level (D7) were measured before the experiment (20 April, 1994) and at the end of October every year. Plant growth was compared in relation to water availability.

Leaf toughness of 10 leaves on each of the 6 trees in each treatment group was measured using a "penetrometer" as described by Feeny (1970). Leaves were dried at 60ºC in an electric dryer, and the dry weight of 10 leaf disks (2 cm in diameter) on each of the 6 trees in each group was used as an index of leaf thickness.

Dried leaves were ground to pass through a 100-mesh sieve, approximately 0.1 mm in diameter, and this leaf powder was used for chemical analysis. Foliar nitrogen was measured by a CHNS/O Analyzer (Perkin-Elmer PE2400 Series II) to the nearest 0.01 %. Approximately 20 mg of the leaf powder was used for one measurement. Foliar tannins were determined by the Folin-Denis method.

Beech caterpillar performance

The *S. punctatella* used in the experiment originated as eggs collected from a population in Appi (141°00′ E, 40°00′ N, 600 m elev.), located in northern Honshu, the main island of Japan. No defoliations have been recorded there (see Kamata and Igarashi, 1995b). *S. punctatella* egg masses were adjusted to 30 eggs and attached to the abaxial sides of beech leaves, one egg mass per leaf, on about 30 June each year. The larvae were reared in fine mesh enclosures to exclude predators. The enclosures were checked at intervals of approximately two days; the number of larvae was counted. Larvae were occasionally shifted from one plant to another so that food was always plentiful and starvation did not limit larval survivorship. Mature larvae were put individually into plastic caps with moist tissue paper and kept under dark conditions. Survivorship and pupal weight were compared among experimental groups.

Experimental design

On 20 April, 1994, three-year-old beech saplings (ca. 30 cm tall) were transplanted to 6-liter pots containing vermiculite and then the pots were moved to the greenhouse. Complete fertilizer (N-P-K; 14-18-16, 3g pot-1) was applied to every pot once a year before the start of flushing. Pots were sufficiently irrigated every day for a month after transplanting; thereafter water availability varied according to treatment. Pots were irrigated daily by an automatic drip system that controlled the length of time of dripping. When on, water dripped at the rate of 2 liters per hour (0.556 ml/second). Treatments 1, 2, 3, 4, 5 and 6 consisted of irrigating for 300 seconds (167 ml), 180 seconds (100 ml), 120 seconds (67 ml), 100 seconds (56 ml), 90 seconds (50 ml) and 80 seconds (44 ml) a day, respectively. The soil water availabilities for the six treatments, measured by a tension meter, were 1.47, 1.55, 2.24, 6.97, 17.06, and 24.82 -Kpa, respectively.

To test the constitutive and rapidly induced defense responses, *S. punctatella* was reared on these beech saplings under all treatments for each of the years of 1994-1996. The number of sapling replicates was three for each experimental plot for each year. Beech foliage was sampled from these experimental saplings and from the control in early August when the final instar larvae were feeding. Foliar nitrogen and leaf texture on the control saplings were determined. Foliar tannins were compared between leaves injured by the insects and 'healthy' leaves on the control saplings.

Beech foliage was also sampled in early August of 1995 and 1996 from saplings that had suffered insect defoliation the previous year to determine delayed induced defense response under water-stressed conditions. Foliar nitrogen and tannins of these saplings were compared with that of the control.

RESULTS

Plant growth under water-stressed conditions

Figure 1 shows the declining growth of *F. crenata* saplings under a gradient of water availability. There was no significant difference in tree height among plots at the time (spring 1994) when we started to control water availability. However, in the following two years, trees in the well irrigated plots tended to grow taller, though difference were not significant. Tree diameters behaved similarly. The mortality rate of the beech trees tended to increase under low water availability. The survival rates of trees in Treatments 1-6 in the fall of 1996 were 85.9 %, 86.6%, 83.3 %, 66.7 %, 70.0 %, and 57.0 %, respectively, suggesting that water stress was quite severe in the latter three plots. These results indicate that water stress can be an important factor determining the growth of beech trees.

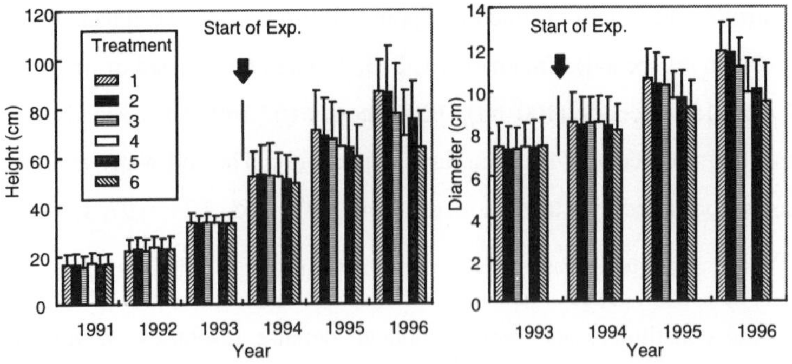

Figure 1. Growth of *Fagus crenata* saplings under a gradient of water availability. The water was provided daily by an automatic drip system. Treatment 1 received the most water and Treatment 6 received the least water. The irrigation control started from the spring of 1994. Diameter was measured at 7 cm above ground level. Mean +- SD are shown.

The physiological response of beech trees under water stress was as follows: at the individual plant level, the average photosynthesis tended to be low under high water-stressed conditions, because the investment in foliage, represented by the leaf area and leaf mass ratios, decreased, although the photosynthetic rate of each leaf, which was represented by photosynthetic rate per leaf area, per leaf mass, and per nitrogen, improved. Leaves tended to be thicker under high water-stressed conditions, and both nitrogen contents and nitrogen concentrations tended to be higher. However, leaf texture and foliar nitrogen in relation to

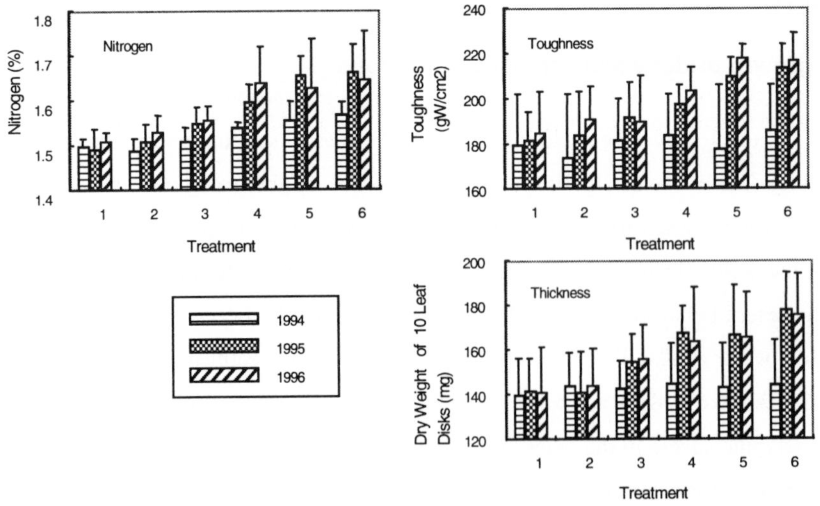

Figure 2. Foliar nitrogen and leaf physical traits of *Fagus crenata* under a gradient of water availability. (Mean +- SE)

water stress differed greatly between the first year of the experiment and the latter years (fig. 2). These results are probably related to the fact that the characteristics of the foliage were basically determined by the environment in the previous year.

As for constitutive and rapidly induced defensive properties, *S. punctatella* seemed to prefer beech foliage under high water stress conditions. Insect performance tended to improve on water-stressed beech trees; the insects tended to be larger on heavily water-stressed beech (fig. 3) and the survival rate during the larval stage also tended to be greater (fig. 4), although the difference was not so clear as the difference in body size. These results seemed to relate both to the higher nitrogen contents and to the low rate of increase in tannins (tannins in injured leaf/healthy leaf) under high water-stressed conditions (fig. 5).

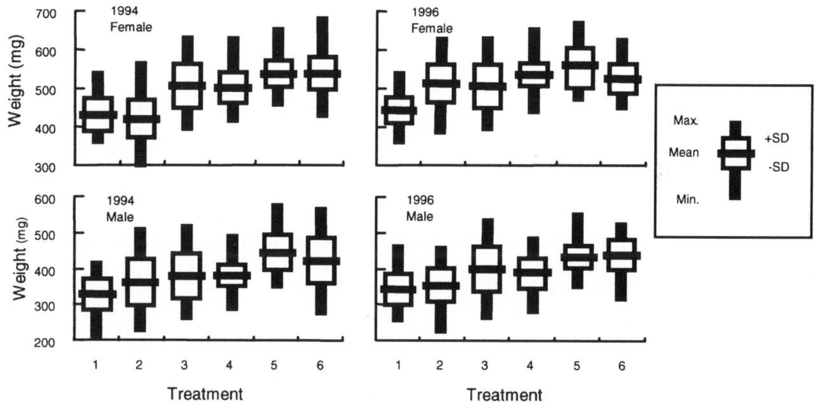

Figure 3. Weight of mature larvae of *Syntypistis punctatella* reared on *Fagus crenata* saplings under a gradient of water availability. The results of each sex were shown for the first year of irrigation control (1994) and the third year (1996).

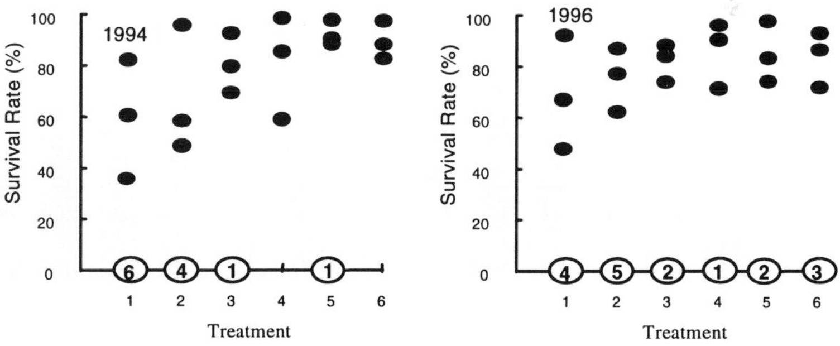

Figure 4. Survival rate during the larval stage of *Syntypistis punctatella* reared on *Fagus crenata* saplings under a gradient of water availability. The rate was shown for each cohort starting from 30 eggs. The number inside an open circle indicates the number of cohorts in which no *S. punctatella* survived until maturing. The results were shown for the first year of irrigation control (1994) and the third year (1996).

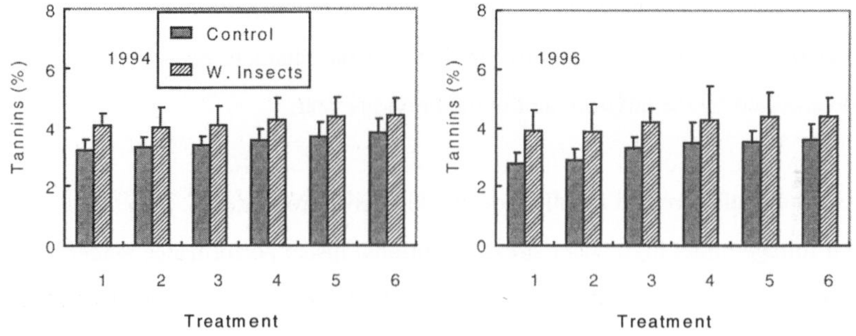

Figure 5. Foliar tannins of *Fagus crenata* under a gradient of water availability in the presence and absence of *Syntypistis punctatella*.(Mean +- SE).

As for the delayed induced defense response, the results were completely opposite to those observed in the rapid induced response. Foliar nitrogen tended to be low but tannins tended to be high under high water-stressed conditions when trees were defoliated by *S. punctatella* in the previous year (fig. 6). It has been known that a nitrogen deficit is the main cause of DIR. Beech trees usually recover most of the nitrogen from foliage before natural defoliation in the fall. Because plants under water stress concentrated a high percentage of the nitrogen in foliage, the nitrogen deficit must have been more severe in these plants in the year following the severe insect defoliation.

CONCLUSION

From this experiment using beech saplings, beech foliage tended to be a better food

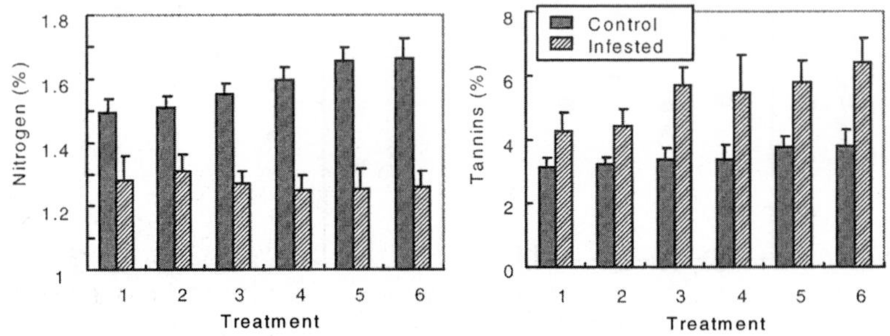

Figure 6. Foliar nitrogen and tannins of *Fagus crenata* under a gradient of water availability in the year following severe defoliation by *Syntypistis punctatella* (Mean +- SE). The results are shown for saplings defoliated the previous year (Infested) and those with no insect defoliation (Control).

for *S. punctatella* under water-stressed conditions; foliar nitrogen was high and the increase of tannins was relatively low. Insect performance tended to be high on these water-stressed beeches; survivorship and pupal weight improved on this foliage. Changes in leaf physical traits and foliar nitrogen in relation to water stress differed greatly between the first year of the experiment and the latter years. This is due to the fact that the characteristics of the foliage were basically determined by the environment in the previous year. The DIR under water stress was completely different from RIR; foliar nitrogen tended to be low and tannins tended to be high under high water-stressed conditions.

The preceding results can explain the relationship between *S. punctatella* population cycles and host plant properties in relation to weather. Successive years of dry summers make beech foliage properties more attractive to *S. punctatella*: the foliage has a higher nitrogen concentration and a relatively low rate of increase of tannins, and these two changes trigger gradual increase of the moth population. However, when the population reaches the outbreak level and beech trees are heavily defoliated, the delayed induced defensive response appears prominently in the following year. The moth population is depressed greatly by this 'stronger' defensive response of beech trees, although other factors, notably natural enemies such as infectious diseases, parasitoids, and predators, are also involved (Kamata & Igarashi, 1995a; Kamata *et al.*, 1997; Kamata, in press).

REFERENCES

BLAIS J.R., PRENTICE R.M., SIPPELL W.L., WALLACE D.R., 1955. Effects of weather on forest tent caterpillar, *Malacosoma disstria* HBN. in central Canada in the spring of 1953. *Can. Entomol.*, 87, 1-8.

BODENHEIMER F.S., 1930. Über die Grundlagen einer allgemeinen Epidemiologie der Insektenkalamitäten. *Z. angew. Entmol.*, 16, 433-450.

FEENY P., 1970. Seasonal changes in oak leaf tannins and nutrients as a cause of spring feeding by winter moth caterpillars. *Ecology*, 51, 565-581.

HARDY Y.V., LAFOND A., HAMEL L., 1983. The epidemiology of the current spruce budworm outbreak in Quebec. *Forest Science*, 29, 715-725.

IGARASHI M., 1975. The beech caterpillar, *Quadricalcarifera punctatella* (MOTSCHULSKY) (Lep., Notodontidae), as an important defoliator of the beech, *Fagus crenata* BLUME. *Monthly Report of Tohoku Research Center, Forestry and Forest Products Research Institute*, 162, 1-4. (in Japanese).

KAMATA N., (in press). Periodic outbreaks of the beech caterpillar, *Quadricalcarifera punctatella*, and its population dynamics: the role of insect pathogens. *In*: McManus M. & Novotony J. (Eds.) : *Population dynamics and integrated control of forest defoliating insects.* Radnor, PA, USDA Forest Service, Northeastern Forest Experiment Station, General Technical Report NE-XXX

KAMATA N., IGARASHI Y., 1993. Factors influencing long term population dynamics of a beech caterpillar, *Quadricalcarifera punctatella* (MOTSCHULSKY) (III): Larval growth associated with water stressed beech. *Trans. Ann. Mtgs. Tohoku Branch Jpn. For. Soc.*, 45, 75-77. (in Japanese)

KAMATA N., IGARASHI Y., 1994. Influence of rainfall on feeding behavior, growth, and mortality of larvae of the beech caterpillar, *Quadricalcarifera punctatella* (MOTSCHULSKY) (Lep. Notodontidae). *J. Appl. Ent.*,

118, 347-353.

KAMATA N., IGARASHI Y., 1995a. An example of numerical response of the carabid beetle, *Calosoma maximowiczi* Morawitz (Col., Carabidae), to the beech caterpillar, *Quadricalcarifera punctatella* (Motschulsky) (Lep., Notodontidae). *J. Appl. Ent.*, 119, 139-142.

KAMATA N., IGARASHI Y., 1995b. Synchronous population dynamics of the beech caterpillar, *Quadricalcarifera punctatella* (MOTSCHULSKY): rainfall is the key. *In*: Haine F., Salom S.M., Ravlin W.F., Payne T., Raffa K.F. (Eds.) : *Behavior population dynamics and control of forest insects.* Wooster, OH, The Ohio State University, p.452-473.

KAMATA N., SATO H., SHIMAZU M., 1997. Seasonal changes in the infection of pupae of the beech caterpillar, *Quadricalcarifera punctatella* (MOTSCH.) (Lep., Notodontidae), by *Cordyceps militaris* LINK (Clavicipitales, Clavicipitaceae) in the soil of the Siebold's beech forest. *J. Appl. Ent.*, 121, 17-21.

KAMATA N., TAKAGI Y., 1991. Factors influencing long term population dynamics of a beech caterpillar, *Quadricalcarifera punctatella* (MOTSCHULSKY) (I) Comparison with fluctuating pattern of temperature and precipitation. *Trans. Ann. Mtgs. Tohoku Branch Jpn. For. Soc.*, 43, 136-138. (in Japanese)

LIEBHOLD, A. M., KAMATA, N., JACOB, T., 1996. Cyclicity and synchrony of historical outbreaks of the beech caterpillar, *Quadricalcarifera punctatella* (MOTSCHULSKY) in Japan. *Res. Pop. Ecol.*, 37, 87-94.

MARTINAT P.J., 1987. The role of climatic variation and weather in forest insect outbreaks. *In*: Barbosa P., Schultz J.C. (Eds) : *Insect Outbreaks.* San Diego, CA, Academic Press, p.241-268.

MATTSON W.J., HAACK R.A., 1987. The role of drought in outbreaks of plant-eating insects. *Bioscience*, 37, 110-118.

MORRIS R.F., 1964. The value of historical data in population research with particular reference to *Hyphantria cunea* DRURY. *Canad. Entomol.*, 96, 356-368.

MYERS J.H., 1988. Can a general hypothesis explain population cycles of forest Lepidoptera? *Adv. Ecol. Res.*, 18, 179-242.

MYERS J.H., 1990. Population cycles of western tent caterpillars: experimental introductions and synchrony of fluctuations. *Ecology*, 71, 986-995.

RHOADES D.F., 1985. Offensive-defensive interactions between herbivores and plants: Their relevance in herbivore population dynamics and ecological theory. *Am. Nat.*, 125, 205-238.

ROYAMA T., 1984. Population dynamics of the spruce budworm *Choristoneura fumiferana. Ecol. Monogr.*, 54, 429-462.

SHEPHERD R.F., BENNETT D.D., DALE J.W., TUNNOCK S., DOLPH R.E., THIER R.W., 1988. Evidence of synchronized cycles in outbreak patterns of Douglas-fir tussock moth, *Orgyia pseudotsugata* (MCDUNNOUGH) (Lepidoptera: Lymantriidae). *Mem. Entomol. Soc. Can.*, 146, 107-121.

SWETNAM T.W., LYNCH A.M., 1993. Multicentury, regional-scale patterns of western spruce budworm outbreaks. *Ecol. Monogr.*, 63, 399-424.

THOMPSON A.J., SHEPHERD R.F., HARRIS J.W.E., SILVERSIDES R.H., 1984. Relating weather to outbreaks of western spruce budworm, *Choristoneura occidentalis* (Lepidoptera: Tortricidae), in British Columbia. *Can. Entomol.*, 116, 375-381.

WALLNER W.E., 1987. Factors affecting insect population dynamics: differences between outbreak and non-outbreak species. *Ann. Rev. Entomol.*, 32, 317-340.

WELLINGTON W.G., 1952. Air-mass climatology in Ontario north of Lake Huron and Lake Superior before outbreaks of the spruce budworm, *Choristoneura fumiferana* (CLEM.), and the forest tent caterpillar, *Malacosoma disstria* HBN. *Can. J. Zool.*, 30, 114-127.

WELLINGTON W.G., 1957. The synoptic approach to studies of insects and climate. *Annu. Rev. Entomol.*, 2, 143-162.

WHITE T.C.R., 1974. A hypothesis to explain outbreaks of looper caterpillars, with special reference to populations of *Selidosema suavis* in a plantation of *Pinus radiata* in New Zealand. *Oecologia(Berlin)*, 16, 279-301.

YANBE T., IGARASHI M., 1983. Outbreaks of beech caterpillar and its parasite *Cordyceps militaris. Forest Pests (Japan)*, 33, 115-119. (in Japanese).

Physiology and Genetics of Tree-Phytophage Interactions
Gujan (France), August 31 - September 5, 1997
Ed. INRA, Paris, 1999 (Les Colloques, n°90)

Insects on drought-stressed trees: four feeding guilds in one experiment

CHRISTER BJÖRKMAN, STIG LARSSON

Department of Entomology, Swedish University of Agricultural Sciences, P.O. Box 7044, S-750 07 Uppsala, Sweden

RESUME

Plants exposed to environmental stress (e.g. drought) are often more attacked by herbivorous insects than plants not exposed to this stress. Among the possible explanations behind these observations, the plant quality hypothesis has achieved most interest. It states that plants exposed to stress become a better food source for insects through increased nutritional value and/or reduced resistance (e.g. lowered concentrations of secondary compounds), leading to higher insect densities. Reviews of the literature indicate that insects with different modes of feeding may vary in their sensitivity to stress-induced changes in their host plants. The ranking of feeding guilds with respect to their sensitivity to stress-induced changes has been suggested to be the following: sucking>mining>chewing>gall-forming. We tested this prediction by comparing the performance (survival, growth, size etc.) of one sucking aphid (*Cinara costata*), one mining lepidoptera (*Epinotia tedella*), one chewing sawfly (*Gilpinia hercyniae*) and one gall-forming aphid (*Sacchiphantes abietis*) on drought-stressed Norway spruce (*Picea abies*) trees with the performance on control trees. Our results generally confirm this prediction, but there were two major exceptions: the mining lepidopterans achieved a lower weight on control than on experimentally drought-stressed trees and the occurrence of galls was higher on drought-stressed trees than on control trees. Our explanations for these exceptions are that insects may differ in their responsiveness to stress-induced changes in their host plant depending on what tissue age they feed on (old tissue should respond more dramatically than young tissue) and that different life-stages in one and the same insect species may respond as if they were from different feeding guilds.

INTRODUCTION

The often made observation that plants or stands of plants exposed to environmental stress (e.g. drought, pollution) are more often and/or more severely attacked by herbivorous insects than unstressed plants (White 1974, Mattson & Haack 1987) has so far evaded general explanation. It is clear, however, that plants exposed to stress undergo biochemical changes that may affect the performance and eventually insect population dynamics (White 1974, 1984, Rhoades 1983, Mattson & Haack 1987, Waring & Cobb 1992). A common pattern is that the level of soluble nitrogen increase whereas the concentration of defensive compounds decrease in stressed plants (Rhoades 1983, Larsson 1989). Insects belonging to different feeding guilds vary with respect to how much they are affected by different types of changes; e.g. sucking insects feeding on phloem sap are primarily affected by changes in soluble nitrogen whereas externally chewing insects are also affected by any change in the concentration of defensive compounds. This could explain the poor consensus among studies on insect responses to stress-induced changes in their host plants, and suggests insect feeding guilds should be treated separately in these studies (Larsson 1989). The following ranking among insect feeding guilds with respect to their sensitivity to stress-induced changes in the host plant, from most positive to most negative, has been suggested: sucking>mining>chewing>gall-making (Larsson 1989). One difficulty when trying to evaluate this hypothesis is that most studies have only covered one (or at the most two) insect feeding guilds in one and the same experiment (Larsson & Björkman 1993).

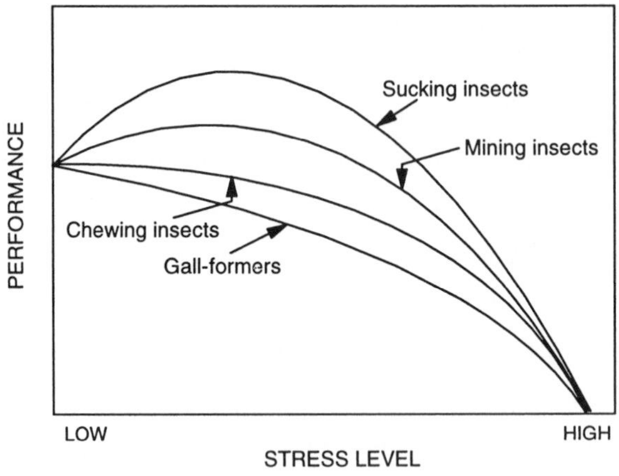

Figure 1. Hypothetical representation of predicted insect performance in relation to host-tree stress level for different insect feeding guilds. Reproduced from Larsson (1989). (© Oikos).

In this paper we report how one sucking, one mining , one chewing and one gall-making insect species respond when their host plant experienced drought stress. We predicted that the sucking insect should perform clearly better on drought-stressed than on control trees, that the mining insect should perform less but significantly better on drought-stressed trees, that the chewing insect should perform equaly well on drought-stressed and control trees and that the gall-former should perform worse on drought-stressed than on control trees This is the first study in which insects from four feeding guilds have been tested on one host plant species under the same experimental conditions.

MATERIALS AND METHODS

Study site

The studies were performed in a Norway spruce (*Picea abies*) stand at Skogaby, 30 km south of Halmstad in southwest Sweden (56°N33'N, 13°13'E; altitude 95-115 m). The stand, planted in 1966, was the second rotation of coniferous forest on a former heathland. In 1987-88, when the experiment started, the stand contained 2285 trees ha^{-1}, had a basal area of 24.4 m^{-2} and a mean breast-height diameter of 11.3 cm. The trees are of Polish origin. Skogaby was the main site of a national research effort to investigate mechanisms behind forest decline. Soil conditions have been experimentally manipulated in several ways, both with respect to water and nutrients (Nilsson & Wiklund 1992). In this paper we will concentrate on the control and the drought-stress treatment.

The drought-stressed plots were 1000 m^2, whereas control plots had an area of 2000 m^2. Trees close to the edge of plots were avoided when randomly selecting the trees included in the studies. For the studies of sucking, chewing and mining insects we used two control and two drought-stressed plots. For the gall-making insect, all four available plots of both treatments were used, mainly because of low gall densities.

Drought treatment

During May 1 — October 1, 1988 and April 1 — October 1, 1989 the drought-stressed plots were covered with a plastic "roof" (70 cm above ground) which prevented about two-thirds or 67 % of the throughfall from reaching the soil. During the rest of the year all precipitation was allowed to infiltrate the soil profile. In 1990, there was no treatment of these plots.

Estimations of drought effects

The soil water content for 1989 was estimated by simulations based on data on soil water potentials collected at regular intervals during the growing season. Tree basal area growth for all three years (1988, 1989, 1990) was measured as described by Nilsson & Wiklund (1992).

Insect species and performance traits

The aphid *Cinara costata* Zett. (Homoptera: Aphididae) was used as a representative of sucking insecst because of its commonness in the area. *C. costata* feeds primarily on shoots and thin branches. On May 2, 1989 two branches on ten trees per plot were each supplied with one second-instar stem-mother collected in the area. The branches were enclosed in sleeve cages after all other insects had been removed. The aphids were left to reproduce. Branches were taken to the laboratory on June 20 and aphids were counted and classified into three age classes based on the number of antennal segments. We also noted if the aphids in the largest class had wing buds or not. A more detailed description can be found in Larsson & Björkman (1993).

The mining insect we studied was *Epinotia tedella* (Cl.) (Lepidoptera: Tortricidae). This moth species was, among other things, chosen because it is one of the few species for which there is strong indications that the population dynamics are driven by stress-induced changes in host plant quality (Münster-Swendsen 1987). The primary mechanism seems to be that drought increases plant quality which results in larger and more fecund adults (Münster-Swendsen 1987). A larva mines approximately 30 old needles before pupating in the soil, leaving characteristic clusters of dry hollow needles on trees. In 1988, 1989 and 1990, larvae present in plots were sampled in funnel traps (n=25 on each plot) when descending from the canopy in late autumn. Traps were emptied every week in all the years, and larval samples were taken to the laboratory where larvae were counted, and degree of parasitism and body weight were determined. A detailed description of the methods used for this species can be found in Münster-Swendsen (1987).

The sawfly *Gilpinia hercyniae* Htg. (Hymenoptera: Symphyta) was chosen to represent chewing insects. *G. hercyniae* occurs naturally in the area, but at the time of these studies population were at such low densities that larvae from a laboratory culture had to be used. Female sawflies were allowed to oviposit on spruce branches in the laboratory. Newly emerged larvae were transferred to experimental branches (one per each of ten trees per plot) enclosed in sleeve cages. Larvae were left undisturbed until cocoon spinning except for one point estimate of "developmental time" at August 29, 1989 when the proportion of larvae that had spun cocoon at that date was determined. At the end of the experiment, the cocoons, all females due to the parthenogenetic life style, were counted and weighed. A detailed description of the methods used for this species can be found in Larsson & Björkman (1993).

The aphid *Sacchiphantes abietis* (L.) (Homoptera: Adelgidae) was used as a model organism for the gall-forming insects. The pineapple-shaped galls induced by this species are deformed buds. One randomly selected branch was sampled from the middle to upper part of the crown from 25 to 100 trees from each of four control and four drought-stressed plots. Sampling took place in late autumn 1990. Occurrence and size of galls produced in 1988, 1989 and 1990 could be estimated from this sampling because old galls remain on the branch for several years. Occurrence of galls was determined in two ways: (1) the relative change from 1988 to 1990 in the proportion of trees with galls (i.e. a value of 1 means no change in the proportion of trees with galls whereas a value less than 1 indicate a decrease and a value larger than 1 an increase in this proportion) and (2) the mean density of galls (i.e. galls per available galling site) on trees with galls in 1989. A detailed description of the methods used for the gall-maker can be found in Björkman (1997).

Thus, the sucking aphid and the chewing sawfly were only studied in 1989. For the mining lepidopteran and the gall-making aphid data from 1988 to 1990 was included in the analyses.

RESULTS

Soil water content

In the early season of 1989, which was a very dry period, the soil water content showed only small differences between treatments (Larsson & Björkman 1993). In late 1989, and probably in 1988 which was a year with more precipitation, there were substantial differences between treatments; i.e. the content was almost twice as high in control than in drought-stressed plots (Larsson & Björkman 1993).

Tree growth

Basal area growth was lower on drought-stressed plots in all years (mean difference almost 30 %), but the difference was less pronounced in 1990, the year when the "roofs" had been removed (Nilsson & Wiklund 1992, Larsson & Björkman 1993).

Insect responses

Sucking aphid

There was no significant difference in the build-up of aphid densities between drought-stressed and control trees ($F_{1, 38}$=2.03, p=0.16), although there was a trend towards higher densities on the drought-stressed trees (Table 1). The proportion of aphids with wing buds was significantly higher on drought-stressed trees than on control trees (Table 1; $F_{1, 38}$=4.29, p<0.05; tested with arcsine-transformed values).

Mining lepidopteran

Contrary to what was predicted, the weight of *E. tedella* larvae was lower on drought-stressed trees than on control trees (Table 1; $F_{1, 298}$=18.07, p<0.001). This difference was most pronounced in 1989. There was no difference in the number of larvae spinning down from control and drought-stressed trees ($F_{1, 298}$=0.00, p>0.97). Rates of parasitism was slightly higher (approx. 4 units of %) among larvae from drought-stressed trees than among larvae from control trees ($F_{1, 298}$=4.16, p<0.05).

Chewing sawfly

As predicted, there was no significant differences between *G. hercyniae* larvae reared on drought-stressed trees and larvae reared on control trees in any of the studied performance traits: Survival (Table 1; $F_{1, 38}$=0.35, p=0.56), proportion of larvae that had spun cocoon on August 29 (Table 1; $F_{1, 38}$=0.37, p=0.55) and cocoon dry weight (Table 1; $F_{1, 38}$=2.75, p=0.11).

Gall-forming aphid

Two of the results from the gall-forming *S. abietis* was opposite to what we expected: Gall density (only measured on trees with galls) was higher on drought-stressed than on control trees (Table 1; p<0.05, Tukey's test). The relative change in proportion of trees with galls from 1988 to 1990 was larger on drought-stressed plots than on control plots (Table 1; p<0.05, Tukey's test).

There was a positive relationship between gall size and tree growth was as predicted, but this relationship was not very strong. In fact, it was only significant at the level of individual shoots; there was a positive, but not very high, correlation between the diameter of the shoot fostering the gall (the mother shoot) and the diameter of the gall (r=0.291, p<0.05, n=49). Treatments did not have any significant effect on gall size (Table 1; p>0.05, Tukey's test).

Table 1. Performance of insects from four feeding guilds on drought-stressed and control Norway spruce (*Picea abies*) trees. Means±S.E. are presented, n=20 per treatment. Significant differences between treatments are indicated by p-values. Data on sucking and chewing insects taken from Björkman & Larsson (1993) and data on the gall-forming insect from Björkman (1997).

FEEDING GUILD - *Species* Insect trait	Control	Drought	p-value
SUCKING INSECT - *Cinara costata*			
Number of progenies per stem-mother	33.1±4.8	40.1±8.2	0.16
Prop. of individuals with wing buds	0.02±0.01	0.09±0.04	<0.05
MINING INSECT - *Epinotia tedella*			
Larval dry weight (mg)	2.22±0.03	2.09±0.04	<0.001
CHEWING INSECT - *Gilpinia hercyniae*			
Survival	0.74±0.05	0.76±0.04	0.56
Proportion that had spun cocoon by Aug 29	0.54±0.09	0.46±0.08	0.55
Cocoon dry weight	24.6±0.5	23.3±0.4	0.11
GALL-FORMING INSECT - *Sacchiphantes abietis*			
Gall frequency - positive effect of drought-stress			
Relative change in proportion of trees with galls[1]	0.75±0.24	2.58±1.10	<0.05
Density of galls on galled trees	0.09±0.02	0.28±0.06	<0.05
Gall size[2] - negative effect of drought stress			
Gall width	8.2±0.4	7.6±0.5	>0.05
Gall length	10.4±0.7	10.1±0.5	>0.05

[1] relative change from 1988 — 1990 in proportion of trees with galls, i.e. a value of 1 means no change in the proportion of trees with galls whereas a value less than 1 indicate a decrease and a value larger than 1 an increase in this proportion.
[2] n=24 and 20 for control and drought, respectively.

DISCUSSION

The general picture that emerges from this study, on the response of four insect species (from different feeding guilds) to experimentally drought-stressed host plants, is that even the modified Plant Stress/Insect Performance Hypothesis (Larsson 1989) may need some further modifications. However, the basic idea that insects with different modes of feeding differ in their response to experimentally induced changes in host plant quality appear to be supported (Figure 2). There are no other studies in which more than one (or at the most two) insect feeding guilds has been studied in the same experiment. This justifies our attempts to generalize although the data base is limited. To clarify. our arguments, we will also speculate on the possible mechanisms behind the observed responses.

Starting with the data supporting the modified Plant Stress/Insect Performance Hypothesis we first notice the lack of response for the chewing sawfly *G. hercyniae* to drought-stressed trees, in accordance with the hypothesis.

The second insect species for which data support the hypothesis is the sucking aphid *C. costata*. The response was, however, weaker than in many other studies on aphids (see Larsson & Björkman 1993). Our experiment involved mature trees whereas most other studies have been conducted with saplings (e.g. Braun & Flückiger 1984, Bolsinger & Flückiger 1987, Kidd 1990, Jones & Coleman 1991). This difference in the age of experimental trees may have affected the results also for the chewing, mining and gall-forming insects. Biochemical changes in mature trees may be less dramatic, but in the same direction, than in saplings (Figure 3).

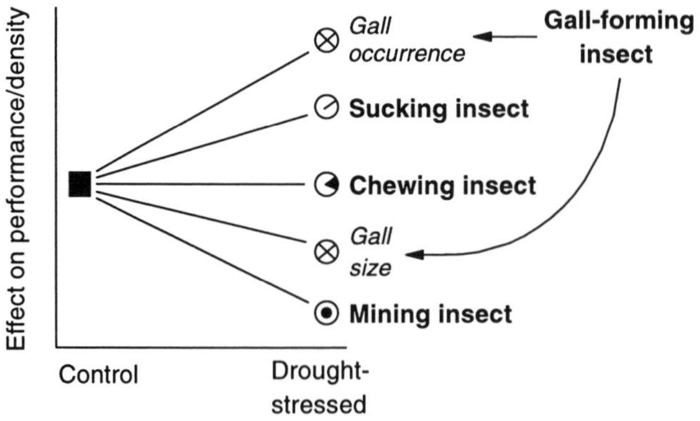

Figure 2. A simplified graphical presentation of the results from our study on the effect of drought-stress on insects from different feeding guilds. Note the dual and opposing effect on the gall-forming insect.

In addition, the drought treatment may have been so strong that the trees were pushed beyond the point where the effect of stress on performance turns from positive to negative (Figure 1), but still with the net result of stress being positive (Figure 2 & 4). Admittedly, both of these arguments are mainly speculative, with little empirical support. A circumstance that may have decreased the difference between treatments, was the fact that 1989 was exceptionally dry during the feeding period of *C. costata* (Figure 2). Thus, the control trees may also have been drought-stressed.

For both the chewing and the sucking insect species we transferred specimens to branches choosen by us. It is difficult to know to what extent this may have affected the result. However, because the trees were fairly tall we had to use branches in the lower part of the crown. It is possible that there is intra-crown variation with respect to stress response. The lower part is probably less sensitive than the upper part (Larsson & Björkman 1993). If so, this could partly explain why the sucking aphids in our study did not respond as strongly as in most other studies.

Completely opposite to our prediction, *E. tedella* achieved a lower weight on drought-stressed trees than on control trees. In a long-term study of this species Münster-Swendsen (1987) reported that there is a negative correlation between precipitation in May - September (in the current and previous years) and insect weight (i.e. fecundity). This, in turn, seems to be the driving force in the population dynamics of this species.

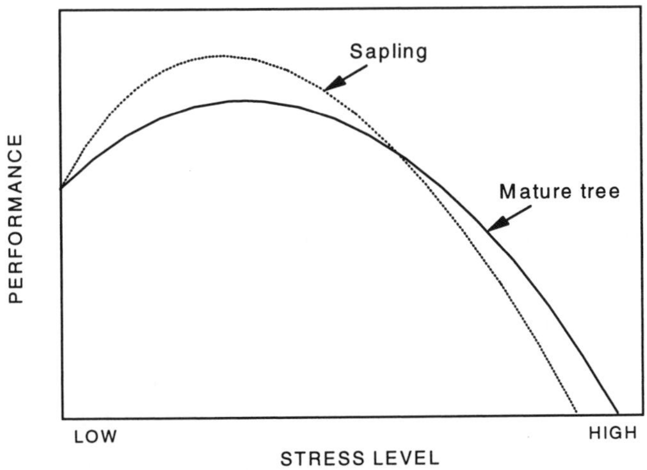

Figure 3. A graphical representation of the suggested difference in stress response between saplings and mature trees and its effect on the performance of (sucking) insects.

The effect of drought stress on host plant quality in our study may simply have been stronger than any naturally occurring effects. However, because all the insect species in our study were feeding on trees exposed to the same level of stress, this strong effect suggests that the response curve of *E. tedella* differs from that of other mining insects (see Fig. 1). That *E. tedella* preferentially feeds on old needles (2 - 4 year old) whereas most other mining insects on spruce occurring in Sweden feed on young needles (Björkman & Larsson 1991) may offer a mechanistic explanation to the results found here; a plant exposed to stress is probably more prone to sacrifice old needles (with low productivity) than young needles contributing more to growth, resulting in a much steeper response curve in old tissue (Figure 4). Thus, because the other species in this study seemed to respond more as predicted, it is possible that *E. tedella* is more responsive to changes in the host plant than the other insect species (Figure 5). At a first glance, this speculative explanation seems to be contradicted by the change in larval weight over years; *E. tedella* larvae grew largest on both control and drought-stressed trees in 1989, the driest year during the study period.(C. Björkman unpublished data). However, the quality of the old (2 - 4 year) needles fed upon by *E. tedella* is probably more affected by the climatic conditions during the year when they were formed. This hypothesis gains support when we look at the precipitation some years back; e.g. 1987 was an exceptionally wet year.

The response of the galling aphid *S. abietis* was, on one hand, as predicted. Gall size was negatively correlated with the growth potential of the attacked bud, as estimated by the diameter of the mother shoot. By using the diameter of a neigbbouring shoot (i.e. a shoot of the same age on the same shoot as the galled one), which may give a more direct measure of growth potential, a similar relationship was found but with a lower n-value. The fact that we used mature trees may explain why the difference in gall size between treatments was statistically non-significant. On the other hand, however, aphid response to drought stress was opposite to our prediction:: Gall occurrence, both measured as the relative change in proportion of trees with galls and as the density of galls on galled trees, was higher on drought-stressed than on control plots. We suggest that the most likely explanation for this somewhat unexpected result is reduced resistance in drought-stressed trees and/or a delayed crown closure (Björkman 1998). Both of these mechanisms would act on the aphid stage initiating the gall. Reduced resistance through a higher survival and delayed crown closure through greater influx of light, making more buds suitable for gall-induction. Thus, we may here have an example where different life-stages in one and the same insect species respond as if they were from different feeding guilds (Figure 5). For galling insects this may actually be more of the rule than an exception (Björkman 1997), because gall initiation probably is more affected by plant resistance than by plant growth rate (Figure 6). Thus, one step towards better predicting how an insect species will respond to environmental stress is to study all of the stages that could be sensitive to changes in host plant quality.

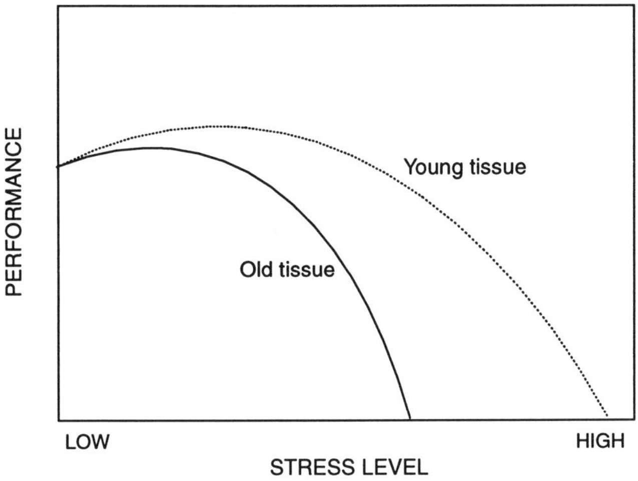

Figure 4. Hypothetical representation of how the relationship between performance of a (mining) insect and stress level of the host plant could be affected by tissue age fed upon by the insect.

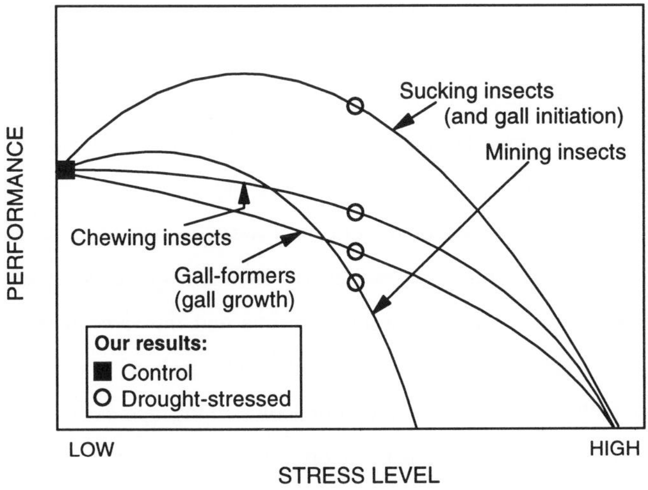

Figure 5. A modified version of Figure 1, with the modified response curve for mining insects feeding on old tissue and our observed results for each feeding guild, respectively, on control and drought-stressed trees included.

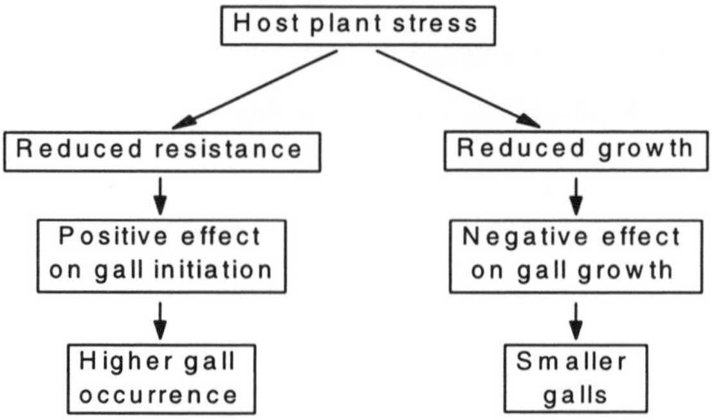

Figure 6. The dual and opposing effect that host plant stress may have on gall-forming insects. This means that different life stages in one and the same insect species may respond as if they were from different feeding guilds.

CONCLUSIONS

The prediction that different feeding guilds should respond differently to the same stress-induced changes in the host plant is corroborated here. However, we found exceptions to the earlier proposed ranking of guilds with respect to their sensitivity, suggesting that the modification of the Plant Stress/Insect Performance Hypothesis suggested by Larsson (1989) may need some further modifications. The main modifications are (1) that mining insects seem to be more sensitive to drought-stress induced changes in the host plant than earlier expected, probably because they feed on old needles which, in turn, may respond more dramatically to stress than young, high-activity, needles and (2) that the response of galling insects need to be divided into at least two separate aspects: gall occurrence and size. Occurrence should, as a consequence of the effects that stress may have on gall initiation, respond positively to drought-stress whereas growth should respond negatively. Thus, we have here an example where different life-stages in one and the same insect species may respond as if they were from different feeding guilds. The lack of effect on the chewing sawfly, the smaller galls and the higher proportion of sucking aphids with wing buds on drought-stressed trees are, in accordance with the original hypothesis.

ACKNOWLEDGEMENTS

We thank Richard Hopkins, and Mike Wagner for valuable comments on the manuscript. Financial support has been provided by the Swedish Council of Forestry and Agriculture and National Swedish Environmental Protection Board.

REFERENCES

BOLSINGER M., FLÜCKIGER W. 1987. Enhanced aphid infestation at motorways, the role of ambient air pollution. *Ent. Exp. Appl.*, 45, 237-243.

BRAUN S., FLÜCKIGER W., 1984. Increased population of the aphid *Aphis pomi* at a motorway. Part 2. The effect of drought and deicing salt. *Environ. Pollut. (Series A)* 36, 261-270.

BJÖRKMAN C., 1997. Opposite, linear and non-linear effects of plant stress on a galling aphid. *Scand. J. For. Res.*, 12: (In press)

BJÖRKMAN C., LARSSON S, 1991. Host-plant specialization in needle-eating insects of Sweden. *In:* Baranchikov Y.N., Mattson W.J., Hain F.P., Payne T.L. (eds): Forest insect guilds: patterns of interaction with host trees. U.S. Dep. Agric. For. Serv. Gen. Tech. Rep. NE-153. P. 1-20.

JONES C.G., COLEMAN J.S., 1991. Plant stress and insect herbivory, toward an integrated perspective. *In:* Mooney H.A., Winner W.E., Bell, E.J. (eds): *Response of plants to multiple stresses.* Academic Press, San Diego, p. 249-280.

KIDD N.A.C., 1990. The effects of simulated acid mist on the growth rates of conifer aphids and the implications for tree health. *J. Appl. Ent.*, 110, 524-529.

LARSSON, S., 1989. Stressful times for the plant stress-insect performance hypothesis. *Oikos*, 56, 277-283.

LARSSON, S. BJÖRKMAN, C., 1993. Performance of chewing and phloem-feeding insects on stressed trees. *Scand. J. For. Res.*, 8, 550-559.

MATTSON, W.J., HAACK, R.A., 1987. The role of drought stress in provoking outbreaks of phytophagous insects´. *In:* Barbosa, P., Schultz, J.C. (eds): *Insect outbreaks*. Academic Press, San Diego, p. 365-407.

MÜNSTER-SWENDSEN, M., 1987. The effect of precipitation on radial increment in Norway spruce (Picea abies Karst.) and on the dynamics of a lepidopteran pest insect. *J. Appl. Ecol.*, 24, 563-571.

NILSSON, L.-O., WIKLUND, K., 1992. Influence of nutrient and water stress on Norway spruce production in south Sweden - the role of air pollutants. *Plant and Soil,* 147, 251-265.

RHOADES, D.F., 1983. Herbivore population dynamics and plant chemistry. *In:* Denno, R.F., McClure, M.S. (eds): *Variable plants and insect herbivores in natural and managed systems.* Academic Press, New York, p. 155-220.

WARING, G.L., COBB, N.S., 1992. The impact of plant stress on herbivore population dynamics. *Insect Plant Interactions,* 4, 167-226.

WHITE, T.C.R., 1974. A hypothesis to explain outbreaks of looper caterpillars, with special reference to populations of *Selidosema suavis* in a plantation of *Pinus radiata* in New Zealand. *Oecologia,* 22, 119-134.

WHITE, T.C.R. 1984. The abundance of invertebrate herbivores in relation to the availability of nitrogen in stressed food plants. *Oecologia,* 63, 90-105.

Physiology and Genetics of Tree-Phytophage Interactions
Gujan (France), August 31 - September 5, 1997
Ed. INRA, Paris, 1999 (Les Colloques, n°90)

Resistance of fertilized Norway spruce (*Picea abies* (L.) Karst.) and Scots pine (*Pinus sylvestris* L.)

H. VIIRI [1], M.KYTÖ[2], P.NIEMELÄ[1]

[1] *Faculty of Forestry, University of Joensuu*
P.O.Box 111, FIN-80101 Joensuu, Finland

[2] *Finnish Forest Research Institute*
P.O.Box 18, FIN-01301 Vantaa, Finland

RESUME

The ability to react to wounding with resin flow and rapid synthesis of defence chemicals is an important means of resistance in conifers. Strong resin flow and rapid accumulation of phenolics and stilbenes in the phloem around a wounded site can prevent the invasion of bark beetles and associated fungi. As growth is considered the primary sink for assimilates, a relationship, even a trade-off is expected to exist between growth and defense.

We have tested how fertilization can affect resin flow and phloem phenolics in Norway spruce, Picea abies, and Scots pine, Pinus sylvestris. In Norway spruce, nitrogen fertilization increased the stem diameter growth and the vigour index, but did not affect resin flow, phloem phenolic concentrations or the lesion length caused by C. polonica. However, in Scots pine, with low vigour index resin flow was either weak or strong, whereas trees with high vigour index were never associated with high resin or phenolic content. The observation that high vigour and strong defense never occurred together is in agreement with the growth-differentiation balance hypothesis.

INTRODUCTION

A major part of the symbiosis between bark beetles and associated fungi is their joint action to overcome the resistance mechanisms of their host trees. The conifers defend against the attack of bark beetles and associated fungi with both constitutive defense, mainly based on primary resin, and with induced responses by producing secondary resins and phenolics. In spite of the constitutive and induced defenses working together to defend the tree, in some circumstances fungi can escape from the entrapping lesion. In the induced response, the lesion formation and terpene synthesis represent two independent activities; necrosis proceeding more rapidly than terpene synthesis (Raffa and Berryman, 1982; Cheniclet et al., 1988). Thus, the fungus is first confined by the removal of essential nutrients from the entry site, and only secondly by resinosis (Wong and Berryman, 1977; Raffa and Berryman, 1982).

Stand and climatic conditions often reduce plant assimilation and may consequently lower the tree's ability to resist the attack of bark beetles and associated fungi. The threshold density of successful bark beetle attack defines the resistance level of the tree and is dependent on the vigour of the host (Waring and Pitman, 1983; Mulock and Christiansen, 1986). Consequently, measurements of the tree vigour are widely used to determine risk of attack by bark beetles. Tree growth efficiency, as measured by stemwood production per unit of foliage area, has been suggested as a universal tree vigour index (Waring, 1983).

The carbon-nutrient balance (CNB) hypothesis, a special case of the growth-differentiation balance (GDB) hypothesis, predicts that environmental factors can modify plants' phenotypical responses and allocation of resources to defense and growth (Bryant, et al. 1983; Lorio, 1986; Herms and Mattson, 1992; Tuomi, 1992). Growth is considered the primary sink for assimilates during favourable conditions and differentiation during growth-limiting conditions. For example, carbon-based secondary metabolites tend to accumulate in conditions of moderate nutrient limitation. On the other hand, increased nutrient availability can cause a relative decrease in secondary metabolites if assimilated carbon is rapidly converted to growth.

Nitrogen is usually the growth limiting factor in boreal forests and hence fertilization has been a common silvicultural practise. In this paper we review some experiments on the effect of nitrogen fertilization on growth, vigour and defense responses of conifers. Specifically, the suitability of carbon-nutrient balance hypothesis and growth-differentiation balance hypothesis for conifers are considered. We have used stem resin flow and phloem phenolics in Norway spruce and Scots pine as indicators of defense responses (Kytö et al., 1996; 1998). Tree vigour was measured by vigour index (stemwood production by unit of leaf area) (Waring, 1983).

DEFENSE RESPONSES AFTER NITROGEN FERTILIZATION

Trade-off predictions

In our earlier experiments on spruce, fertilization treatments had no significant effect on resin flow or length of the lesion caused by blue-stain fungus, Ceratocystis polonica Siem. Moreau (Kytö et al., 1996). However, resin flow increased two-fold in trees wounded one year earlier, indicating an induced component of the resin production. The growth response of spruce to fertilization was clear but the only indication that increased growth might reduce the level of resistance was the modest positive correlation between lesion length and annual ring width (Kytö et al., 1996). The fact that resistance against blue-stain fungus correlated negatively with a stem diameter increment, might be an indication of a genetic rather than physiological trade-off between growth and defense. Resource allocation to defense might be regulated genetically rather than by the availability of resources.

In the case of Scots pine, fertilization treatments increased the stem diameter growth and tree vigour index (Kytö et al., 1998). In most of the sites resin flow was highest in non-fertilized treatments, but individual fertilization treatments did not affect resin flow in any of the experimental sites. There was no significant correlation between the phenolic concentration and amount of resin flow in any of the experiments. The concentration of total phenolics was unaffected by changes in the growth rate (Kytö et al., 1998).

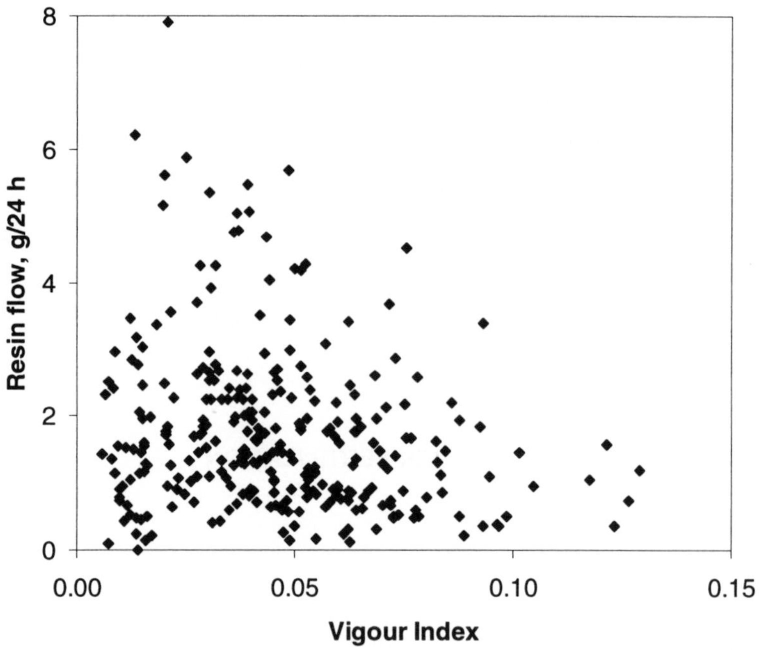

Figure 1. The amount of resin flow plotted against the vigour index in 291 Scots pine trees in seven different field experiments. Each point represents the mean of two samples from one tree.

The relationship between resin flow and tree vigour index in seven different field experiments is shown in Fig. 1. The consequent relationship between concentrations of total phenolics in the phloem and vigour index is shown in Fig. 2. Interestingly, high resin content or high total phenolic content never occurred together with high vigour index. Trees with low vigour index resin flow was either weak or strong, while trees with relatively high vigour index never had strong resin flow. Exactly the same pattern holds for the total phenolics of phloem and vigour index.

These relationships are consistent with growth-differentiation model (Herms and Mattson, 1992). According to the model three phenotypes are predicted 1) rapid growth coupled with low secondary metabolism, 2) slow growth coupled with high secondary metabolism, and 3) slow growth coupled with low secondary metabolism (with high carbohydrate storage in sink limited plants, and low carbohydrate storage in source limited plants). Further, the relationship between growth, photosynthesis and secondary metabolism is nonlinear (Tuomi, 1992). Because photosynthesis was not measured in this study and where on the continuum of resource availability fertilization treatments fell, it is not possible rigorously to determine from the data if there is an actual trade-off between growth and defense.

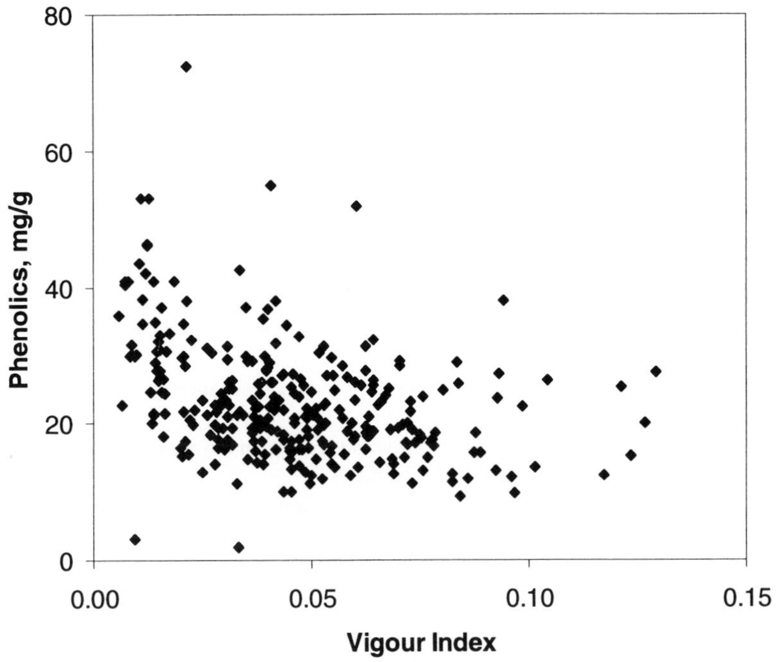

Figure 2. The concentration of total phenolics (mg/g dry weight, tannic acid equivalents) in the phloem plotted against the vigour index of the same trees as in Figure 1.

CONCLUSION

Previously mentioned theories predict that there might be a decrease in the defense level due to fertilization. According to Waring and Cobb (1989) coniferous trees do not elicit a strong positive herbivore response when fertilized. In our experiments the growth response to fertilization in both Scots pine and Norway spruce was not clearly reflected in the resin flow or phloem phenolic concentration. However, a noteworthy feature in the results was that combination of simultaneous high resin or phenolic content and high vigour index (or high growth) seem to be mutually exclusive (Fig. 1, Fig. 2). Whether this combination is infeasible due to morphological constraints or resource based trade-offs is difficult to resolve without knowing the morphological and resource limitations, assimilation capacity and allocation patterns of the trees (Mole, 1994).

REFERENCES

BRYANT, J.P., CHAPIN, F.S., III, KLEIN, D.R., 1983. Carbon/nutrient balance of boreal plants in relation to vertebrate herbivory. *Oikos*, 40, 357-368.

CHENICLET, C., BERNARD-DAGAN, C., PAULY, G., 1988. Terpene Biosynthesis Under Pathological Conditions. *In*: Mattson, W.J., Levieux, J., Bernard-Dagan, C. (Eds.): *Mechanisms of Woody Plant Defenses Against Insects. Search for Pattern.* Springer Verlag, p. 117-130.

HERMS, D.A., MATTSON, W.J., 1992. The dilemma of plants: to grow or to defend. *Q. Rev. Biol.*, 67, 28-335.

KYTÖ, M., NIEMELÄ, P., ANNILA, E., 1996. Vitality and bark beetle resistance of fertilized Norway spruce. *For. Ecol. Manag.,* 84, 149-157.

KYTÖ, M., NIEMELÄ, P., ANNILA, E., 1998. Effects of vitality fertilization on the resin flow and vigour of Scots pine in Finland. *For. Ecol. Manag.*, 102, 121-130.

LORIO, P.L., Jr., 1986. Growth-differentiation balance: a basis for understanding southern pine beetle-tree interactions. *For. Ecol. Manag.*, 14, 259-273.

MOLE, S., 1994. Trade-offs and constraints in plant-herbivore defense theory: A life-history perspective. *Oikos*, 71, 3-12.

MULOCK, P., CHRISTIANSEN, E., 1986. The threshold of successful attack by *Ips typographus* on *Picea abies*: A field experiment. *For. Ecol. Manag.*, 14, 125-132.

RAFFA, K.F., BERRYMAN, A.A., 1982. Accumulation of monoterpenes and associated volatiles following inoculation of grand fir with a fungus transmitted by the fir engraver, *Scolytus ventralis* (Coleoptera: Scolytidae). *Can. Ent.*, 114, 797-810.

TUOMI, J., 1992. Toward Integration of Plant Defence Theories. *Tree,* 11, 365-367.

WARING, R. H., 1983. Estimating forest growth and efficiency in relation to canopy leaf area. *Adv. Ecol. Res.*, 13, 327-354.

WARING, G.L., COBB, N.S., 1989. The Impact of Plant Stress on Herbivore Population Dynamics. *In*: Berrays E.A. (Ed.): *Insect Herbivore Interactions.* CRE Press, p. 167-226.

WARING, R.H., PITMAN, G.B., 1983. Physiological stress in lodgepole pine as a precursor for Mountain pine beetle attack. *Z. ang. Ent.*, 96, 265-270.

WONG, B.L., BERRYMAN, A.A., 1977. Host resistance to the fir engraver beetle. 3. Lesion development and containment of infection by resistant *Abies grandis* inoculated with *Trichosporium symbioticum. Can. J. Bot.*, 55, 2358-2365.

Chapter 6

Theories and Mechanisms

Physiology and Genetics of Tree-Phytophage Interactions
Gujan (France), August 31 - September 5, 1997
Ed. INRA, Paris, 1999 (Les Colloques, n°90)

Inducible defense responses: mechanisms of general aggressor perception are conserved in plants

J.M. DAVIS[1], H.WU[1,2], M.E. TIGNOR[1]

[1]*School of Forest Resources and Conservation, PO Box 110410, University of Florida, Gainesville, FL 32611 USA*

[2]*current address: Department of Medicine, Brigham and Women's Hospital and Harvard Medical School, Boston MA 02115 USA*

RESUME

Our research goal is to understand the mechanisms by which a tree "perceives" an aggressor and initiates a defense response. To gain insight into these mechanisms, we identified a gene -- which codes for a defense enzyme, chitinase -- whose mRNA accumulates after treatment of pine cells with the general elicitor chitosan. This gene acts as a reporter gene for the induction of a defense response, since it is transcribed into mRNA after an aggressor is perceived by a pine cell. We asked whether the pine chitinase gene could still perceive chitosan after the gene was removed from pines and introduced into tobacco plants *via* genetic engineering. This experiment allowed us to distinguish whether the aggressor perception mechanisms in pines and in tobacco plants were similar, or dissimilar. We found that the pine gene was still transcribed in response to chitosan treatments in transgenic tobacco, supporting the hypothesis that aggressor perception mechanisms, mediated through signal transduction pathways, are similar in gymnosperms and angiosperms. Given that these pathways are similar in trees and other higher plants, we describe genetic variants within the species *Arabidopsis thaliana* that serve to illuminate the range of genetic variation that could be observed among tree genotypes with respect to these pathways.

INTRODUCTION

Tree defenses can be subdivided into two categories, constitutive and inducible. Constitutive defenses are pre-formed; they are already present prior to interaction of the plant with an aggressor. Inducible defenses, on the other hand, are activated in response to interaction with an aggressor. We are interested in inducible defenses and how they are regulated in trees. We want to better understand how inducible defenses are activated so that we can explain how tree genetic variation affects the nature and timing of inducible defenses, and in turn how these defenses impact tree:phytophage interactions.

As a first step toward meeting these overarching goals, we developed an experimental system that was amenable to molecular analysis and in which we could induce a defense response reliably and rapidly. We used pine cell cultures because they exhibit a dramatic defense response to chitosan that has been extensively characterized (Lesney, 1989; Popp *et al.*, 1997). Cell cultures are advantageous in that they are genetically uniform, physiologically synchronized for growth, and can be treated *en masse* with compounds that elicit defense responses. When treated with the general elicitor chitosan, pine cells undergo a synchronized and massive defense response that mimics many aspects of a defense response in intact plant tissues. The cells accumulate peroxidase and produce lignin (Lesney, 1989), evolve ethylene, and produce the hydrolytic defense enzymes chitinase and glucanase (Popp *et al.*, 1997). Ethylene production, lignification, and hydrolytic enzyme production are all well-characterized inducible responses to mechanical injury and/or fungal elicitors in herbaceous crops (Stintzi *et al.*, 1993).

By analogy to herbaceous crops, gene expression was probably required for many aspects of the induced defense response in pines. If a gene was expressed during an induced response, then its messenger RNA would be elevated after treatment with chitosan. Indeed we identified several mRNAs that were elevated in abundance after chitosan treatment (Mason and Davis, 1997). One of the mRNAs encoded chitinase, a pathogen-related (PR-) enzyme which was known from previous experiments to be induced in pine cell cultures (Popp *et al.*, 1997). The gene encoding chitinase, *Pschi4*, was used in the studies reported in this paper.

One can view the chitinase gene as a downstream target for an aggressor-induced signal transduction pathway. According to this view, the gene is activated by intracellular signals generated by the cell's perception of an aggressor. In the experiments reported herein, we asked the question: Is the signal transduction pathway that activates the chitinase gene in pine similar to, or dissimilar to, the pathway in tobacco, an herbaceous crop plant?

MATERIALS AND METHODS

Cell cultures of slash pine (*Pinus elliottii* var. *elliottii,* genotype 52-56) were initiated from cambium tissue, maintained in continuously shaken liquid cultures, and treated with the general elicitor chitosan using previously described methods (Lesney, 1989). Previous work established that the *Pschi4* gene was chitosan-induced in the 52-56 cell line (Wu *et al.*, 1997; Mason and Davis, 1997). To determine if *Pschi4* was inducible in transgenic tobacco, we introduced a 7 kb genomic fragment containing the coding sequence of *Pschi4* along with flanking sequences into the *Agrobacterium* binary vector pCIB10, and then into transgenic tobacco plants using previously described methods (Wu *et al.*, 1997). Nine independent transgenic plants were randomly selected for testing chitosan-induced expression of *Pschi4* using RNA gel blot analysis. Briefly, young leaves were excised from young transgenic tobacco plants grown on MS agar in culture vessels. Leaf sections were removed and incubated in culture dishes with buffer only (50 mM KCl), buffer plus chitosan (60 mg/ml final concentration), or left on the plant and wounded with a pair of hemostats. Plants transformed with pCIB10 lacking *Pschi4* were used as controls. RNA was extracted and analyzed using standard procedures (Davis *et al.,* 1991). The probe for *Pschi4* expression was a 668 bp *Sac*I-*Bam*HI fragment that is part of the coding region of *Pschi4* (Wu *et al.*, 1997). Equal loading of RNA was confirmed by ethidium bromide staining of the gels. The *Pschi4* gene was considered chitosan-induced if the autoradiograph showed higher signal intensity in the chitosan-treated sample, compared to the buffer-treated sample.

Table 1. Chitosan-induced accumulation of the pine *Pschi4* messenger RNA in transgenic tobacco plants containing the *Pschi4* transgene.

transgenic lines	CIB10	4.2	4.6	4.7	4.8	4.9	4.10	4.11	4.12	4.14
chitosan induction	no*	yes**	?***	yes	yes	?	yes	yes	yes	yes

* no expression of *Pschi4* was detected in these plant lines
** chitosan treated samples showed higher *Pschi4* mRNA levels
*** chitosan treated samples showed higher *Pschi4* mRNA, but interpretation was ambiguous due to unequal loading

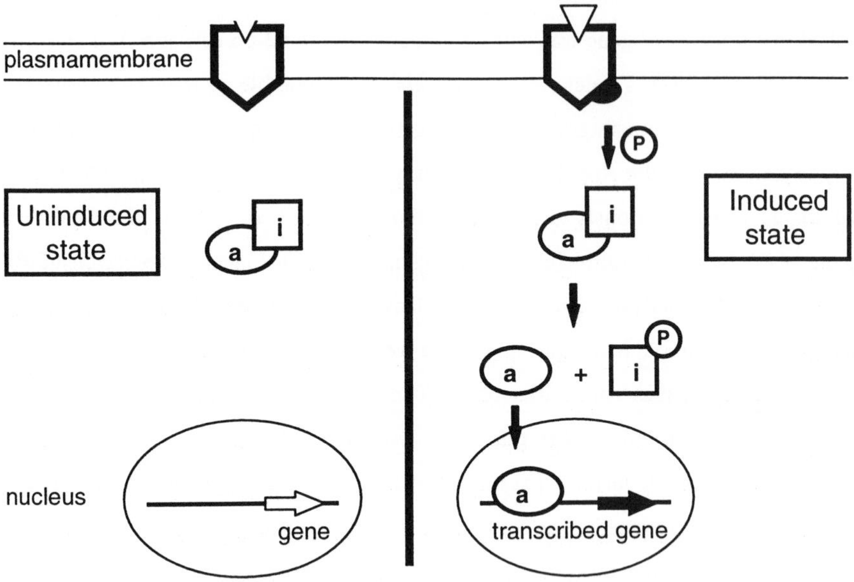

Figure 1. Model with predicted protein components of an inducible signal transduction pathway. Components of the pathway include a plasmamembrane receptor (pentagon) for chitosan (inverted triangle), a transcriptional activator (a), an inhibitor capable of binding the activator (i), and inorganic phosphate (P).

RESULTS

Pine *Pschi4* is transcribed in tobacco

Seven out of nine transgenic tobacco lines showed inducibility of the *Pschi4* transgene in response to chitosan treatment (Table 1). Two of the nine lines showed higher apparent expression of the transgene in chitosan-treated samples, but the RNA samples were unequally loaded which made interpretation of the results ambiguous. *Pschi4* mRNA levels also increased after mechanical wounding (data not shown), indicating that the regulatory region of *Pschi4* also contains a wound-response element. As expected, samples from tobacco plants transformed with pCIB10 only (which lacks the *Pschi4* gene) showed no signal on the RNA gel blots. This result confirmed that the mRNA transcripts we detected with our probe were in fact *Pschi4* transcripts, and were not transcripts from related chitinase genes in tobacco.

A model for an inducible signal transduction pathway

Models are useful frameworks for conducting experiments, and serve to illustrate emerging ideas about how inducible signal transduction pathways are regulated. Based on our results, we developed a model for the proteins that interact in a chitosan-activated signal transduction pathway (Figure 1). Cells contain a chitosan receptor in the plasmamembrane, a complex of two proteins (an activator and an inhibitor) in the cytoplasm, and PR (pathogen-related, e.g., Pschi4) genes in the nucleus. In uninduced cells, no signal flux occurs to the nucleus because the activator protein is bound to an inhibitor protein. In the induced state, the chitosan:receptor complex alters the conformation of the receptor protein, allowing it to phosphorylate the inhibitor protein. There is no direct evidence for a specific chitosan receptor, but there is evidence that plant cells can specifically recognize the general elicitor chitin at picomolar concentrations (Felix et al., 1993). Upon phosphorylation, the inhibitor protein dissociates from the activator protein, exposing a nuclear localization signal on the activator.

The activator diffuses into the nucleus, where it interacts with the promoter region of one or more PR genes and recruits the transcriptional apparatus. The components of the model are based on the NF-kB proteins that mediate responses to acute oxidative stress in animal systems (Thanos and Maniatis, 1995).

CONCLUSION

Pathways induced by general elicitors and wounding are conserved

We identified a gene from pine trees that is strongly up-regulated during an induced defense response to chitosan. Upon transfer into transgenic tobacco plants, the gene remains responsive to chitosan. These data indicate that the signal transduction pathway that activates the gene in pine cells is very similar in tobacco, suggesting functional homology between the components of the signal transduction pathway in gymnosperms and angiosperms. Our major conclusion is that aggressor perception mechanisms appear to be highly conserved in higher plants, based on our observations that an inducible gene from a gymnosperm is properly regulated in an evolutionarily distant angiosperm.

These results have important implications for aggressor perception mechanisms in trees. If *Pschi4* was not chitosan induced in tobacco, it would seem likely that pines utilized signaling components that were different than those in angiosperms. Our observation that *Pschi4* is properly regulated by chitosan and by wounding in tobacco suggests that mechanisms for general perception of aggressors are conserved in modern day pines and distantly related angiosperms. If our supposition is correct -- that the inducible pathways in angiosperms and gymnosperms are similar -- then the genes that regulate inducible defense responses are likely to be similar in pines and in angiosperms like tobacco (and by extension, *Arabidopsis*).

A model provides a context for genetic interpretation and hypothesis testing

The model helps illustrate that inducible signaling is under genetic control, and guides our expectations as to the type of genetic variation that is possible in forest trees. Because the pathway is composed of both positively acting components (receptor and activator) and negatively acting components (inhibitor), the inducibility of the pathway is tightly regulated. Because signal transduction pathways are composed of proteins, the genes that encode those proteins are subject to mutation. When a mutation renders a signal transduction protein nonfunctional, that mutation can affect signal flux through the signal transduction pathway.

We hasten to add that the model is probably too simple, with too few proteins involved. For example, *Pschi4* mRNA increases 3 hours after chitosan treatment (Wu *et al.*,

1997), whereas this pathway would be expected to be induced within seconds or minutes. This suggests there are probably additional steps that occur between chitosan recognition and *Pschi4* transcription. In addition, only protein components are included in the model; other molecules (*e.g.*, salicylic acid, active oxygen and/or jasmonic acid) probably play key roles. These caveats notwithstanding, the model provides a framework to better understand the genetic basis of inducible defense responses. We cite two examples of genetic variants in *Arabidopsis thaliana* to illustrate this point.

Genetic variation in signal transduction pathways

Single gene mutations can have dramatic effects on inducible defenses. Two lines of *Arabidopsis* are particularly informative. One of these lines (*npr1*) contains a mutation in a gene that makes the plant a ***n***on-expressor of ***p***athogen-***r***elated genes (Cao *et al.*, 1994). This genotype is unable to induce PR genes -- part of its defense response -- when challenged by an aggressor. Loss of pathway inducibility implies that the mutation destroyed a protein that promotes signal flux through the pathway (a non-functional activator would be unable to stimulate PR gene transcription, even when free from the inhibitor). The defective and the functional copies of the *npr1* gene have now been cloned, and as predicted, the normal protein functions similarly to the activator proposed in Fig. 1 (Cao *et al.*, 1997).

Another line (*cpr1*) contains a mutation in a gene that makes the plant a ***c***onstitutive expressor of ***p***athogen-***r***elated genes (Bowling *et al.*, 1994). Constitutive regulation of a normally inducible pathway implies that the mutation destroyed a protein that normally acts to inhibit signal flux through the pathway (a non-functional inhibitor would create a large pool of unbound activator, which would constitutively stimulate PR gene transcription). The cloning of the *cpr1* gene has not yet been reported. Interestingly, *Arabidopsis* lines that exhibit constitutive defenses are stunted compared to their wild-type counterparts (Bowling *et al.*, 1994), which would be expected if there is a carbon cost associated with constitutive defense. Such lines would be useful to quantify those energetic costs.

These *Arabidopsis* mutant lines illustrate that the physiological capacity of a plant to induce a defense response is under the control of genes. There are many unanswered questions regarding how much genetic variation exists in trees with respect to inducible defenses, and most importantly how that genetic variation impacts tree:phytophage interactions. If inducible defense signal transduction pathways are conserved in trees and herbs (as our data imply), then cloning the relevant genes in *Arabidopsis* will accelerate the pace of gene discovery in trees. Cloning the tree genes should help address some important fundamental questions, and ultimately make these pathways subject to manipulation in transgenic trees to improve tolerance to aggressors.

ACKNOWLEDGMENTS

We gratefully acknowledge support from the USDA-Forest Service (North Central and Southern stations).

REFERENCES

BOWLING S.A., GUO A., CAO H., GORDON A.S., KLESSIG D.F., DONG X. 1994. A mutation in *Arabidopsis* that leads to constitutive expression of systemic acquired resistance. *The Plant Cell*, 6, 1845-1857.

CAO H., BOWLING S.A., GORDON A.S., DONG X. 1994. Characterization of an *Arabidopsis* mutant that is nonresponsive to inducers of systemic acquired resistance. *The Plant Cell*, 6, 1583-1592.

CAO H., GLAZEBROOK J., CLARKE J.D., VOLKO S., DONG X.N. 1997. The *Arabidopsis NPR1* gene that controls systemic acquired resistance encodes a novel protein containing ankyrin repeats. *Cell*, 88, 57-63.

DAVIS J.M., CLARKE H.R.G., BRADSHAW H.D. JR, GORDON, M.P. 1991. *Populus* chitinase genes: structure, expression, and similarity of translated sequences to herbaceous plant chitinases. *Plant Molecular Biology*, 17, 631-639.

FELIX G., REGENESS M., BOLLER T. 1993. Specific perception of subnanomolar concentrations of chitin fragments by tomato cells: induction of extracellular alkalinization, changes in protein phosphorylation, and establishment of a refractory state. *Plant Journal*, 4, 307-316.

LESNEY M.S. 1989. Growth responses and lignin production in cell suspensions of *Pinus elliottii* elicited by chitin, chitosan, or mycelium of *Cronartium quercuum* f.sp. *fusiforme*. *Plant Cell Tissue and Organ Culture*, 19, 23-31.

MASON M.E., DAVIS J.M. 1997. Defense response in slash pine: chitosan treatment alters the abundance of specific mRNAs. *Molecular Plant-Microbe Interactions*, 10, 135-137.

POPP M.P., LESNEY M.S., DAVIS J.M. 1997. Defense responses elicited in pine cell suspension cultures. *Plant Cell, Tissue and Organ Culture*, 47, 199-206.

STINTZI A., HEITZ T., PRASAD V., WEIDEMANN-MERDINOGLU S., KAUFFMANN S., GEOFFROY P., LEGRAND M., FRITIG B. 1993. Plant pathogenesis-related proteins and their role in defense against pathogens. *Biochimie*, 75, 687-706.

THANOS D., MANIATIS T. 1995. NF-kB: a lesson in family values. *Cell*, 80, 529-532.

WU H., ECHT, C.S., POPP M.P., DAVIS J.M. 1997. Molecular cloning, structure and expression of an elicitor-inducible chitinase gene from pine trees. *Plant Molecular Biology*, 33, 979-987.

Physiology and Genetics of Tree-Phytophage Interactions
Gujan (France), August 31 - September 5, 1997
Ed. INRA, Paris, 1999 (Les Colloques, n°90)

What do low-density inoculations with fungus tell us about fungal virulence and tree resistance?

P. KROKENE[1], H. SOLHEIM

Norwegian Forest Research Institute N-1432 Ås, Norway

[1] Corresponding author: telephone 4764 949090,
fax 4764 942980, e-mail paal.krokene@nisk.no

RESUME

The length of phloem necrosis induced by low-density inoculation (less than ca. 20 inoc./tree) of blue-stain fungi is often used as a measure of fungal virulence or level of tree resistance, with longer lesions implying a more virulent fungus or a physiologically weaker host tree. Although the rationale for using necrosis length as a measure of virulence or resistance seems clear, low-density fungal inoculations in Norway spruce (*Picea abies*) do not always give results that are consistent with results from studies using other inoculation techniques. In trees inoculated at low densities (3 inoc./fungus/tree) with four different species of blue-stain fungi *Ceratocystis polonica*, a virulent blue-stain fungus associated with the spruce bark beetle *Ips typographus*, did not induce significantly longer necroses than the other, less virulent blue-stain fungi. However, when the same fungi were mass-inoculated into trees (at about 270 inoc./tree) *C. polonica* induced much longer phloem necroses than the other fungi, and it also induced more extensive symptoms in the cambium and sapwood. When the resistance of 20 different Norway spruce clones was tested using either a few (12) or many (about 170) *C. polonica* inoculations per tree, necrosis lengths induced by the two different treatments were only weakly correlated. These results suggest that phloem necrosis length following low-density inoculations is not always an accurate estimate of fungal virulence or tree resistance. Mass-inoculation, which overwhelms the total defensive capacity of susceptible trees, probably better estimates fungal virulence and tree resistance. Furthermore, host symptoms in the sapwood and fungal colonisation of sapwood may be more relevant measures of virulence or resistance, since the cause of death of trees colonised by blue-stain fungi seems to be disruption of sapwood water transport.

INTRODUCTION

Phytopathogenic fungi associated with aggressive bark beetles are thought to assist the beetles in overcoming the resistance of their conifer host trees (Hemingway *et al.*, 1977; Whitney, 1982; Stephen *et al.*, 1993). The fungi in question are mostly blue-stain fungi in the genera *Ceratocystis* and *Ophiostoma* (Harrington, 1993a; 1993b; Paine *et al.*, 1997). Most blue-stain fungi are associated with bark beetles, and most conifer bark beetles vector some species of these fungi (Harrington, 1988; Perry, 1991)

Much effort has been put into determining the pathogenicity of the fungal associates of economically important bark beetle species. The most widely used technique for studying fungal virulence has been to inoculate fungi into the bark of host trees, and to measure the length of the resulting lesions. When conifers are inoculated with a blue-stain fungus at a low density (1 to about 20 inoculations per tree), the tree is always able to confine the fungal infection within discrete lesions produced by the induced wound response (e.g. Berryman, 1972; Paine, 1984; Christiansen *et al.*, 1987; Cook and Hain, 1987; Raffa and Smalley, 1988; Parmeter *et al.*, 1989; Ross *et al.*, 1992; Krokene and Solheim, 1997). With a low number of inoculations the response at each inoculation point probably represents the most efficient defensive response the tree can mobilise towards that particular pathogen (Raffa and Berryman, 1983; Cook and Hain, 1987). If it is assumed that the defensive response of the tree is designed to conserve tissue and energy, it follows that a tree that resists fungal invasion will produce a lesion that is only as large as necessary to confine the fungus. Thus, the efficient response of a resistant tree will produce a small lesion, while a longer lesion generally is considered to imply either a physiologically weaker host tree or a more virulent fungus.

Although the rationale for using phloem necrosis length as a measure of fungal virulence or tree resistance seems clear, we will in this paper show that low-density fungal inoculations not always give reliable estimates of these variables. The system we have studied is Norway spruce (*Picea abies* (L.) Karst.) inoculated with the blue-stain fungus *Ceratocystis polonica* (Siem.) C. Moreau and other fungal associates of different bark beetles colonising this host. *Ceratocystis polonica*, which is associated with the aggressive spruce bark beetle *Ips typographus* L., is the most important fungus in this system. It colonises sapwood and phloem extensively, and may kill healthy trees when inoculated at high densities (Horntvedt *et al.*, 1983; Christiansen, 1985a; Solheim, 1988).

MATERIAL AND METHODS

Experiment 1: Fungal virulence

Norway spruce trees were inoculated with the following four fungi (numbers in parentheses refers to the Culture Collection of Norwegian Forest Research Institute): *Ceratocystis polonica* (93-208/115), *Ophiostoma piceae* (Münch) H. and P. Sydow (94-169/56), an apparent *Ambrosiella* sp. (93-208/44), and a sterile fungus with dark mycelium (Dark sterile sp. A) (94-166/39). The fungi were originally isolated from five species of bark beetles that colonise Norway spruce (Krokene and Solheim, 1996). Trees were inoculated by removing a bark plug with a 5-mm cork borer, inserting inoculum in the wound, and replacing the bark plug. Inoculum consisted of actively growing mycelium on malt agar (2% malt, 1.5% agar) and sterile malt agar as a control.

On May 31 1995, one tree from each of 12 different clones were inoculated three times with each of the four fungi and three times with the control (Krokene and Solheim, 1997). The trees, planted in 1970, were growing in Ås, Norway. Tree diameter at breast height (DBH) ranged from 12.4 to 18.2 cm. The 15 inoculations per tree were evenly distributed in three rings encircling the stem at 1, 1.5 and 2 m height, with each fungus and the control occurring once in each ring. Trees were felled 5 weeks after inoculation and three 15-cm stem sections containing the inoculations were removed from each tree and taken to the laboratory. The bark around each inoculation point was removed to the sapwood and full length of the necroses was measured on the phloem surface. The sapwood was split radially through the inoculation point to measure depth of desiccated sapwood beneath each inoculation.

On June 5-7 1995, 40 trees of similar size (range DBH 16.4-19.4 cm) and age (range 35-48 yr) were selected from a stand in Ås, Norway. The trees were mass-inoculated at 400 inoculations/m^2 over a 1.2 m wide band from about 0.8 to 2 m above ground with the four fungi and the control (Krokene and Solheim, 1998). Eight trees were randomly assigned to each of the five treatments. On September 12-13, we removed the outer bark over six of the uppermost and six of the lowermost inoculation sites on each tree and measured maximum length of the necrosis surrounding each inoculation point. Necrosis length was measured from the centre of the inoculation wound and in one direction away from the inoculated band. This was done because necroses often coalesce in the inoculation band on trees inoculated with *C. polonica*. Trees were felled 15 weeks after inoculation. From the central 0.6 m of the inoculated stem sections we cut two 5 mm thick stem disks about 0.1 m from the upper and lower end. The area of blue-stained sapwood was outlined on the upper surface of each disk, and the surface area was determined with a computer-connected planimeter (Krokene and Solheim, 1998). Along the circumference of each disk we measured the fraction of living and dead cambium. On each 0.6 m section we removed the outer bark and traced all phloem necroses in a 0.062 m^2 area onto clear plastic foil. Total area of dead phloem was later determined from the foils by planimetry.

All data were analysed using ANOVA (Krokene and Solheim, 1997; 1998). Analyses were performed with the general linear models (GLM) procedure of SAS (SAS Institute, 1987).

Experiment 2: Tree resistance

In 1995, five ramets were selected from each of 20 Norway spruce clones growing in Ås, Norway, and inoculated with *C. polonica* (93-208/115). The trees, planted in 1970, had a DBH of about 14 cm and were about 13 m high. On 31 May–2 June, two ramets were selected from each clone and mass-inoculated at 400 inoculations/m^2 in the same way as described for experiment 1. Trees were felled 16 weeks after mass inoculation, and phloem necrosis length and blue-stained sapwood area were measured as for the mass-inoculated trees in experiment 1. On 19–20 June, the remaining three ramets from each clone were inoculated with six inoculations per ring in two rings encircling the stem at 2 and 2.5 m height. Four months later we removed the outer bark over the inoculation sites and measured full phloem necrosis length. Mean length of phloem necrosis in the low-density inoculated ramets was compared with mean necrosis length or mean percent blue-stained sapwood in the mass-inoculated ramets of the same clone using linear regression. Analyses were performed with JMP (SAS Institute, 1989).

RESULTS

Experiment 1: Fungal virulence

In the low-density inoculated trees there was little variation in phloem necrosis length between the different fungi. Five weeks after inoculation, necroses induced by *C. polonica*

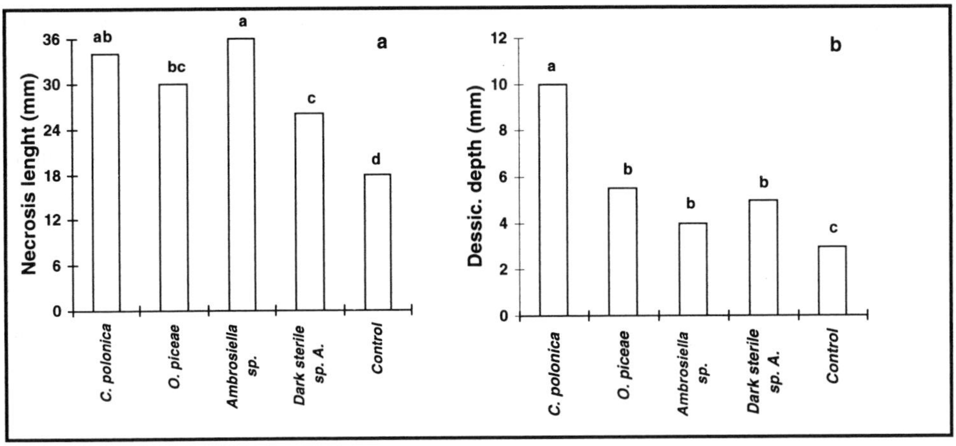

Figure 1. Phloem necrosis length (a) and sapwood desiccation depth (b) in Norway spruce 5 weeks after inoculation with four different blue-stain fungi and sterile agar control. Treatments within (a) and (b) with the same letter are not significantly different (Duncan's multiple range test at $p < 0.05$ following ANOVA).

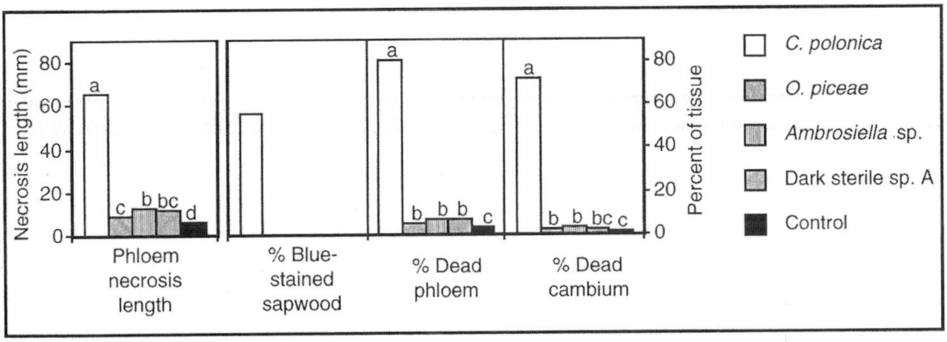

Figure 2.: Different criteria of fungal colonisation success measured 15 weeks after mass-inoculation of Norway spruce with four different blue-stain fungi and sterile agar control. For the different criteria columns with the same letter are not significantly different (Duncan's multiple range test at $p < 0.05$ following ANOVA).

were not significantly longer than those induced by *O. piceae* and the unidentified *Ambrosiella* species (Fig. 1a). Depth of desiccated sapwood differed more between treatments, with *C. polonica* inducing significantly deeper desiccation then all other treatments (Fig. 1b).

In the mass-inoculated trees *C. polonica* induced much longer phloem necroses than the other fungi, and it also induced more extensive symptoms in the sapwood and cambium. It was the only fungus that caused blue-stain, and it induced 21 times more dead cambium circumference, 11 times more dead phloem surface area and five times longer phloem necroses than any other fungus (Fig. 2). The other fungi differed very little in pathogenicity. They were all significantly different from the control, except for percent dead cambium for the dark sterile fungus (Fig. 2).

Experiment 2: Tree resistance

For the low-density inoculated trees there was relatively little variation in mean phloem necrosis length between ramets within a clone (range SD=0.4-12.7), while the variation between clones was larger (SD=20.7, Fig. 3). In the mass-inoculated ramets there was huge variation in necrosis length both within clones (SD from 0.6 to 409.2) and between clones (SD=149.8, Fig. 3). Seven mass-inoculated ramets that belonged to four different clones with very long phloem necroses (170-810 mm) also had much blue-stained sapwood ($\bar{X}$=75%), indicating that they had been successfully colonised by the fungus.

Overall, there was a weak, but statistically significant correlation between mean phloem necrosis length in low-density and mass-inoculated ramets of the same clone (p=0.01, r^2=0.30, Fig. 3). Many clones that differed much in their response to low-density inoculations produced relatively short and very similar necrosis lengths when they were mass-inoculated (Fig. 3, open symbols). However, six clones produced very long necroses after mass-inoculation, and for these clones there was a stronger, but not significant, correlation between necrosis length in low-density and mass-inoculated ramets (p=0.12, r^2=0.50, Fig. 3). The correlation between symptoms in low-density and mass-inoculated ramets did not improve if necrosis length in low-density inoculated ramets was correlated with percent blue-stained sapwood in mass-inoculated ramets (p=0.04, r^2=0.22, data not shown). Percent blue-stain and necrosis length in the mass-inoculated ramets were strongly correlated ($p<0.00001$, r^2=0.80).

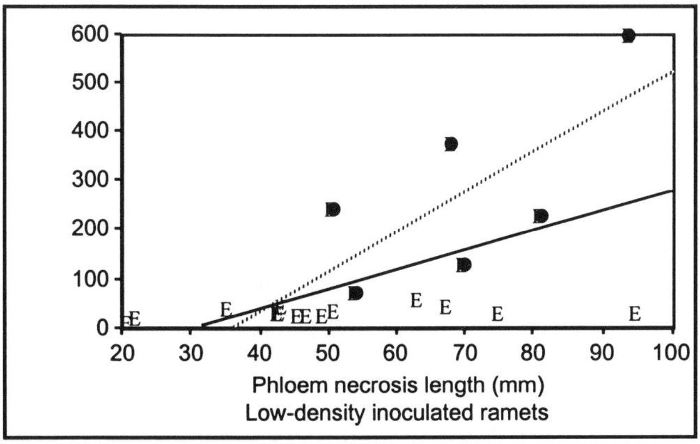

Figure 3. Linear regression of mean phloem necrosis length in 20 Norway spruce clones that were mass-inoculated (ca. 170 inoc./tree) or low-density inoculated (12 inoc./tree) with the blue-stain fungus *Ceratocystis polonica* (continuous line). Two ramets per clone were mass-inoculated and three ramets were low-density inoculated. The dashed line shows the linear regression for six clones (filled symbols) where at least one of the mass-inoculated ramets was successfully colonised by the fungus (i.e. > 40% sapwood area was blue-stained).

DISCUSSION

Phloem necrosis length after low-density inoculations did not give an accurate estimate of the virulence of the different fungi used in experiment 1. The results from the low-density inoculation suggest that *C. polonica* was about equally virulent as the other three blue-stain fungi, but mass-inoculations have shown it to be a much more virulent fungus (Horntvedt *et al.*, 1983; Christiansen, 1985a; Krokene and Solheim, 1998). Previously, *Ophiostoma penicillatum* (Grosm.) Siem., another fungal associate of *I. typographus*, has been shown to induce longer phloem necroses in Norway spruce than *C. polonica*, although it is less able to colonise sapwood and cause tree mortality (Horntvedt *et al.*, 1983; Solheim, 1988). Thus, phloem necrosis length after low-density inoculations is probably not always the best estimate of fungal virulence. Depth of desiccated sapwood after low-density inoculations seems to be more useful in determining the virulence of different fungi.

Phloem necrosis length after low-density inoculations did not accurately predict the clones' resistance to massive fungal infection. Similar results have been obtained for lodgepole pine *Pinus contorta* Douglas var. *latifolia* Engelmann inoculated with *O. clavigerum* (Robinson-Jeffrey and Davids.) Harrington (Raffa and Berryman, 1982a). Phloem necrosis length after low-density inoculations could not be used to distinguish between trees that were resistant and susceptible to subsequent mass-attack by *Dendroctonus ponderosae* Hopkins. However, concentration and rate of accumulation of monoterpenes inside necroses successfully predicted tree resistance (Raffa and Berryman, 1982a; 1982b). Resin concentration in phloem necroses has also been found to correlate with resistance of Norway spruce towards mass-inoculation with *C. polonica* (Christiansen, 1985b).

Overwhelmed host defences may be one explanation for the weak correlation between the results obtained with low-density inoculation and mass-inoculation. All trees seem to have a threshold of successful infection, and below this threshold the tree is able to resist fungal infection and confine all attacks within relatively short reaction zones (e.g. Christiansen *et al.*, 1987, Raffa and Berryman, 1983). Above the threshold the fungus breaks through the reaction zones, colonises phloem and sapwood extensively and eventually kills the tree. Thus, after mass-inoculation we would expect resistant trees to produce relatively short necroses, while susceptible trees that are overwhelmed by the fungus will produce very long necroses. Mass-inoculation, which overwhelms the total defensive capacity of susceptible trees, probably better estimates fungal pathogenicity and tree resistance than low-density inoculations.

There are more aspects of fungal pathogenicity than only the ability to colonise phloem and induce phloem necroses. The most pathogenic blue-stain fungi associates of several aggressive bark beetles seem to be quite tolerant to low oxygen levels, and this probably enables them to be the first colonisers of sapwood of attacked trees (Solheim, 1991; 1992; 1995; Solheim and Krokene, 1998). Amount of blue-stained sapwood or extent of fungal penetration into sapwood may be more relevant measures of fungal virulence, since the primary cause of death of trees colonized by blue-stain fungi seems to be disruption of sapwood water transport and not girdling of the phloem (Reid *et al.*, 1967; Fares *et al.*, 1980; Ross *et al.*, 1992). In experiment 1, depth of desiccated sapwood in the low-density inoculated trees agreed better with what is known about the relative pathogenicity of the experimental fungi than phloem necrosis length.

REFERENCES

BERRYMAN A.A., 1972. Resistance of conifers to invasion by bark beetle-fungus associations. *BioScience*, 22, 598-602.

CHRISTIANSEN E., 1985a. *Ips/Ceratocystis*-infection of Norway spruce: what is a deadly dosage? *Z. ang. Ent.*, 99, 6-11.

CHRISTIANSEN E., 1985b. *Ceratocystis polonica* inoculated in Norway spruce: blue-staining in relation to inoculum density, resinosis and tree growth. *Eur. J. For. Path.*, 15, 160-167.

CHRISTIANSEN E., WARING R.H., BERRYMAN A.A., 1987. Resistance of conifers to bark beetle attack: searching for general relationships. *For. Ecol. Manage.*, 22, 89-106.

COOK S.P., HAin F.P.., 1987. Susceptibility of trees to southern pine beetle, *Dendroctonus frontalis* (Coleoptera: Scolytidae). *Environ. Entomol.*, 16, 9-14.

FARES Y., GOESCHL J.D.., SHARPE P.J.H., 1980. Dynamics of bark beetle-fungus symbiosis. I. Pine tree anatomy and fungus growth pattern. *In* Stephen F.M., Searcy J.L., Hertel G.D. (Ed.) : *Modeling southern pine beetle populations. Symp. Proc.* Asheville, N. C., USDA For. Serv. Tech. Bull. No. 1630, p. 54-60.

HARRINGTON T.C., 1988. *Leptographium* species, their distributions, hosts and insect vectors. *In* Harrington T.C., Cobb F.W., Jr. (Ed.) : Leptographium *root diseases in conifers.* St. Paul, Minnesota, APS Press, p. 1-39.

HARRINGTON T.C., 1993a. Biology and taxonomy of fungi associated with bark beetles. In Schowalter T.D., Filip G.M. (Ed.) : Beetle - pathogen *interactions in conifer forests.* London, Academic Press, p. 37-58.

HARRINGTON T.C ., 1993b. Diseases of conifers caused by species of *Ophiostoma* and *Leptographium. In* Wingfield M.J., Seifert K.A., Webber J.F. (Ed.) : *Ceratocystis and Ophiostoma. Taxonomy, ecology, and pathogenicity.* St. Paul, Minnesota, APS Press, p. 161-172.

HEMINGWAY R.W., MCGRAW G.W., BARRAS S.J., 1977. Polyphenols in *Ceratocystis minor* infected *Pinus taeda*: fungal metabolites, phloem and xylem phenols. *J. Agric. Food Chem.*, 25, 717-722.

HORNTVEDT R., CHRISTIANSEN E., SOLHEIM H., WANG S., 1983. Artificial inoculation with *Ips typographus*-associated blue-stain fungi can kill healthy Norway spruce trees. *Medd. Nor. Inst. Skogforsk.*, 38, 1-20.

KROKENE P., SOLHEIM H., 1996. Fungal associates of five bark beetle species colonizing Norway spruce. *Can. J. For. Res.*, 26, 2115-2122.

KROKENE P., SOLHEIM H., 1997. Growth of four bark beetle-vectored blue-stain fungi in relation to the induced wound response in Norway spruce. *Can. J. Bot.*, 75, 618-625.

KROKENE P., SOLHEIM H. , 1998. Phytopathogenicity of four blue-stain fungi associated with aggressive and non-aggressive bark beetles. *Phytopathology*, 88, 39-44.

PAINE T.D., 1984. Seasonal response of ponderosa pine to inoculation of the mycangial fungi from the western pine beetle. *Can. J. Bot.*, 62, 551-555.

PAINE T.D., RAFFA K.F., HARRINGTON T.C., 1997. Interactions among scolytid bark beetles, their associated fungi, and live host conifers. *Ann. Rev. Entomol.*, 42, 179-206.

PARMETER J.R. Jr., SLAUGHTER G.W., CHEN M., WOOD D.L.., STUBBS H.A., 1989. Single and mixed inoculations of ponderosa pine with fungal associates of *Dendroctonus* spp. *Phytopathology*, 79, 768-772.

PERRY T.J., 1991. *A synopsis of the taxonomic revisions in the genus* Ceratocystis *including a review of bluestaining species associated with* Dendroctonus *bark beetles.* USDA For. Serv. Gen. Tech. Rep. SO-86, 16 p.

RAFFA K.F., BERRYMAN A.A., 1982a. Physiological differences between lodgepole pines resistant and susceptible to the mountain pine beetle and associated microorganisms. *Environ. Entomol.*, 11, 486-492.

RAFFA K.F., BERRYMAN A.A., 1982b. Accumulation of monoterpenes and associated volatiles following inoculation of grand fir with a fungus transmitted by the fir engraver *Scolytus ventralis* (Coleoptera: Scolytidae). *Can. Ent.*, 114, 797-810.

RAFFA K.F., BERRYMAN A.A., 1983. Physiological aspects of lodgepole pine wound responses to a fungal symbiont of the mountain pine beetle, *Dendroctonus ponderosae* (Coleoptera: Scolytidae). *Can. Ent.*, 115, 723-734.

RAFFA K.F., SMALLEY E.B., 1988. Response of red and jack pines to inoculation with microbial associates of the pine engraver, *Ips pini* (Coleoptera: Scolytidae). *Can. J. For. Res.*, 18, 581-586.

REID R.W., WHITNEY H.S., WATSON J.A., 1967. Reactions of lodgepole pine to attack by *Dendroctonus ponderosae* Hopkins and blue stain fungi. *Can. J. Bot.*, 45, 1115-1126.

ROSS D.W., FENN P., STEPHEN F.M., 1992. Growth of southern pine beetle associated fungi in relation to the induced wound response in loblolly pine. *Can. J. For. Res.*, 22, 1851-1859.

SAS INSTITUTE, 1987. *SAS/STAT™ guide for personal computers, version 6 edition.* SAS Institute Inc., Cary, NC, 1028 p.

SAS INSTITUTE, 1989. *JMP* user's *guide*. SAS Institute Inc., Cary, NC, 584 p.

SOLHEIM H., 1988. Pathogenicity of some *Ips typographus*-associated blue-stain fungi to Norway spruce. *Medd. Nor. Inst.* Skogforsk., 40, 1-11.

SOLHEIM H., 1991. Oxygen deficiency and spruce resin inhibition of growth of fungi associated with *Ips typographus*. Mycol. *Res.*, 95, 1387-1392.

SOLHEIM H., 1992. The early stages of fungal invasion in Norway spruce infested by the bark beetle *Ips typographus. Can. J. Bot.*, 70, 1-5.

SOLHEIM H., 1995. A comparison of blue-stain fungi associated with the North-American spruce beetle *Dendroctonus rufipennis* and the Eurasian spruce bark beetle *Ips typographus. In* Aamlid D. (Ed.) : *Forest pathology* research *in the Nordic countries 1994.* Aktuelt fra Skogforsk 4, p. 61-67.

SOLHEIM H., KROKENE P., 1998. Growth and virulence of mountain pine beetle associated blue-stain fungi, *Ophiostoma* clavigerum and *O. montium. Can. J. Bot.*, in press.

STEPHEN F.M., BERISFORD C.W., DAHLSTEN D.L., FENN P., MOSER J.C., 1993. Invertebrate and microbial associates. *In* Schowalter T.D., Filip G.M. (Ed.) : *Beetle - pathogen interactions in conifer forests.* London, Academic Press, p. 129-153.

WHITNEY H.S., 1982. Relationships between bark beetles and symbiotic organisms. *In* Mitton J.B., Sturgeon K.B. (Ed.) : *Bark beetles in North American conifers. A system for the study of evolutionary biology.* Austin, University of Texas Press, p. 183-211.

Physiology and Genetics of Tree-Phytophage Interactions
Gujan (France), August 31 - September 5, 1997
Ed. INRA, Paris, 1999 (Les Colloques, n°90)

Induced resistance against insects in European forest ecosystems

JÖRG LUNDERSTÄDT

Institut für Forestzoologie Büsgenweg 3 D 37077 Göttingen

ABSTRACT

Passive and induced resistance are presented as defence mechanisms against insect feeding using the examples: *Fagus sylvatica – Phyllaphis fagi, Fagus sylvatica – Cryptococcus fagisuga, Larix decidua – Colephora laricella, Larix decidua – Ips cambrae, Picea abies – Ips typographus* and *Pinus sylvestris – Lymantria monacha.* The dependence of the type of resistance with respect to genotype and physiological age of the host tree, intensity of the attack by phytopages, site stand treatment, and weather are discussed from an ecosystemic point of view.

INTRODUCTION

Mass outbreaks of phytophagous insects are an integral component of stand life of natural and commercial forests (Schimitscheck, 1969 ; Duncan and Hodson, 1958 ; Benz, 1974 ; Mattson and Addy, 1975). A key position for a feedback-controlled, resource-adjusted plant growth is held in by many insects bound species-specifically to the natural development stages of forests (young growth, brushwood, high polewood, mature forest) ; (Schowalter et al., 1991 ; Wickmann, 1980 ; McNaughton, 1983).

The regulation of the amount of plant biomass transferred into phytophagous biomass is bound to different grades of resistance depending on whether the impact of the phytophagous is disenhancing, neutral, or enhancing for the plant. In the latter case the individual plants will exhibit on the population level a spectrum of drifting transitions from resistant to susceptible stages depending on the genetic, time, and space structure of the stand.

Two groups of natural compounds are involved predominantly in the resistance reaction : proteins as biocatalysts in the metabolic turnover and urgently required source for the synthesis of animal mass, and secondary compounds as inhibitors of enzyme activity and of the protein transfer from the plant to the animal.

It is the aim of this paper to demonstrate different aspects of defence mechanisms after attack by insects of four main European forest species, i. e. larch (*Larix decidua*), beech (*Fagus sylvatica*), spruce (*Picea abies*) and Scot pine (*Pinus sylvestris*).

RESULTS

The resistance reaction is dependent on the physiological age of the host

The varying readiness for the activation of induced resistance as dependent on physiological age is demonstrated with Fagus sylvatica seedlings and 10-15 year old beech saplings which were infected at the same time and at the same location with Phyllaphis fagi, a leaf phloem feeder (Gora *et al* , 1994a). The procyanidin titre is raised moderately in the leaves of seedlings and saplings. This is a general, undirected wound reaction due to the puncture wounds at beginning of the feeding process. However, stronger changes occur at the specific location of the actual interaction, i. e. the phloem. In the phloem of seedlings, the defence by procyanidins is started by the fourfold raised level of their precursor, quinic acid. But, by this time, the defence reaction in saplings is already completed, the level of quinic acid is lowered to zero, and the procyanidin titre has been elevated up to 20 fold, depending on the infestation intensity.

The same principle is observed after the attack of *Larix decidua* needles by *Coleophora laricella*, a needle miner (Habermann, 1995). In young trees (4 year olds) an immediate systemic reaction in the attacked as well as in the unattacked needles of the whole tree is induced, the procyanidin contents are elevated, the protein contents are lowered. In older trees a two-step reaction occurs. In the first step, up to 25% of the needles are dropped, causing a high mortality rate of the mining larvae. In the second step the procyanidin titre is raised to 10 fold over 3 years while the protein content is lowered continuously. The effectiveness of this defence becomes obvious in the tendency towards a decrease of the mines infestation two years later and the collapse of its population 5 years later.

Gradation of the induced resistance reation

Gradation of induced resistance and simultaneous intensification of passive resistance occur after attacks of varying intensity on *Larix decidua* by *Ips cembrae*, and on *Picea abies* by *I. typographus*, both bark phloem feeders (Rohde et al., 1996). Independent of an attack the procyanidin titre in the phloem of larcn is markedly raised and the protein titre is lowered during the flight periods of the beetle (May and August). Dependent on the actual infestation density at the time of attack this reaction is markedly intensified by induced resistance, then persisting on a high level for at least one year.

Comparative studies of the carbohydrate, protein and procyanidin contents in uninfested tissue, and infested tissue at a decreasing distance from the site of atack by Ips cembrae on larch and by *Ips typographus* on spruce demonstrate the very high energy requirements of the induced defense reaction (Jung et al., 1994), Rohde *et al.*, 1996).

The resistance reaction on a population level

The system *Fagus sylvatica* and *Cryptococcus fagisuga*, a bark parenchyma feeder, shows that induced resistance is not a static process because a temporary reinforcing defensive reaction develops in addition to passive resistance (Gora *et al.*, 1996). In a sample of 419 mature trees, the infestation status was constant or oscillated during a 5-year period in 50% of the trees. In the other half there was either decreasing or increasing infestations. On six pairs of beeches which were uninfested and infested, respectively, in 1989 an increase of the infestation occurred in the formerly uninfested trees until 1993, accompanied by a general increase of the procyanidin titre and a parallel decrease of the protein titre. Within the procyanidin fraction the concentration of glucodistylin and taxifolin increased while the concentration of cis-coniferin decreased (Dübeler *et al.*, 1997).

Induced resistance as influenced by abiotic parameters

The influence of weather conditions in different years and of specific site qualities is demonstrated in an eight year investigation into the physiological age class bond between the flushing status of beech and their infestation status by *Cryptococcus fagisuga* (Lunderstädt, in press). The regression lines for both parameters under varied conditions (8 years, six sites, two thinning regimes, three diameter classes) represent a measure of the stand dependence on the induced resistance and can be arranged in a continuous order showing the promotion of the infestation by accelerated flushing in cool, unthinned valley positions to promotion of the infestation by reduced flushing on warm, thinned plateau positions.

Induced resistance as influenced by stand treatment

The pattern of attack and resistance can be altered artificially by changing the micro stand and the competition status by thinning. This is shown with the example of the non moth, *Lymantria monacha* and Scots pine (Hagermann and Bester, 1997). Large numbers of trees of poor growth and therefore of poor resistance form attraction centres for the nun moth. These centres are subjected to a high probability of heavy defoliation and little or no probability of regeneration. Trees with a high social position are surrounded by trees with a low social position the insect pressure is concentrated noticeably on the latter because induced resistance which will be developed in trees of all social positions is expressed much more strongly in the members of the higher social classes. Ideally, the aggressiveness of the nun moth population will be reduced by the stronger physiological resistance of these trees and will be diverted during the retrogradation phase onto the weaker and suppressed trees.

DISCUSSION

The possible ecosystemic role of induced resistance

From an ecosystemic point of view, resistance must be considered as a limited evolutionary barrier, susceptibility as a limited evolutionary gate. Because of this inconstancy of either traits within a natural population, different types of resistance and susceptibility are coexistent. Passive resistance is directed against disturbing events which vary in their frequency and intensity within the statistical norm of stand life. The respective defence processes are integrated into the framework of the general plant metabolism, demanding a bearable share within the common metabolic output for growth, reproduction, and defense. However, if disturbing effects occur as single events (like weather abnormalities) in overstocked stands with high intraspecific competition, a reaction cascade is released. The resulting answer in the form of induced resistance ifs effective but metabolically expensive. Therefore, it an only last for a single individual for a relatively short period.

A shown in the example of the trend analysis of the Cryptococcus infestation in a beech stand during 5 years (Gora *et al.*, 1996), by the analysis of the genetical background of resistance of the respective trees (Gora *et al.*, 1994b) and by their spatial distribution in time (Gora et al., 1996) the ecological mechanism of keeping up an effective level of induced resistance could be as follows : induced resistance is activated to a different degree in changing members of the tree population by reducing the infestation of single individuals and spreading the infestation pressure on others within the whole host population, thus counteracting inter- and intraspecific competition within the plant community of the stand. In commercial forests the competition status can by modified by man.

REFERENCES

BENZ G., 1974. Negative Rückkoppelung durch Raum- und Nahrungskonkurrenz sowie zyklische Veränderungen der Nahrungsgrundlage als Regelprinzip in der Populationsdynamik es Grauen Lärchenwidklers *Zeiraphera diniana* (Guenée) (Lep., Tortricidae). *Z. ang. Ent.* 76, 196-228.

DÜBELER A., VOLTMER G., GORA,V., LUNDERSTÄDT J., ZEECK A., 1997. Phenols from *Fagus sylvatica* and their role in defence against *Cryptococcus fagisuga*. *Phytochemistry* 45, 51-57.

DUNCAN D. P., HODSON A. C., 1958. Interference of the forest tent caterpillar upon the aspen forests of Minnesota. *Forest science* 4, 71-93.

GORA V., KÖNIG J., LUNDERSTÄDT J., 1994a. Physiological defence reactions of young beech trees (*Fagus sylvatica*) to attack by *Phyllaphis fagi*. *For. Ecol. Manage.* 70, 245-254.

GORA V., STARKE R., ZIEHE M., KÖNIG J., MÜLLER-STARCK G., LUNDERSTÄDT J., 1994b. Influence of genetic structures and silvicultural treatments in a beech stand (*Fagus sylvatica*) on the population dynamics of beech scale (*Cryptococcus fagisuga*) *For. Genet.* 1, 157-164.

GORA V., KÖNIG J., LUNDERSTÄDT J., 1996. Population dynamics of beech scale (*Cryptococcus fagisuga*) (Coccina, Pseudococcidae) related to physiological defence reactions of attacked beech trees (*Fagus sylvatica*). *Chemoecology* 7, 112-120.

HABERMANN M., 1995. Physiologische Reacktionen in Lärchennadeln (*Larix* spp.) nach Befall durch die Lärchenminiermotte *Coleophora laricella* Hbn (Lepidoptera, Coleophoridae). *Mitt. Dtsch. Ges. allg. angew.* Ent. 10, 91-94.

HABERMANN M., BESTER R., 1997. Influence of stand structure and needle physiology on the development of outbreaks of the nun moth (*Lymantria monacha* L.) in pine stands (*Pinus sylvestris* L.) in a permanently damaged area of Lower Saxony. *Allg. Forst- u. J. Ztg.* 168, 157-162.

JUNG P., ROHDE M., LUNDERSTÄDT J., 1994. Induzierte Resistenz im Leitgewebe der europäischen Lärche Larix decidua (Mill) nach Befall durch den großen Lärchenborkenkäfer *Ips cembrae* (Heer) (Col., Scolytidae). *J. Appl. Ent.* 117, 427-433.

LUNDERSTÄDT J., 1998. Impact of external factors on the population dynamics of beech scale (*Cryptococcus fagisuga*) in beech – (*Fagus sylvatica*) stands during the latency stage. *J. Appl. Ent.*, 122, 319-322.

MATTSON W. I., ADDY N. D., 1975. Phytophagous insects as regulators of forest primary production. *Science* 190, 515-522.

McNAUGHTON S. J., 1983. Compensatory plant growth as a response to herbivory. *Oikos* 40, 329-336.

ROHDE M., WALDMANN R., LUNDERSTÄDT J., 1996. Induced defence reaction in the phloem of spruce (*Picea abies*) and larch (*Larix decidua*) after attack by *Ips typographus* and *Ips cembrae*. *For. Ecol. Manage.* 86, 51-59.

SCHIMITSCHEK E., 1969. *Grundzüge der Waldhygiene*. Paul Parey, Hamburg und Berlin.

SCHOWALTER T. D., SABIN T. E., STAFFORD S. G., SEXTON J. M., 1991. Phytophage effects on primary production, nutrient turnover, and litter decomposition of young Douglas fir in Western Oregon, *For. Ecol. Manage.* 42, 229-243.

WICKMANN B. E., 1980. Increased growth of white fir after a Douglas-fir Tussock Moth outbreak. *J. Forestry* 31-38.

List of participants

ACEBES J.L
Universidad de Leon
Faculdad de Ciencias Biologicas
Departamento de Biologia Animal (Zoologia)
Campus de Vegazana S/N
Leon 24071
Spain

ALFARO Rene
For. Insect Res.
506 W. Burnside Rd.
Pacific Forest Research Centre
Victoria
B. C. V8Z 1M5
Canada

AUGUSTIN Sylvie
Station de Zoologie Forestiere
INRA
Avenue de la Pomme de Pin
BP 20619 ARDON
F-45166 - OLIVET Cedex
France

BAIER Peter
Institute für Forstentomologie, Forstpathologie
und Forstschutz
Universität für Bodenkultur
Hasenauerstraasse 38
A-1190 Wien
Austria

BASTIEN Catherine
Station d'Amélioration des Arbres Forestiers
INRA
Avenue de la Pomme de Pin
BP 20619 ARDON
F-45166 - OLIVET Cedex
France

BERRYMAN Alan A.
Department of Entomology
Forest Entomology Res.
Washington State University
Pullman,
WA 99164-6432
USA

BJÖRKMAN Christer
Department of Entomology
Swedish University of Agricultural Sciences
P.O. Box 7044
S-750 07 Uppsala
Sweden

BOIS Evelyne
Station de Zoologie Forestière
INRA
Avenue de la Pomme de Pin
BP 20619 ARDON
F-45166 - OLIVET Cedex
France

BORG-KARLSON Anna-Karin
Royal Institute of Technology (KTH)
Department of Organic Chemistry
S-10 044 Stockholm
Sweden

BOUHOT-DELDUC Laurence
Dept. de la Sante des Forets
19 Avenue du Maine
Ministère de l'Agriculture
75732 Paris Cedex 15
France

BRATT Katharina
Institute of Chemistry
Department of Organic Chemistry
Uppsala University
P.O. Box 531
S-751 21 Uppsala
Sweden

BRIDGES Robert J.
USDA Forest Service
Forest Insect & Disease Research
P.O. Box 96090
Washington
DC 20090
USA

BURBAN Christian
Unité de Zoologie Forestière
INRA
Domaine de l'Hermitage
Pierroton
F-33610 Cestas
France

BYERS John A.
Swedish Agricultural University
Department of Plant Protection
P.O.Box 44
S-230 53 Alnarp
Sweden

CARCREFF Emmanuel
Unité de Zologie Forestière
INRA
Domaine de l'Hermitage
Pierroton
F-33610 Cestas
France

CHEN Shanna
Yunnan University
Laboratory of Plant Physiology
Kunming
Yunnan
650091
P.R. CHINA

CHRISTIANSEN Erik
Norwegian Forest Reseach Institute
Hogskoloveien 12
P.O. Box 61
N-1432 Ås -NLH
Norway

CLANCY Karen M.
Entomology Research Program
U.S.D.A. Forest Service
Rocky Mountain Forest & Range Exp. Station
Southwest Forest Science Complex
2500 S. Pine Knoll Dr.
Flagstaff
AZ 86001.6381
USA

CROISE Luc
Station de Zoologie Forestière
INRA
Avenue de la Pomme de Pin
BP 20619 ARDON
F-45166 - OLIVET Cedex
France

DAVIS John M.
School of Forest Resources and Conservation
Plant Molecular and Cellular Biology Program
Box 110410
University of Florida
Gainesville FL 32611
USA

DAY Keith R.
Environmental Research
University of Ulster
Coleraine
Northern Ireland BT 52 1SA
United Kingdom

DELPLANQUE Andre
Station de Zoologie Forestiere
INRA
Avenue de la Pomme de Pin
BP 20619 ARDON
F-45166 - OLIVET Cedex
France

DE SOUSA Edmundo M. R.
Departamento de Proteção Florestal
Estação Florestal Nacional
Quinta do Marqês
Rua do Borja 2
P-2780 Oeiras
Portugal

DING Huasun
Yunnan University
Biology Department
Kunming
Yunnan
650091
P.R. CHINA

DREYER Erwin
Station d'Ecophysiologie Forestière
INRA
Centre de Nancy
F-54280 Champenoux
France

FERNANDEZ Mercedes F.
Universidad de Leon
Faculdad de Ciencias Biologicas
Departamento de Biologia Animal (Zoologia)
Campus de Vegazana S/N
Leon 24071
Spain

FOGGO Andrew
Marine Biology and Ecology Group
Department of Biological Sciences
University of Plymouth
Drake Circus
Plymouth
England PL4 8AA
United Kingdom

FÜHRER_Erwin
Institut für Forstentomologie & Forstschutz
Hasenauerstrasse 38
Universität für Bodenkultur
A-1190 Wien
Austria

GERI Claude
Station de Zoologie Forestiere
INRA
Avenue de la Pomme de Pin
BP 20619 ARDON
F-45166 - OLIVET Cedex
France

GREGOIRE J.C.
Lab. de Biologie Animale
CP160/12
Université Libre de Bruxelles
50 Avenue F.D. Roosevelt
B-1050 Bruxelles
Belgique

GUERARD Natacha
Station de Zoologie Forestiere
INRA
Avenue de la Pomme de Pin
BP 20619 ARDON
F-45166 - OLIVET Cedex
France

HAUKIOJA Erkki
Laboratory of Ecological Zoology
Department of Biology
University of Turku
FIN-20500 Turku
Finland

HEIDGER Christa
HTWS (FH)
Zittau/Gorling
Theodor Korner Allee 16
D-02763 Zittau
Deutschland

HERMS Daniel A.
Department of Entomology
Ohio State University - OARDC
Wooster
Ohio 44691
USA

ILLMAN Barbara
Forest Products Laboratory
USDA Forest Service
1 Giffort Pinchot Drive
Madison
WI 53705
USA

JACTEL Hervé
Unité de Zoologie Forestière
INRA
Domaine de L'Hermitage
Pierroton
33610 Cestas
France

KAMATA Naoto
Forest & Forestry Products Research Institute.
Tohoku Research Center
Nabeyashiki 72
Shimokuriyagawa
Morioka
Iwate 020-0123
Japan

KLEIHENTZ Marc
Unité de Zoologie Forestière
INRA
Domaine de L'Hermitage
Pierroton
33610 Cestas
France

KORICHEVA Julia
Department of Entomology
Swedish University of Agricultural Sciences
P.OBox 7044
S-750 07 Uppsala
Sweden

KROKENE Paal
Norwegian Forest Research Institute
Hogskoloveien 12
P.O.Box 61
N-1432 Ås NLH
Norway

KYTO Maarit
Finnish Forest Research Institute
Vantaa Research Center
Jokiniemenkuja 1
P.O. Box 18
FIN 01301 Vantaa
Finland

LÅNGSTRÖM Bo
Division of Forest Entomology
Swedish University of Agricultural Sciences
P.O. Box 7044
S-750 07 Uppsala
Sweden

LAVALLEE Robert
Canadian Forestry Service
C.P. 3800 Sainte-Foy
Quebec G1V 4C7
Canada

LI Lisha
Yunnan Academy of Forest Sciences
Heilontang
Kunming
Yunnan
650204
P.R. China

LIANG Chuan
Forest Protection Division
Department of Yunnan Province
87 qinguam road
Kunming
Yunnan
P.R. China

LIEUTIER François
Station de Zoologie Forestiere
INRA
Avenue de la Pomme de Pin
BP 20619 ARDON
F-45166 - OLIVET Cedex
France

LIU Hongpin
Yunnan Academy of Forest Sciences
Heilontang
Kunming
Yunnan
650204
P.R. China

LORIO Peter L.
USDA Forest Service
SRS-4501
2500 Shreveport Highway
Pineville
LA71360.2009
USA

LOUSTAU Marie-Laure
Station de Pathologie Vegetale
INRA
Domaine de la Grande Ferrade
BP81
33883 Villenave d'Ornon Cedex
France

LUNDERSTÄDT Jorg
Institut Forst Zoologie
Georg-August Universität Göttingen
Busgenweg 3
D-37077 Göttingen
Deutschland

MARTIKAINEN Petri
Department of Ecology and Systematics
Division of Population Biology
POBox 17
University of Helsinki
FIN-00014 Helsinki
Finland

MATTSON William J
Forestry Sciences Laboratory
North Central Forest Research Station
5985 Highway K
Rhinelander
WI 54501
USA

MORAAL Leen G.
Institute for Forestry and Nature Research
(IBN-DLO)
P.O. Box 23
NL-6700 AA WAGENINGEN
The Netherlands

NAGELEISEN Louis Michel
Antenne Spécialisée du DSF
INRA
Centre de Nancy
F-54280 Champenoux
France

NIEMELÄ Pekka
Faculty of Forestry
Forest Protection
University of Joensuu
P.O. Box 111
FIN-08101 Joensuu
Finland

PAN Yongzhi
Southwest Forest College
White Dragon Temple
Kunming
Yunnan
650224
P.R. China

PASHENOVA Nataly V.
Institute of Forest SB RAS
Academgorodok
Krasnoyarsk
RU-660036
Russia

PASQUIER Florence
Station de Zoologie Forestiere
INRA
Avenue de la Pomme de Pin
BP 20619 ARDON
F-45166 - OLIVET Cedex
France

PAYNE Tom
Agricultural Experiment Station
116 Agricultural Administration Building
2120 Fyffe Rd.
Ohio State University
Colombus OH 43210
USA

ROBIN Cecile
Station de Pathologie Végétale
INRA
Domaine de la Grande Ferrade
B.P. 84
33883 Villenave d'Ornon Cedex
France

RODEN David
Great Lakes Forestry Research Center
P.O. Box 490
Canadian Forestry Service
Sault Ste Marie
Ontario P6A5M7
Canada

ROQUES Alain
Station de Zoologie Forestiere
INRA
Avenue de la Pomme de Pin
BP 20619 ARDON
F-45166 - OLIVET Cedex
France

ROUSI Matti
Finnish Forest Research Institute
Punkaharju Research Station
Finlandiantie 18
FI-58450 Punkaharju
Finland

ROUSSELET Jerome
Station de Zoologie Forestiere
INRA
Avenue de la Pomme de Pin
BP 20619 ARDON
F-45166 - OLIVET Cedex
France

SOUSA SANTOS Maria Nartecia
Departamento de Proteção Florestal
Estação Florestal Nacional
Quinta do Marqês
Rua do Borja 2
P-2780 Oeiras
Portugal

SAUVARD Daniel
Station de Zoologie Forestiere
INRA
Avenue de la Pomme de Pin
BP 20619 ARDON
F-45166 - OLIVET Cedex
France

SCHLYTER Fredrik
Chemical Ecology
Plant Protection Sciences
Swedish Agricultural University
P.O. Box 44
S-23053 Arnalp
Sweden

SCHOPF Axel
Institute of Forest Entomology
Universität für Bodenkultur
HasenauerStraasse 38
A-1190 Wien
Austria

SUNNERHEIM Kerstin
Institute of Chemistry
Department of Organic Chemistry
Uppsala University
Box 531
S-751 21 Uppsala
Sweden

VETROVA Valentina
Sukachev Institute of Forest
Institute of Forest SB RAS
Academgorodok
Krasnoyarsk
RU-660036
Russia

VIIRI Heli
Faculty of Forestry
University of Joensuu
P.O. Box 111
SF-80101 Joensuu
Finland

VOLNEY Jan
Natural Resources Canada
Canadian Forestry Service
Northern Forestry Center
5320-122 Street
Edmonton, AB T6H 3S5
Canada

WAGNER Michael R.
School of Forestry
Northern Arizona University
P.O.Box 15018
Flagstaff
AZ-86011.00
USA

WANG Hailin
Southwest Forest College
White Dragon Temple
Kunming
Yunnan
650224
P.R. China

WHITE Eleanor
Canadian Forestry Service
Pacific Forestry Centre
506 West Burnside Road
Victoria, B.C. V8Z 1M5
Canada

WILSON G. F.
Departamento de Biologia Generale
ICB/Univsidad Fed. Minas Gerais
Caixa Postal 2486
S0161-970 Belo Horizonte MG
Brazil

WINGFIELD Michael
Tree Pathology Cooperative Programme
Forestry and Agricultural Biotechnology Institute
Faculty of Biological and Agricultural Sciences
University of Pretoria
Pretoria 0002
South Africa

YANCHUCK Alvin C.
Research Branch
BC Forest Service
31 Bastion Square
Victoria, B.C. V8W 3E7
Canada

YART Annie
Station de Zoologie Forestiere
INRA
Avenue de la Pomme de Pin
BP 20619 ARDON
F-45166 - OLIVET Cedex
France

YE Hui
Yunnan University
Institute of Ecology and Geobotany
Kunming
Yunnan
650091
P.R. CHINA

YLIOJA Tiina
Forest Research Institute
Punkaharju Research Station
Finlandiantie 18
FIN-58450 Punkaharju
Finland

INRA Editions, Route de St Cyr, 78026 Versailles Cedex, France
Dépôt légal : 2ème trimestre 1999
ISSN : 0293-1915
ISBN : 2-7380-0883-6

Impression : Bialec S.A., 54000 Nancy - D.L. n° 50029